FLOAT
PILKINGTONS' GLASS REVOLUTION

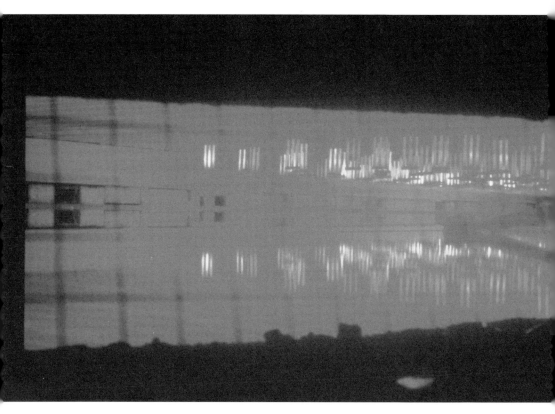

Frontispiece: the interior of a float bath.

FLOAT

Pilkingtons'
Glass Revolution

DAVID J. BRICKNELL

CRUCIBLE

To Ilush

Float: Pilkingtons' Glass Revolution

Copyright © David J. Bricknell, 2009

First published in 2009 by
Crucible Books

Crucible Books is an imprint of
Carnegie Publishing Ltd,
Carnegie House,
Chatsworth Road,
Lancaster LA1 4SL
www.cruciblebooks.com

British Library Cataloguing-in-Publication data
A catalogue record for this book is available from the British Library

ISBN 978-1-905472-11-6

Designed, typeset and originated by Carnegie Book Production, Lancaster
Printed and bound by Cromwell Press Group, Trowbridge

Contents

CHAPTER ONE

Introduction

WINDOW GLASS was originally intended simply to let light in and to keep the weather out, but its use and application have steadily expanded until today it has evolved into a huge family of products. It can be modified to keep heat in or keep heat out. It may be coloured to impact upon its environment or it can be reflective to blend with it. It may be thick enough to stop a bullet or thin enough to be sent into space. The prime quality of glass is that it is invisible. The less you are conscious of the glass itself (rather than its colour or coating), in a window, a car windscreen or a mirror, the more valuable it is. The magic of the float process is that it gave the world the capability of making a valuable, invisible product more cheaply than ever before. To achieve invisibility glass has to be flawless: perfectly flat, totally uniform, and free from any distortion or contamination. We now take this for granted, but in the early 1950s, before the advent of the float process, this perfection was rare and expensive.

Building design in the second half of the twentieth century was inextricably bound up with glass. The development of the curtain wall in the 1950s and 1960s was critical to the emergence of tower blocks with the cheapest construction cost and the maximum rental space.[1] The development of inexpensive, high-quality glass allowed the fulfilment of the architects' new designs and the emphasis on the façade of the building. The float process has brought cheap, perfect glass to the whole of the world and with it a new range of design possibilities that has changed the environment we live in.

This book is an account of the strategy for the invention and exploitation of the float process, 'one of the great process inventions of the [twentieth]

Norman Foster's iconic building at 30 St Mary Axe in the City of London, one of the most spectacular uses of float glass in modern architecture. Despite the shape, the main panes of glass are flat rather than curved.

BY COURTESY OF NIGEL YOUNG / FOSTER + PARTNERS (ARCHITECTS)

1

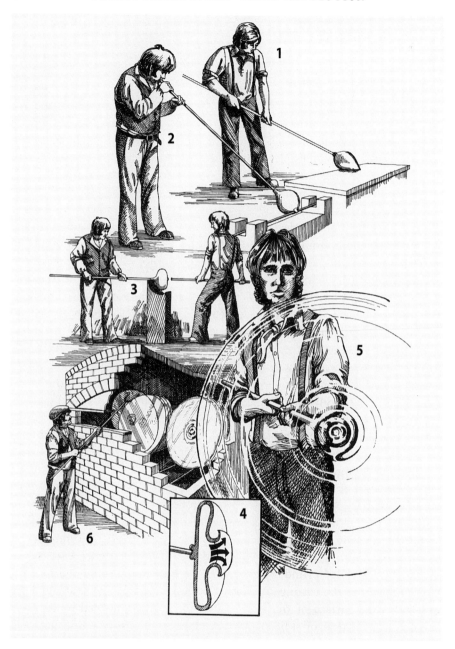

The manufacture of crown glass. A lump of molten glass is gathered on the blow pipe (1) and is blown to form a bubble (2). This is then transferred to a solid rod (3), the glass is re-heated so that it is molten, the open end is pulled out (4), and then quickly spun on the rod so that it forms a flat table of glass (5). The tables are then stacked in the annealing furnace to be cooled in a controlled manner (6).

PILKINGTON ARCHIVE

century',[2] the decisions that shaped the strategy and the factors, conscious and unconscious, which shaped these decisions.

A brief history of window glass[3]

The Egyptians had discovered the technique for making glass as early as 2000 BC, but only for small ornamental pieces. By the time of the Roman empire glass could be made in pieces large enough for windows, although it was rare and expensive. Techniques of manufacture did not change substantially until the end of the seventeenth century when the French, at St Gobain in Picardy, invented the process for making plate glass to meet the demand for the best-quality glass, for uses that included mirrors and coach windows. This process involved melting a pot of glass, pouring it on to a table and allowing it to set, when the top and bottom of the resulting sheet could, in turn, be ground and polished to give a highly transparent finish. With care in the selection of raw materials and their melting the glass was white and relatively fault free.

The quality of glass for windows was not so exacting, except for the most expensive of houses. The glass could often be greenish and badly flawed yet still be weatherproof and let the light in. The method generally used in Europe – the broad glass process – involved blowing a balloon of glass which was swung until it formed into a cylinder. This was allowed to cool and then split, re-heated and flattened into a single sheet. The resulting sheets of glass were quite large, but the surface of the glass was marked in the flattening process. Broad glass was made in Britain initially, but in the eighteenth century was replaced by the crown process which could produce thinner glass that had the glossy, fire finished surface preferred by the customers. In the crown process a blob of molten glass was collected on the end of a metal rod and spun so that it formed a round table of glass of relatively uniform thickness.

Although there was waste in the central bullion and in the cutting of square plates from a round table, the crown process was the predominant method in Britain until it was superseded by improved blown glass techniques of forming and splitting the glass in the middle of the nineteenth century. The new method – called cylinder glass – still involved the blowing and forming of a cylinder, but the cutting and flattening processes entailed relatively little damage to the surface of the glass. However, it was a manual process and required a great deal of skill to produce glass of a consistent thickness and in large sizes. The limit was a sheet measuring about 7ft × 4ft. Towards the end of the nineteenth century the cylinder process was mechanised, allowing sheets of up to 40ft × 8ft with a fired finish. The process was only phased out in Britain in about 1930, and in older houses it can be recognised by the deformity of parallel lines in the reflective surface of the glass, created when the cylinder was flattened.

The manufacture of cylinder glass. A lump of molten glass is gathered on the blowpipe (1), and is blown into a bubble (2). This is repeatedly reheated, swung in a pit next to the glass blower and blown again so that the bubble of glass is shaped into a cylinder (3). After the glass has cooled the ends of the cylinder are cut off, the inside is scored so that the glass cracks (4) and the glass is reheated so that it can be flattened out into a sheet (5).

PILKINGTON ARCHIVE

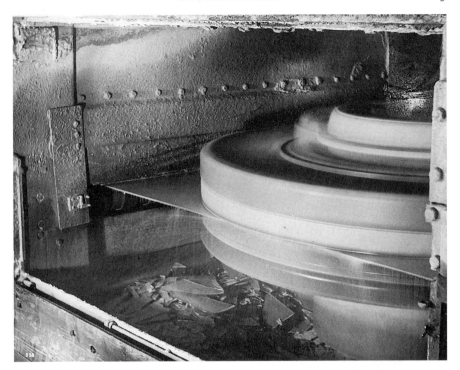

Plate glass grinding. The fragile ribbon of opaque glass passes between two grinding wheels to semi-finish the glass on both sides before it goes to the polisher.

PILKINGTON ARCHIVE

Only one piece of glass was produced at a time in both the cylinder and the plate processes (which had been mechanised but was still essentially the same as that invented in St Gobain). Adaptations of the Siemens furnace, as early as 1870, enabled the continuous melting of glass, but it was not until the 1920s that the production of a continuous ribbon of glass was commercialised. Two similar processes, the Fourcault and Colburn, were invented in the early twentieth century, but both took some fifteen years to become fully commercial and widely adopted. In both methods a horizontal bar was dipped into a reservoir of molten glass; the glass adhered to the bar, which was then lifted. The viscosity of the glass was such that a ribbon formed, which could then be drawn continuously away from the reservoir, cooled in a controlled manner (or annealed) in a lehr* and then cut for the warehouse. An improved method of making sheet glass was invented by Pittsburg Plate Glass (later PPG Industries Inc) (PPG) in the late 1920s, and it was this process that was regarded as the

---

* A specialised, temperature-controlled kiln for annealing glass.

best method of making good-quality window glass until the advent of the float process, although the Fourcault process was the most widely adopted.

By the early 1900s the plate process involved pouring a large pot of molten glass onto a casting table, allowing it to cool, cutting it into plates as large as could be handled, bedding the plates in plaster of Paris and then grinding the top surface with successively finer grades of sand and rouge until a completely flat, polished and transparent surface was produced. The plate was then removed from the table, turned over, laid on cloth and the second surface ground and polished. About half of the glass melted was lost. It was the Ford Motor Company that set about the modernisation of the plate process. Ford had started making its own glass and, in keeping with its mass production mentality, endeavoured to develop a continuous process. It asked for help in the continuous melting of glass from Pilkington (American glass-makers were not anxious to help a newcomer), and by the early 1920s Ford and Pilkington could produce a constant ribbon of plate-quality glass. It still required grinding and polishing – areas in which Pilkington had done much development work – and in 1923 Pilkington launched its continuous grinding and polishing technology which, over the next fifteen years, it licensed to all the plate glass producers. Pilkington was now seen as the leader in quality glass manufacturing, a role it was to retain for the rest of the century. By 1935 further development had enabled Pilkington to grind both surfaces of the glass at once (dubbed the 'Twin' process). Although the Twin was licensed to St Gobain in 1935, the licensing programme for this technology was interrupted by the Second World War and licences were still being granted into the 1950s despite the fact the technology was by then over twenty years old.

Glass in St Helens; the birth of Pilkington

Prior to the end of the eighteenth century glass-making in Britain was localised and relatively small scale, and high-quality glass was imported from the Continent, mainly from France. However, the growing demand for high-quality glass for use in housing led English entrepreneurs to set up an English plate glass factory in 1776, when the St Helens Ravenhead works started producing plate glass using St Gobain expertise. It was one of the largest industrial buildings in the UK at the time and was still in use (though no longer for plate glass manufacture) in the mid-1980s, when it was destroyed by fire.

St Helens was an ideal site for glass production. It lay on a coalfield, important at a time when eight tons of coal were needed to make one ton of glass. The soda ash for glass-making came from the new chemical industry based on the nearby salt mines in Cheshire. The new Sankey Canal, the first non-waterway canal in England, provided transport linked to the Mersey for

Artist's impression of Pilkington's plate glassworks at Cowley Hill, 1879.
PILKINGTON ARCHIVE

both the bulk raw materials and the fragile glass, and the growing port of Liverpool was available for shipping glass to the rest of the UK and overseas. In the early days sand was shipped in from the east coast of England, but St Helens was given a huge competitive advantage when it was discovered that there were extensive deposits of glass-quality sand just north of the town. By the early 1800s St Helens was famed for the quality of its plate glass, and the vast Ravenhead factory was one of the sights of southern Lancashire.

In 1826 a group of local entrepreneurs, including William Pilkington, the son of a local doctor who had made his money as a wine and spirit merchant, set up a new firm to make crown glass, the St Helens Crown Glass Company. William was later joined by his elder brother, Richard and in 1849 they bought out the other partners and renamed the firm Pilkington Brothers. By the middle of the century crown glass was being phased out and replaced by cylinder, the last crown glass being made in 1872. Pilkington was also moving into plate glass. In 1876 it built a new factory at Cowley Hill, on the northern edge of St Helens, on slightly elevated ground so that the liquid waste from the grinding and polishing process could be piped away.

The first and second generations of the family brought a range of skills to the business, and the sheer number of offspring (the two brothers produced fourteen sons) ensured that only the most able were given positions in the firm. Their astute business sense, both commercial and technical, kept them ahead of their UK rivals, who found it very difficult to compete against the Europeans, particularly the Belgians who had become the predominant glass-making nation, efficiently exporting large quantities of cheap glass. In the 1860s Belgium was exporting as much glass as was being made in the whole of Britain. The firm's Pilkington technical expertise was also being noted, and William Windle Pilkington (the son of the founding brother, Richard) made a succession of crucial inventions in the later 1800s. He developed the Siemens furnaces in order to deliver a continuous flow of glass rather than the intermittent pot method. Over a period of years he developed much more efficient lehrs (the furnace for cooling, or annealing, the glass in a controlled way to make it less fragile), reducing the annealing time of plates of glass from days to hours. By 1902 annealing was a continuous process through a single tunnel. The grinding and polishing processes were mechanised for improved flow of throughput. All these improvements were essential predecessors to the production of a continuous ribbon of glass, in the 1920s, in conjunction with Ford.

In 1901 Pilkington (which had become a limited company rather than a partnership in 1894) bought out the owners of the first plate glass works at Ravenhead, which had ceased production some time before, and became the only British manufacturer of plate glass. The other producers had been unable to compete with the St Gobain glass and that made in Belgium, particularly after the lucrative US market was appropriated by Pittsburgh Plate Glass (PPG) in the years following their start-up in 1870. By the turn of the century Pilkington's only real competitor in the UK was Chance Brothers of Birmingham. Chance Brothers made their early reputation on the quality of their sheet glass, providing the glass for Paxton's glasshouse at Chatsworth in 1839 and for the Crystal Palace in London in 1851. But they failed in the production of plate, and by 1900 their prosperity was based on the quality of their rolled glass. In this process the molten glass was formed into a ribbon between two rollers, which governed the ribbon's flatness and thickness. Inevitably, the rollers marked the surface of the glass, but this was made a virtue by imparting various patterns onto the surface making the glass opaque and decorative.

In 1909 Pilkington brought in from the USA the new mechanised form of cylinder glass production, the Lubbers process. By the early 1920s this form of production was being outmoded by the new flat drawn sheet processes from Fourcault and Colburn (now owned by Libbey-Owens in the USA), but Pilkington could not get the right terms nor decide on which process

Plate glass polishing. The semi-finished glass is cut and then passed through the high-speed polisher.

to license. While it dithered, it lost position in relation to its sheet glass competitors, but was therefore free to license an improved version of the sheet process from PPG in 1930. Despite its poor performance in sheet glass at this time, the firm's world leading expertise in the continuous manufacture of plate glass kept it viable and in 1951 Pilkington bought out its last remaining UK competitor, Chance Brothers. The company was now well placed, in both the size of its market and the level of its technical expertise, to compete with its foreign rivals.

In the late 1940s, as the glass industry turned its mind to the demands of post-war reconstruction, it was recognised that neither the plate process nor the sheet process was ideal for the manufacture of flat glass. The sheet process was relatively cheap, both in terms of its initial capital cost and its running costs, and it produced a 'fire-finished' glass, bright and shiny as the surface was not touched from the time it emerged, molten, from the tank until it had been cooled enough to be too hard to mark. However, drawing the glass from the tank exaggerated any tiny faults in the glass by elongating them, and the process also suffered distortion caused by any minor variation in the uniformity of the 'metal' (molten glass) and temperature fluctuations at the time of forming the ribbon.

Plate plants were far more costly both to build and to run. Plants were huge, some 500m long (compared with the 200m of a modern float plant) and each consuming 1.5 MW of electricity. They were two to three times more expensive to build than sheet plants. More than 20 per cent of the glass was still lost in the grinding and polishing process alone.[4] The key selling point was that the optical quality of the glass was very high. The surface was perfectly flat; the two surfaces were perfectly parallel; and the body of the glass was free from distortion if the melting tank was delivering good glass to the process. However, the surface was relatively dull as a result of the grinding and polishing, and the dream of the glass-making industry was a glass with the lack of distortion of plate with the fire finish of sheet and particularly without the expense of grinding and polishing.

A large part of the flat glass market was for processed glass, which required high-quality glass. Glass may be processed in a number of ways:

• Lamination: two layers of glass are sandwiched with an interlayer of plastic to form a safety glass which is difficult to penetrate and will remain intact even when broken, reducing the risk of laceration. Any defects in the glass are exaggerated when looking through the two layers together.

• Toughening; the glass is subjected to rapid cooling in a carefully regulated manner, setting up internal stresses in the glass which make it much harder to break, and when it does so it forms the now-familiar small dice which will not cause deep lacerations. If the glass is not well made, particularly if it contains any foreign matter, it may shatter on the thermal shock of toughening. Toughening is critical for both automotive glass and for the glazing of high-rise buildings.

• Glass can be made into mirrors by applying a reflective material to one face of the glass and then protecting this material with paint. Any fault is exaggerated by its reflection and by the fact that you are looking at the glass rather than through it.

Cowley Hill plate works 1950. The semi-opaque ribbon of glass (centre foreground) enters the twin grinding machine in the first stage of producing clear glass.
PILKINGTON ARCHIVE

In 1950 all of the world's leading glass-makers were expecting a rapid increase in demand for increasingly high-quality glass with strong downward pressure on price. Any company who made a breakthrough on price or quality – or preferably both – was going to be in a position to become the dominant force in glass-making for the remainder of the century.

This book explores how it came to be that Pilkington Brothers, one of the smallest of the plate glass producers, came to be that dominant force, through a mixture of brilliance, skill, bravery, hard work and luck. However, before proceeding with the story it is necessary to explain why the history is written as a series of stories about individual decisions – at first glance a somewhat disjointed approach – rather than as a simple, chronological narrative.

Decisions, decisions ...

The chronology of the development of float glass is straightforward to recount, but this alone would make it difficult to understand why the board of Pilkington acted in the way they did. Decisions made by the board would seem strange when taken out of context. It is too easy to criticise when we, with the benefit of hindsight, and in possession of more complete information, judge a decision to be poor. Sir Alastair Pilkington was very clear that a good decision, based on good analysis and the exercise of expert judgement, could still have a poor outcome. Equally, the outcome might be good but result from a poor decision, based on weak analysis or judgement.

In order to gain a better understanding of the workings of the decision-making process, the story of float is split into the account of six critical, strategic decisions. Using primarily contemporary records from the company archives, with some interviews of eye witnesses as well as some personal recollection, I have tried to recreate what was in the minds of the directors at the time they made those decisions, whether explicitly or intuitively. Putting this process in context gives us a clearer picture of whether the decision process was a 'good' one, whether decisions were difficult, and whether the outcomes were favourable and in what way.

The six decisions have been chosen as being the most important in each phase of the exploitation of technology: in its infancy, the taking of the invention through to production; in adolescence, the decision whether to keep the monopoly of the technology or to share it with others; in adulthood, whether the initial strategy was correct or should be widened; in maturity, how to capitalise on the strategic power given by the technology (there are two contrasting decisions in this phase); and, in old age, how to preserve as long as possible the new-found strength as the technology becomes generic. The total period covered by this account is more than half a century, and the decisions are well spaced so that each can be examined within its own context.

Strategic decision-making ... the Pilkington way

A company board, in theory, might be characterised as a rational choice processor, which reviews a management paper setting out the problem, the alternative solutions, their consequences in financial terms, and a recommended choice of action. The board – omniscient in deliberation – fine tunes the analysis, having discussed each aspect rationally, and confirms or varies the recommendation with a view to maximising the profit to the company. The reality is much more subtle and far less perfect. The following account is of a typical Pilkington board meeting in the 1980s (it was not materially different during the period 1950–87).

The heart of the company's strategic decision-making is the board meeting in the boardroom, the temporal, physical and mental focal point at which the company's decision-making is enacted. There is an element of ritual about the board meetings, to underline the importance of the debate in the minds of the directors, and to endow the outcome with gravitas when it is communicated to the management. Two weeks or so prior to the meeting the secretary (the administrator of the board) agrees the agenda with the chairman and advises the directors or senior managers what discussion papers are required in addition to the routine reports. The papers are collected by the secretary and are sent out in folders to each director some days prior to the meeting to allow for reading, assimilation and some consultation. On the day of the meeting the directors assemble in the boardroom and take their allotted places, strictly in order of appointment to the board (except for the chairman and the vice-chairman) at the horseshoe shaped table (see Figure 1.1 below and the photograph on page 147). The chairman is at the external apex and the secretary at the internal apex.

The boardroom, used for no other purpose than meetings of the board and its committees, is panelled in dark woods to match the rosewood table, unadorned by paintings and insulated from the ante-room by two sets of doors to ensure there is no risk of being overheard. Although one wall is of glass, overlooking one of the company's factories and the town of St Helens, on winter afternoons it can be gloomy and the lights cast a disconcerting pattern which looks, from certain angles, like a halo over the chairman's head.

All directors have an equal right of audience, but the junior members have to raise their voices to be heard by the chairman, particularly when

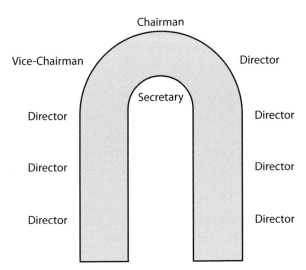

Figure 1.1
The board table.

the full board of twenty members is meeting. Senior directors can speak more quietly, more personally, to the chairman. As juniors speak to the back of the secretary's head, they cannot be sure their comments are noted. The senior directors, and especially the chairman, can catch the secretary's eye to reinforce a point worthy of noting in the minutes. The secretary has no right of audience except on a point of order or elucidation of fact.

The papers are taken as read, although on rare occasions the author of the paper might be asked to summarise a complex case. Management authors might be invited into the meeting to present their papers as a test of their character or as a sop to their egos. The recommendation might be adopted without debate but, whether debated or not, it is reasonable to assume that the contents of the paper are at the front of the directors' minds. The debate has some structure (depending on the style of the chairman) and is reasonably logical, but there is no expectation that it is comprehensive. To the contrary, points are discussed as matters of exception, the debate concentrates on issues of novelty or difficulty. The remaining relevant, but unexceptional, points are left implicit. In addition there are other tacit issues which are deep within the minds of the directors, not only unvoiced but incapable of being voiced. An uninitiated observer may take the discussion to be illogical, even irrational. It jumps from point to point of the argument as the directors make the necessary connections in their minds without the need to voice them, knowing what their colleagues are thinking. This is especially true when there are no new non-executive directors on the board who have to have matters explained to them. During most of the period under review the executive directors had all spent most of their careers in the company, and even the non-executives had spent some years on the board and had been inducted into the relevant history.

If the debate is clear-cut the chairman will state the consensus. (There was only one vote in the whole of the period under review, and that was at a committee of the board.) If the debate was diffuse the chairman might say that the matter would be discussed again when the board had seen the minute, i.e. when a thoughtful summary of the debate had been prepared. Draft minutes were prepared by the secretary. They were not a verbatim report of the meeting, nor even a pure condensation of what was said. The decision, if any, was recorded, but the language used by the directors might be tempered to make the message more palatable to a recipient, to keep it within the law or to give the board some room to manoeuvre in the future. Key points voiced in the debate might be mentioned, together with key points in the paper which had not been mentioned and even other matters (such as legal constraints) of which the secretary was aware, to flesh out the logic of the record. The tedious, mundane or irrelevant would be omitted. The company secretary in the late 1970s described the result to me as 'what the directors would have said had they had time to think'. This draft was submitted to the chairman for comment (see Appendix 3.A), and the amended version sent to the directors for their comments. Only after the final revised version was formally adopted at the next meeting did the minute become the record of the meeting. At the moment of formal approval the minute reflected the concurrent, conscious thoughts of the board; the directors were confirming the precise wording of the record and thereby constructing the meeting.

Two aspects in particular are key to the decisions reported in this book:

- the papers and minutes of a specific board meeting are only a partial record of the thinking of the board at that meeting; and

- the conscious thinking of the directors on each decision was, at the moment of decision, only a part of the rationalisation of the directors. A great deal of the rationalisation was unrecorded and unvoiced and therefore, *prima facie*, intuitive.

However, the wider historical record, particularly from the company archive, can show the contexts of the decision and give strong evidence of many more factors implicit in the directors' minds at the moment of decision. It is possible, to a large extent, to reconstruct the perceptions of the directors, both express and implicit, at the time of decision.

A key absentee in most of the formal documentation is any reflection of the personal agenda of the directors, other than the chairman, who was expected to provide leadership to the board and whose personal views are inevitably reflected in all aspects of the board's business. Overt ambition was not well received by the board. On one occasion a potential board candidate who had the temerity to put himself forward for a directorship was promptly taken off the list of candidates. Once an individual had been appointed to the board his personal aspirations were expected to be identical to the company's. An individual would have responsibility for a specific division or function, and would be expected to fight that operation's corner in budget allocations and the like. But it did not pay to be too aggressive, as the following year there might be a change of responsibilities and the aggressor might find himself in charge of a budget loser. In the whole of the period 1950–87 there was little point in jockeying for position for the chairmanship as the succession to the role was very clear-cut. There was inevitably some showmanship in the meetings – you did not get to be a director if you were shy and retiring – but there was no attribution in the minutes, so there was no need to make points in the record for personal aggrandisement. The principle of consensus decisions meant that there were no dissenting voices to be recorded. The decision of the board became the decision of each director and he was expected to abide by it.

Within the board there were relationships which were either close or tinged with animosity, but this was rarely reflected in the behaviour at meetings, let alone in the record. One of the key attributes for promotion to the board was the ability to work as the member of a team and to leave personal feelings, especially animosity, outside. People were expected to be entirely professional and dispassionate in dealings with their colleagues. The consequence of this is that, while personalities were critical in the decisions examined, the contribution was a function of leadership and intellectual input rather than interpersonal conflict. What comes out of the record is the reinforcement of complementary strengths rather than political jockeying for position. Consensus was creative not merely compromise.

A second absentee from the record is the culture of both the company and the industry of which it formed part. Companies such as Pilkington had an extensive history and a tradition of long, trans-generational service. There were many families in St Helens who had provided generations to the firm as the Pilkington family. The employees were very conscious, and proud, that the company had a culture, even if they could not define it. At whatever level in the company, shop floor to boardroom, a senior individual had spent many years in the organisation absorbing from his peers what was, or was not, acceptable behaviour and in turn passing this view of life on to his successors. The learning and teaching were implicit; little or nothing need be said, but this intuitive, cultural knowledge was very enduring and difficult to change, as we shall see.

The glass industry was confined to a relatively small group of manufacturers, and the directors and senior managers of Pilkington had regular contact with their opposite numbers and generally knew them well. In the same way that the individual companies had a culture, so the industry had a culture, an implicit understanding of the way things should be done. This had an even more insidious effect on strategic decisions than the internal culture and was more difficult to change. The directors, without being particularly conscious of it, were constrained in their decision-making by the internal and external cultures. The more a decision required a change in culture, the more difficult it was either to make such a decision or to implement it.

Organisations often talk about their culture without being specific as to what that culture is. Indeed, some aspects of culture are so deep seated in the sub-conscious that they are not capable of being articulated. Yet the culture buried in the intuition of the decision makers is so powerful that it is difficult (some have argued impossible) to make a decision which runs counter to the prevailing culture, particularly that of the industry. This book examines six key decisions, but only one significantly changed the culture, and that only with great difficulty. This is not to say that culture is deterministic, precluding the free will of the directors, but there is a need for decision makers to understand the past, and its power, if decisions are to be the product of such free will.

A tale of three chairmen

Through the 35 years of this story there were only three chairmen of Pilkington, and there was a considerable overlap in their times on the board (see Appendix 1). As the leaders of the company – and they were each, in very different ways, powerful leaders – their personalities are reflected in the style of management of the company and to some extent the strategies. But they shared a sense that the company had an important role to fulfil in the glass industry, and that the float glass process was the key to achieving that destiny. Despite their differences, and the radically changing environment over the 35 years, their shared goals bring a sense of coherence to the overall story of the exploitation of float.

Sir Harry Pilkington
William Henry (Harry) Pilkington was born in 1905, a great-grandson of one of the founding brothers, Richard Pilkington. He was educated at Rugby School and Magdalene College, Cambridge, but for reasons which have not been explained, he excelled at neither. He joined the company in 1927, and quickly demonstrated that, despite his academic record, he had a remarkably retentive memory, particularly for figures, and an analytical approach to any problem. He immediately concentrated on the commercial side of the business, rather than production. His formative years with the company were in the recession of the late 1920s and the intensely competitive environment of the 1930s. Much of his time in this period was spent talking to the other producers in Europe, trying to get some agreement of a reasonable level of competition so that all of the manufacturers could make an acceptable level of profits.

It was this experience that gave him an attitude towards competition which guided him for the rest of his career. An oligopoly (where the industry is controlled by a small number of companies) was a fact of life in a capital-intensive industry such as glass-making. This did not mean that the producers should abuse their position and conspire against the customers to increase profits, but equally it was not in the best long-term interests of customers, or any other stakeholder, if the members of the oligopoly fought against each other so hard that none of them made reasonable profits. For if they did not do so, then only a very few companies would survive, leading to an unsustainable monopoly. Healthy competition, for Sir Harry, was therefore competition where the competitors remained healthy, which, so long as they were not abusive, was best for customers, suppliers, employees and the community generally. Even some economists agree that a benign oligopoly is the ideal form of economy, but the regulatory authorities of the antitrust bodies in the USA and the Competition Commission in Europe are more

Sir Harry Pilikington inspecting the glass stocks, October 1962.
PILKINGTON ARCHIVE

cynical. They do not believe that oligopolists could ever be benign, the latter always turning to abuse when times get tough.

Although Harry Pilkington was well aware of the cynical view, and was always at pains to stress that the company must remain within the letter of the competition law, he seemed to struggle with its philosophy that all trade discussion was, on the face of it, improper collusion. His view was that agreement was acceptable, even desirable, as long as it did not abuse the customer. Despite agreements there was still enough incentive for the business to become ever more efficient. If the sales prices, volumes and capacities of competitors were known, then the way to increase profitability was to become more efficient. The extent of the information sharing that seemed good business planning in the 1950s would not be tolerated today, but Sir Harry should not be judged by today's standards. The mutually assured destructive practices of the inter-war years had endangered or destroyed many businesses. There was a very real fear in the 1950s that the might of the Communist industrial machine would overwhelm European industry and that the glass industry, like iron and steel, with which it had structural similarities, should have a unified approach to the market in order to present a united front to the Eastern Bloc. Indeed, he achieved an acceptable balance for the time, as the UK Monopolies Commission report in 1966 could find no evidence of behaviour that distorted the supply of glass in the UK, despite the close links with the competitors.[5]

Harry Pilkington became a director in 1934, and the following year, at the age of 30, was the most senior executive on the commercial side. He was appointed chairman of the company in 1949. There was no question of Buggin's turn. He was surrounded by very able executives, all of whom had spent most, if not all, of their careers in the company, and there was no easy ride for members of the family. Only the most promising were recruited, and they could only remain if they proved they were sufficiently able for the board. There were no sinecure posts. Sir Harry's ability was later recognised with a series of public appointments, including the chairmanship of two royal commissions, for Doctors' and Dentists' Remuneration in 1957–60 and Broadcasting in 1960–62. He was also president of the Federation of British Industries (the predecessor of the CBI) from 1953 to 1955. He was knighted in 1953, and was thereafter known as Sir Harry in the works, even after his elevation to the peerage in 1968.

Sir Harry had a fearsome reputation for his memory, his absorption of a brief and his grasp of a balance sheet or set of statistics at a glance. Just before the company went public in 1970 the board was advised that it needed a financial policy for review by prospective investors. Shortly thereafter, during an interval in a play he was attending, he wrote the policy on the back of the programme which was later adopted, almost verbatim, by the company. This was typical of Sir Harry's intensive approach to life. He kept a note of the thousands of miles he travelled on business, and was a pioneer of international air travel. He would dictate answers to letters while driving to the airport and fill his weekends serving as a JP or tending his (prize-winning) roses or those of a company pensioner if the welfare gardener was not available. Despite being a workaholic and having one of the sharpest business minds of his day, he had the reputation of being unfailingly kind and courteous with a gentle sense of humour. Joyce Grenfell, who sat with him on his second royal commission, described him as 'an overgrown schoolboy with a good face, wrinkled around the eyes ... full of energy, wit and brain'.[6] He had a joy of life which friends said was enhanced when he married his second wife, Mavis, in 1961, some eight years after his first wife had died. He was regarded by some of the more pompous in the City as eccentric, likely to cycle home from a full dress dinner or cajole colleagues into a game of tennis before work or late into the evening. He had to be persuaded to replace his ageing, and inexpensive, Rover in order that the managers could upgrade their cars. While he was conscious of his image, he was comfortable with it and it was a true reflection of his character. He lived up to his *persona* without making it an artificial creation.

His non-conformist (United Reform) upbringing and life-long adherence gave him an innate sense of fairness to subordinates and colleagues, customers and competitors and a humility about his position. Being asked by him to do something was not an order but a polite request for a favour. Despite all his positive qualities, he was not slow to criticise himself for what he perceived as shortcomings. After the bitter and damaging strike in 1970 (Chapter 8) he wrote a paper to the board in which he criticised his own lack of foresight, and was surprisingly frank about his personal failings. It would be rare for a public figure today to shoulder so much blame, but Pilkington was still a private company and the shareholders were unlikely to be vindictive.

Sir Harry remained chairman until 1973, having been persuaded to stay past retirement age in order to see the company through the trauma of going public in 1970. He remained on the board until 1980 and was still regularly in the office, often hand writing letters of congratulation to pensioners, until his death in 1983.

Lionel Alexander Bethune (Alastair) Pilkington

Alastair Pilkington was not a member of the founding family. Despite the fact that publicity often referred to him as a distant cousin, no link was established between his ancestors and those of the glass-making family. Alastair had been born in 1920 in Calcutta, the son of an English engineer. He was educated at Sherborne, and had just started his mechanical sciences degree at Trinity College, Cambridge, when he volunteered to join the Royal Artillery and was posted to Egypt just before war broke out. When he saw that war was inevitable he declared that he wanted to be part of the professional army, not merely a conscript. In Alexandria on his way out he met the daughter of a senior naval officer, Patricia Elliot, and they started a correspondence which survived through his service in North Africa and Crete, where he was captured, and in prisoner of war camps for the rest of the war. Despite the

Sir Alastair Pilkington,
1974.

distant nature of the courtship, they were married in 1945, just before he returned to Cambridge to finish his degree.

Both Alastair's father and Richard Pilkington had an interest in family history (through which they met) and their mutual researches confirmed that there was no traceable connection between the families. However Richard (who was not part of the company management) commented that Pilkington was looking for high-quality engineers. It was arranged that Alastair would be seen by members of the board over a three-day period. Richard was criticised for the unorthodox manner of the introduction, but Alastair would nevertheless be offered a position. The board minute of 29 November 1945 says:

> Mr LG Pilkington's branch of the family broke away at least 15 generations ago. It was agreed that a member of the family, however remote, could be accepted only as a potential Family Director ...

> Mr AC Pilkington pointed out that our business is largely in the

North of England, that conditions of life in the North of England are very different from those in the South, and that we must be very sure that a potential candidate brought up in the South understands and is willing to take on the obligation of living in the North, both for himself and his Family [sic].

Chandler, the business historian, cites this decision as an example of the parochial attitude of a family company, spending time on the recruitment of a junior manager and giving priority to the interests of the family.[7] In fact they were considering the appointment of a potential director despite the fact he was not family and introducing, as it turned out, the dynamic factor of new blood that Chandler saw lacking in the family company.

There is a wonderful self-centeredness with these minutes. It was the other branch of the family that had 'broken away', and it was worth putting in the minutes that a southerner who had just spent three days in St Helens being interviewed might need reminding that St Helens was not the same as Cambridge. Alastair later wrote to Lawrence Pilkington (Sir Harry's brother), the director in charge of technology, asking if he could recommend any books on glass-making. The reply was that Alastair should concentrate on his physics as Pilkington had its own way of doing things and the books might be misleading. At this time managers were expected to live in St Helens, not to commute in from the more amenable countryside or the distractions of Southport, and the company owned a number of houses to let to managers while they found suitable property. Sir Harry's house, Windle Hall, was a short cycle ride to Cowley Hill. Sir Alastair lived in Rainhill, the southern part of St Helens, in the same house from the time of his return from Doncaster until the late 1980s.

Alastair completed his degree in 1947, having won blues for tennis, fives and squash, and started work as a technical assistant, a lowly appointment, whose duties included clearing clinker from the gas producers that made the fuel for the glass melting tanks. This was part of a thoughtfully designed programme for family members to expose them to all aspects of the business, to groom them for responsibility at an early age, and to expose any weaknesses. In 1949 he was posted to the plate glass works at Doncaster as production manager. He thoroughly enjoyed both the responsibility, the involvement in a relatively small works, and possibly the fact that he was out of sight of head office. As well as his production responsibilities he also had time to identify and supervise some experimental work involving glass and tin, the precursor to the invention of the float process (see Chapter 3).

He returned to St Helens in 1951, to a post which he thought was less demanding and in which he was bored. But he was also given new responsibilities on the Manufacturing Conference (the most senior technical committee, reporting to the board) and the right to lunch in the directors' dining room. This was not a trivial favour. It was a right given to very few, and it exposed him to discussion covering the whole of the business and the strategic thinking behind it. Alastair must have had a character and manner that quickly inspired confidence and trust. This was an era when even the most senior management, who had spent long careers with the company, were given the minimal amount of information about company performance and certainly nothing in relation to profitability; that was strictly for the board. After only four years he was brought into the inner sanctum. He was appointed a sub-director, and to the executive committee, in 1953 and became a full member of the board in 1955, rapid promotion by any standards, let alone for somebody who was not a member of the family.

Sir Alastair shared a number of traits with Sir Harry. Despite his outstanding intellect, he was thoughtful and courteous to colleagues and subordinates, inspiring the very best from them. The story of the development of float glass, covered in detail in Chapters 3 and 4, reflects his intellectual problem-solving skills, his inspirational team leadership, his careful advocacy in the boardroom to obtain further funding, but the ability to stand back and be dispassionate about the progress of the project. He is the only person minuted as expressing reservations about the project's prospects. It was not only in St Helens that he was building his reputation. In 1952–53 he was the project leader supervising the installation of the Twin machinery at LOF in the USA, and they were very impressed with his qualities. He was regarded as an outstanding engineer by other leading engineers, and his expertise, honesty and advocacy were vital in the negotiation of the first licences of the technology.

Sir Alastair (he was knighted in 1970) was equally enthusiastic with his outside interests. He loved the Lake District and had a retreat in an idyllic spot in Patterdale. He inherited from his mother a life-long commitment to Christian Science, which may explain his firm belief in the human will in accomplishment, and was a powerful advocate of strong links between business and academia, with the emphasis on orienting education towards a practical application in business. He could appear somewhat domineering, but he believed firmly in consultation and would listen to, and was capable of being persuaded by, a well argued case. It is the fate of chairmen or chief executives to be perceived as didactic. They did not get to their positions by being diffident, and too often they are surrounded by managers who are overly concerned for their future careers or are not confident enough of their arguments to challenge the statements of their superior, even if the latter would genuinely welcome such contributions. In Sir Alastair's case his commitment to consider all aspects of a problem fully obliged him to listen to suggestions, even from a junior member of the team, although he could be abrupt in demolishing a suspect argument. It was politic for an advisor not to stray too far from his field of expertise, but within that field the advisor could be quite robust in debate and still retain Sir Alastair's confidence.

Sir Alastair retired from executive office, somewhat surprisingly and despite pleas from colleagues, in 1980 at the age of 60, to enjoy other things while he was still active, and finally retired from the board in 1985. He died in May 1995; although he was 75 he was so active that his death still felt premature.

Antony Richard Pilkington

Antony Pilkington was the only member of the fifth generation of the family to become a director. He was born in 1935, son of Arthur Pilkington, possibly Sir Harry's closest colleague on the board, and educated at Ampleforth (his father having been brought up as a Roman Catholic) and Trinity College, Cambridge, where he got an undistinguished degree in history. He did his National Service in the Coldstream Guards and on joining the company in 1959 on the sales side was posted out to France. Although Antony enjoyed his youth, when he developed a taste for fine wine and racing moderately fast

Sir Antony Pilkington, 1986.

cars, he quickly developed a reputation for his business acumen in marketing planning. He established his board credentials with the development of the Scandinavian market for the company from small beginnings to the point where it justified its own float plant in 1976. This had to be accomplished in the face of resistance from the existing market leaders and involved a mixture of guile, diplomacy, charm and occasional flashes of strength. He was appointed to the board in 1973.

In the early days as a director he gave the impression of being very laid-back. Business was important, but that was no reason why it should not be fun. In the early 1970s at a negotiating meeting with senior representatives of LOF, a visitor asked Leslie Wall (then Deputy Chairman) who was going to hold Antony's hand until he grew up. Once he became Chairman in 1980 he was faced with a series of difficult challenges, and he was less relaxed and open with his colleagues than he had been. Arguably it was the most difficult time for the company since the late 1920s, and the low point was the bid from BTR (Chapter 11) when his stance was uncompromising: 'The company is not for sale.' His leadership of the management teams and external advisors was widely acknowledged as masterful, and he was genuinely moved by the warmth of his reception in head office the day after the victory. In a contested bid, an experience most chairmen only have once, it is normal to hand over the conduct of the defence to the advisors. Not with Sir Antony (he was knighted in 1990). While the advice was considered, the company's stance and the tone of the defence were staunchly his own.

Sir Antony had a steely resolve, despite his relaxed manner, and felt deeply his role as trustee of the company, in that he was the custodian of the company for the future. He confessed at the end of the BTR bid that he had felt the pressure of the preceding four generations of the family. He did not want to be the one to give it away. He had a strong strategic instinct and, although his religion rarely surfaced at the office, he had a strong moral sense of what was right in business which was totally in keeping with the views of both Sir Harry and Sir Alastair. Although a company had an obligation to provide an income to its investors, it also had a responsibility to its other stakeholders. This was not in any way charitable but enlightened self-interest. If the company created an environment in which it was respected by its stakeholders then its business position would be enhanced. He too was courteous with colleagues and prepared to listen to, and act on, advice. He was very reserved with most of his team, and his management technique was to praise with faint damns. In the Guards it was well recognised that if your turnout was exemplary you would still be criticised for 'an idle haircut'. Sir Antony's subordinates had to understand that the appraisal of an excellent year was that 'you need to give more attention to detail'. An expectation of overt praise was a waste of effort.

Sir Antony had the widest constituency to reconcile. The shareholders and their advisors were becoming increasingly aggressive about the strategy for a business about which they had only an academic knowledge. The employees and their unions were constantly resistant to the job losses that were an inevitable consequence of the efficiency offered by the float process. Competition was fiercer than for any time in the last fifty years as the ex-licensees tried to recoup lost ground, and there was persistent surplus capacity for the first time since the war. Analysts and commentators were much more public in their criticism of perceived shortcomings. The vogue was for diversification, away from the businesses that the company knew well to some other business about which the management knew little. Sir Antony had to integrate the powerful and independent-minded new acquisitions in Germany and America. Despite these problems, the company achieved record sales and profits under his leadership. It was unfortunate that the last few years in the role were a time of recession and severe restructuring in the industry so that his retirement, in 1995, was at a time of uncertainty for the future. He died, sadly prematurely, in 2000.

The three men were very different in their characters and the range of challenges over which they had to preside, but there were common themes. They were all intellectually powerful and strong-minded. They were collegiate in that they wanted to discuss issues with colleagues and were willing to take advice, although they were not afraid to take the lead. Their various branches of Christianity gave them similar values. In particular, business had far wider responsibilities to the community than merely to give short-term profits to the shareholders. And they shared and reinforced the culture of the organisation, moulding it to reflect the circumstances it faced while retaining the core values of fair dealing in all its relationships.

CHAPTER TWO

The 1950s: a decade of optimism

THE 1950S was a period of great optimism for Pilkington. It had survived the Second World War well and was benefiting from the general recovery in demand. Sir Harry Pilkington's diplomatic expertise and his vision for the glass industry as a whole was giving the company a high standing among its competitors. Pilkington's financial strength, its internal structures and its relationship with its shareholders gave it the freedom to be ambitious, both in the expansion of its existing business and the invention of new processes.

The market and the competitors

Despite its weight and fragility, glass had for centuries been an internationally traded commodity. The Venetians had sold their early plate glass all over Europe, but were supplanted in the eighteenth century by the French, in particular St Gobain, who dominated the European market for plate glass after the Second World War. The USA had been a very important plate glass market for the Europeans, but it diminished rapidly after PPG started to manufacture there in 1870. In the sheet glass market the Belgian glassmakers had become the leading European manufacturers, producing far more than their home market could consume and becoming a major exporter to all the glass markets of the world. Their quality and price set the standard for others to achieve. A manufacturer needed a strong home market to provide a stable base, but all of the leading glass manufacturers also had aspirations to a share of export markets, selling to countries which had little or no indigenous production.

In the 1950s there were very few plate glass manufacturers in the world. PPG was the largest in the USA. Founded in 1870, it had grown rapidly and had largely replaced the lucrative imports from Europe by the mid-1880s. There was limited competition from other plate glass producers in the USA until 1931, when Libbey-Owens-Ford (LOF) started to make plate glass and won the contract to supply General Motors with most of their requirements. The two founders of LOF, Messrs Libbey and Owens, had built a successful and innovative business in glass containers, and in 1916 had set up Libbey Owens Sheet Glass Company to develop the Colburn sheet glass process after the inventor had become insolvent. The process was made to work and was successful commercially, although it was never adopted as widely as the Fourcault process or the later PPG process. In 1930 Libbey Owens was merged with the Edward Ford Glass Company to become LOF. (Edward Ford was not part of the car making dynasty, but the son of the founder of PPG.) As related in Chapter 1, Ford Motor Company was the only other plate glass manufacturer in the USA in the 1950s, but despite having made glass for forty years by the end of the decade, was still not regarded as a true glass-maker by PPG or LOF.

In Europe the position was more complex, but there were still only five plate glass producers in continental Europe when the float process was announced in 1959. St Gobain was the descendant of the firms which had started making plate glass in France as early as the 1680s. It was by far the largest plate glass producer, with operations in France, Germany, Spain and Belgium. By the end of the 1950s the diverse, interlocking Belgian companies had been rationalised into two groups, Glaver and Univerbel. Delog and Detag in Germany had merged, and Boussois was the only other French producer of plate glass. Outside Europe the only producers of plate glass were Asahi Glass and Nippon Sheet Glass, both based in Japan.

Sheet glass manufacture was more widely spread, but in the USA and Europe the plate producers were also the dominant sheet manufacturers, with a limited number of small independent companies. Elsewhere there was a significant number of small producers, most of them independent of the majors, in virtually every country which had a local market large enough to support a plant. LOF, PPG and the Belgian owners of the Fourcault process had all been active in selling the different techniques for making sheet glass. In 1957 there were 34 plate glass plants in the world compared with 130 sheet glass plants. Each of the latter plants might have a number of drawing machines, and the total number of such machines was 336 using Fourcault technology, 129 using PPG technology and 50 machines using Colburn (LOF) technology.[1]

Manufacturing capacity in Europe in the twentieth century had risen rapidly following investment in the new, highly productive technologies for both sheet and plate. The resulting excess capacity and the general recession of the inter-war years resulted in a rapid fall in prices, particularly in sheet glass. As Figure 2.1 shows, Pilkington faced severe competition from imports at home and had a relatively small export market. The company lost money on sheet in the first four years of the 1930s, partly as they had been slow

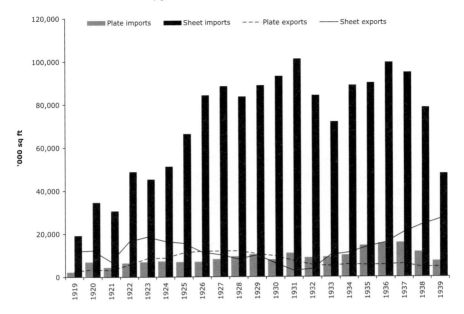

Figure 2.1   UK imports and exports – raw flat glass, 1919–1939
Source: Derived from Barker, T.C. 1977b. *The Glass-makers*. Weidenfeld and Nicolson, London.

to move away from the older, cylinder process. Pilkington were then quick to license the new PPG sheet process, but manufacturing started at a very difficult time for the industry, and it was some years before Pilkington made a profit in sheet glass.

To bring some order to this potentially damaging competition the European manufacturers had established a set of arrangements to control their activities. This was not a new strategy in Europe. In 1904 a group of continental plate glass producers formed the Convention Internationale des Glaceries to ration exports between them and to control prices. Pilkington did not formally sign until 1929, but in the meantime kept generally in line with the lead of the Convention. There was no equivalent in the sheet glass field for many years, reflected in the relative profitability of sheet and plate in the 1930s, but Pilkington made great efforts, with Sir Harry as a prime mover, to bring about a general accord in the mid-1930s. Although it only resulted in a series of bilateral agreements, the negotiations alone may have produced a marked effect on the level of imports into Britain and the profitability of sheet.[2] There may also have been a beneficial effect of a 15 per cent import tariff from 1934. These factors, coupled with the fact that Pilkington had made significant improvements to the licensed PPG sheet technology, resulted in a reduction

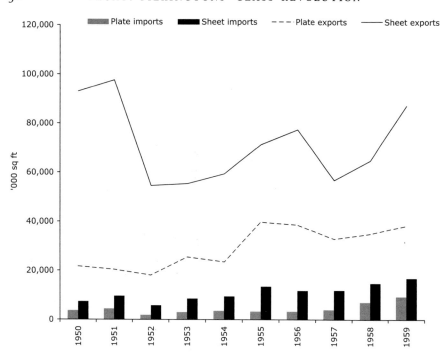

Figure 2.2   UK imports and exports – raw flat glass, 1950–1959
Source: Monopolies Commission report, 1966.

of the imports of sheet and an increase in the exports in the late 1930s.

Pilkington exited the Second World War much stronger than it had entered (see Figure 2.2). Its prime competitors in Europe, the Belgian companies and the St Gobain group of companies, had been precluded from exporting during the war and Pilkington's output had increased to meet the demand both for replacing glass damaged during the Blitz and of export markets previously serviced in competition with the continental manufacturers. Imports into the UK had virtually evaporated, and Pilkington's export markets had been improved dramatically. In 1950 nearly four times as much glass, both sheet and plate, was being sold overseas compared with 1939. In addition, all the agreements with the Continentals had lapsed with the outbreak of the war (by virtue of the Trading With the Enemy legislation) and although Pilkington kept in close touch with the Continentals after 1945, and discussed prices and exports, it saw no immediate need to re-formalise arrangements. Pilkington's prices were very competitive, both in the home market and overseas, and it had much improved relationships with overseas customers as a result of the support they had received from Pilkington during the war. With the recovery of markets in the post-war rebuilding there was plenty of demand for the Continentals to meet in their home markets before becoming over-competitive in the export market.

At the end of 1945 Pilkington's board was told that in the earlier part of the year the company had made 75 per cent of the world's plate glass as PPG and LOF had been on strike;[3] record sales were achieved in October 1946,[4] and again in October 1948[5] (despite stiff price competition in sheet glass markets[6]), and for the six months to September 1950.[7] Sir Harry now took the opportunity to seek to persuade his fellow glass industry leaders that there was plenty of room for everyone to make money without cutting each others' throats. Each manufacturer could stick to his home territory, which was Europe for the Continental producers, and there was plenty of scope to share the uncommitted export markets to absorb any surplus European capacity as it came back on stream. Generally speaking the US producers made enough for their markets in normal years, and looked to the Europeans to act as the swing producers if there was a shortfall in home production. There was a degree of acceptance for Sir Harry's proposals in Europe, although the Belgian sheet glass producers were the least happy with the suggestions. Traditionally they had been huge exporters and thought it was their right to retake these markets.

Throughout Sir Harry's chairmanship, and in particular in the 1950s, he travelled tirelessly across Europe discussing production, prices and export shares and cajoling his fellow leaders to keep order. During the 1950s the board and Group Executive received frequent reports, from Sir Harry in particular, about meetings with both the sheet and plate producers in Europe and their discussions. Despite this Sir Harry was anxious to point out that there were no agreements with the competitors. In working at an industry level to avoid a repeat of the destructive competition of the inter-war years Sir Harry walked a fine line between legality and illegality. In 1950 the board issued the instruction that all sales arrangements were to be overhauled to conform with the monopolies and antitrust rules although it was assured that 'this was uppermost in the minds of the Sales Department'.[8] The company stressed, in a draft memorandum to the Monopolies Commission in 1952 'there is nothing except price, delivery and service that curbs foreign competition [in the UK]',[9] and stated to the Monopolies Commission in 1966 that there were no agreements. There was a draft agreement in 1956 which was never signed, although the provisions were loosely observed,[10] and there were tentative arrangements on prices and discounts in the UK of foreign plate.[11]

There were also regular exchanges of information with PPG and LOF in the USA, but these discussions were carefully circumscribed as the two American companies were expressly prohibited from colluding by virtue of a consent decree of 1948.* The thorough investigation of Pilkington in 1966 by the Monopolies Commission could find no evidence of collusion that inhibited the free working of the UK market for flat glass. None of these arrangements caused the Monopolies Commission to conclude that there was any improper activity as far as the supply of glass in the UK was concerned.[12]

It is interesting that Sir Harry took on, and was allowed by the industry to take on, this leadership role as Pilkington were by no means the biggest in the glass industry. The company was, in the 1950s, about fifth in size in the world league of glass-makers. Pilkington was capitalised at £3 million (approximately $12.8 million), PPG at $89.8 million and LOF at $16 million.[13] St Gobain, based in France but with operations elsewhere in Europe, was much bigger than Pilkington. Although the Belgian glass-makers were smaller as units, there were material interlocking shareholdings between them and they tended to behave as a powerful whole. The Japanese manufacturers were at this time an unknown quantity, concentrating on their own, protected, markets and those of South East Asia, although there were early indications of their interest in the markets of the west coasts of the USA and Canada.

In 1955 there was an uneasy balance of power in the glass markets. The Americans were somewhat short on capacity in plate, but new Twin capacity was being constructed, and Ford were pressing for a Twin licence (although the existing glass-makers were very reluctant to allow a customer into the fold[14]). The Continentals had been expanding their productive capacity, and the need to sell their increasing output was putting strains on the unofficial accords in Pilkington's home and export markets. Profitability was certain to come under pressure. Pilkington needed to invest heavily to increase its capacity just to maintain its market position, let alone to grow it, and its own plate plant was considerably older than much of that now being operated by its competitors.

Pilkington's finances

The 1950s was a period of rapid growth for Pilkington. The post-war rebuilding at home in both domestic and commercial markets, the sharp rise in the automotive market, coupled with the increasing demand for the company's products in overseas markets (see Figure 2.2), particularly the USA (in 1955 the USA was taking as much plate as the whole of the home and export plate markets had in 1939[15]), all combined to give the company the financial strength to fund the float development. Despite the industrial

---

* A consent decree is an agreement made with the US antitrust authorities under the aegis of the courts to behave in a certain way, usually after a finding of suspicious behaviour which does not warrant a prosecution.

discussions through Sir Harry, sheet glass profits hardly grew in the decade, even though there was a 250 per cent growth in sales volume. However, there was a ten-fold increase in plate glass profits as there were periods of under-capacity as installation of new equipment failed to keep up with demand. There was a particular spurt in Pilkington profits in 1956 (at just the time that Pilkington was deciding to commit significant resources to the first float production plant) when the US producers could not meet their home demand and had to buy from Europe. In 1958–59, when the float project was at its most critical, it was ironic that strikes at PPG and LOF entailed large, and profitable, quantities of plate being sold to them to cover their shortfall.[16] Profits from these sales to Pilkington's major competitors effectively funded the float project.

Although UK flat glass was the dominant business of Pilkington, the company as a whole was doing well (see Table 2.1). Turnover rose every year (except 1952/53), from £20 million in 1949 to £51 million in 1959 and trading profit, which more accurately reflected the state of competition in its fluctuations, rose from £1.9 million to £5.6 million.

Table 2.1   *Pilkington group consolidated figures, 1949–1959 (£m)*

	1949	1950	1951	1952	1953	1954	1955	1956	1957	1958	1959
Share capital	3.1	3.1	3.1	3.1	3.1	3.1	3.1	6.0	6.0	6.0	6.0
Reserves	6.5	8.7	10.5	12.3	13.0	15.0	18.8	19.0	21.6	24.5	28.1
Fixed assets	7.8	8.1	9.8	11.8	11.9	11.9	12.7	14.2	17.2	19.4	20.3
Turnover	20.0	22.4	24.8	29.2	27.1	33.4	37.1	42.1	44.1	49.1	51.2
Trading profit*	1.9	2.6	3.1	3.3	1.5	4.7	5.9	5.2	4.3	4.1	5.6
Dividend	0.3	0.3	0.3	0.3	0.3	0.4	0.5	0.6	0.5	0.5	0.6
Cash	0.0	2.0	2.0	–1.0	–0.1	2.9	7.0	6.0	4.3	4.3	7.0

* After depreciation *and* replacement

Source: Pilkington accounts

Critical to the thinking of the board was the ability of the company to finance its expansion internally without recourse to borrowing or raising new capital. The board was very anxious to retain its status as an exempt private company without the obligation to publish its accounts.[17] This entailed keeping the number of shareholders below 50 and, as the majority of the shareholders (all of whom were descendants of the founders) had most of their wealth tied up in the company, there was little scope to raise funds from issues of shares. The share capital only increased from £3.1 million to £6 million during the

1950s. With prudence dictating that there was no outside borrowing (except overdraft facilities to cope with the peaks and troughs of cash flow) all of the expansion had to be funded from internally generated cash.

The strong trading position was fundamental to achieving this goal, but two policies were major contributors. First the dividends were not over-generous, rising from a total of £292,000 in 1949 to £575,000 in 1959; given that the capital had doubled, the rate of return actually dropped over the period. It was only in 1960, when the board seemed satisfied that float was viable, that dividends were increased, to £732,000. It was part of the philosophy of the dividend policy that the shareholders were the custodians of the future of the company and were not investors for short-term profit.

Second, the company was virtually unique in that it not only allowed for depreciation on its assets but also made charges for the replacement cost of its assets, i.e. the reserves covered not just the conventional historic cost of the assets but also any inflation since they were built. In 1958 replacement charges and depreciation were roughly equal,[18] in other words the company was moving to reserves twice the amount of a company using conventional accounting policies. This materially reduced the trading profit but meant that the reserves actually grew faster than the value of the fixed assets, even in a time of rapid investment. Assets grew from £7.8 million in 1949 to £20.3 million in 1959, while reserves grew from £6.5 million to £28.1 million. It is worth noting that the Revenue, despite overtures from the company, did not allow the replacement charges as a deduction against profit and the company therefore incurred an apparently high rate of tax in relation its declared profits.[19]

Last, the cash position was strong throughout despite the capital expenditure and the funding of the float project. There were dips in 1952 and 1957, when profitability dipped, but cash grew from zero in 1949 to £7 million in 1959.

The mid-1950s was a period of extraordinary optimism for the company. On the back of strongly rising markets, a good relationship with its competitors, and the growing belief that the company had a world beater in float, it could plan to invest £9.6 million in plate and sheet plant to keep up with forecast demand,[20] £1 million in a new head office at Prescot Road in St Helens,[21] as well as a large R&D facility at Lathom (about ten miles north of St Helens where the air was cleaner and there was no risk of mining subsidence), a new optical glass factory at St Asaph in north Wales, and the expansion of its overseas facilities and the other UK manufacturing operations of the business. Sir Harry warned shareholders in 1955 that the total capital expenditure plan for the next five years was £15 million at a time when the total turnover was only £37 million p.a.[22]

Shareholders

Pilkington Brothers had been founded as a partnership in 1826. The business had converted into a private limited company in 1894, but even by 1950 had remained very much a family company. All the shares were held by descendants of the two founding brothers. All of the directors held at least a qualifying shareholding and family directors held inherited shares, either in their own right or as trustees. However, a large proportion of the beneficial shareholders were not employed in the business, and their involvement appears to have been very limited. Annual accounts were printed for the shareholders, together with a brief report on the company by the Chairman, but the content was minimal. Although profits were revealed, there is no reference to turnover, and the reports contain no overt comment on the significant expenditure on float until 1959. The only references are oblique: in 1956, for example, the Chairman's report refers to the need to keep 'technical leadership right at the top of the list of our priorities'.[23]

It is possible that there was informal reporting to the shareholders, but there is no reference in the minutes or papers to the interests of shareholders. Despite Chandler's remark that family companies in general, and Pilkington in particular (although to a lesser extent), 'chose to pay dividends rather than to reinvest in research and development',[24] this is not borne out by the evidence. The rate of dividend (see Table 2.1) and the willingness to spend on float (see Chapters 3 and 4) show that the well-being of the shareholders via short-term dividend policy was low on the board's priorities. It was the unwritten but fundamental objective of the board to ensure successful continuity of the company.[25] This objective encompassed not only the shareholders but also the employees, customers and suppliers; the company had an 'obligation' to keep up with the industries who depended on it.[26] The board took a very wide view of the company's role and responsibilities to the community.

Pilkington's status as a private company was fundamental to its ability to fund the float glass project. Sir Alastair Pilkington commented some years later, after the company had gone public, that it was unlikely that the company would have spent the money it had done on developing float if it had been obliged to report openly to independent shareholders.[27] Sir Harry was more cautious in his conclusions in his statement to shareholders in 1973, immediately prior to his retirement from executive office:

The one question often posed that I have never been able to answer with confidence is whether we would have taken all the risks and losses over the long period needed to develop the float process had we been public. This is a completely fair question and demands a completely honest answer, but I cannot say yes or no with certainty.

I am sure that being private made it much easier to spend so much on something which to many knowledgeable people naturally seemed incapable of achievement.[28]

In the 1950s the board could take decisions which had a profound effect on the shareholders without consulting them or even informing them in any meaningful way about the way in which the business was being run. The board had been entrusted with the running of the company for long-term continuity, and the board was trusted to carry out their delegated responsibility without review by those who were not aware of the detail of the business.

The management structure

In float glass's crucial, formative period from 1955 to 1959 the board of Pilkington had 13 members (see Appendix 1); Sir Harry had been Chairman since 1949; Douglas Phelps was chairman of the Group Executive (effectively the CEO); Lord Cozens-Hardy (the 4th Baron), Arthur Pilkington, Roger Percival, Lawrence Pilkington, James Watt, Alan Hudson-Davies (both non-family) and Alastair Pilkington were executive or 'managing' directors, joined by George McOnie in 1958; Colonel Guy Pilkington, Geoffrey Pilkington and Lord Weeks were retired executive directors (Lord Cozens-Hardy, the 3rd Baron, died in 1956). The executive committee of the board, the Group Executive, comprised all the executive directors, and beneath them were the two Divisional boards looking after the Pressed Glass Division and the Flat Glass Division respectively (see Figure 2.3). These committees and divisional boards comprised a mixture of executive directors and senior managers. There were functional committees (*inter alia*) for Finance and Technology

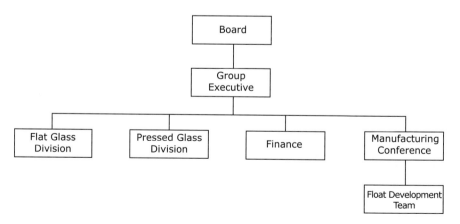

Figure 2.3   Simplified organisation chart, 1955.

The General Board, 1964 (the last meeting at the old head office in Grove Street, St Helens). Seated, left to right: Arthur Pilkington, Douglas Phelps, Guy Pilkington, Harry Pilkington, Geoffrey Pilkington, James Watt. Standing: Lawrence Pilkington, Alan Hudson-Davies, Archie Burns (sub-director), Herbert Cozens-Hardy, David Pilkington, Humphrey Mynors, Fraser Rigby (company secretary), Terry Bird, George McOnie, Alastair Pilkington.

PILKINGTON ARCHIVE

(the Manufacturing Conference) which reported to the Group Executive and which again were composed of a mixture of executive directors and managers. In addition the board members in St Helens on any given day would meet informally over lunch to discuss business, sign documents and, in an emergency, pass resolutions. The Directors' Flat Glass Committee (DFGC) was specifically created in 1958 to deal with policy and long-term issues for the company, undistracted by the examination of the monthly figures and the long list of requisitions for expenditure. There was also the special sub-committee of Douglas Phelps, Sir Harry, Arthur Pilkington and Alastair which had been set up by the Group Executive in January 1956 to consider the exploitation of float.[29]

This structure meant that all the executive directors were involved in various aspects of the detail of the company's operations on a day-to-day basis and were constantly updated on matters of importance. Policy discussion was not necessarily reserved for formal occasions, although decisions would (normally) be ratified at the next appropriate meeting. When decisions were made at the board or Group Executive, most of the executive directors, including the Chairman of the Group Executive and those with specific technical responsibility, would have been fully aware of the state of the project and private doubts or concerns were in all probability dealt with prior to the meetings.

The daily exchange of ideas means that the full rationale of any decision is rarely recorded in the minutes or papers. The decision-making process was extended over a period of time in many different venues, and the formalisation of the decision at a recorded meeting only reflects those aspects of the decision that were voiced on the day and which the Secretary (with the approval of the directors) chose to report. But matters were always (except in an emergency) raised at the board or Group Executive. At this time there was very little delegated authority – even the purchase of a typewriter had to be approved at this level – and there was a strong belief in the formal debating of important matters. Sir Alastair later said; 'I've never taken a major decision without consulting my colleagues. It would be unimaginable to me, unimaginable. I can't even see any point to it.'[30] Many aspects of the business were so deeply ingrained in the psyche of the directors that they were rarely, if ever, expressed. All of the directors had spent many years in the business (see Appendix 1). There were, in 1959, no outside non-executives to whom long-standing policies or practices had to be explained, and key factors were implicitly accepted by all those present. The directors' intuitive expertise reduced the need for conscious discussion and explicit decisions.

The board appears to have been obsessive about secrecy during this period. Full sets of accounts tabled at the board meetings were not filed with the board papers. Turnover statistics in the papers circulated were, until October 1955, removed before the papers were filed. There was much debate about the financial data that could be revealed to the most senior of the management and it was limited to the costs, over which managers had control, and not the sales from their operations; they could not be put in the position to work out the profits. This policy was justified on the grounds that the board desired to 'not overburden managers with unnecessary detail'.[31] On the other hand the directors often called for huge amounts of detail. Many of the directors had been works managers, when they had been expected to be on top of every aspect of their operations. Some found it difficult to abandon this level of detail, and were still receiving copies of works' figures for Cowley Hill even when they had responsibility for plants around the world. It was difficult to become detached from the works where they had built their reputations when they could see them from their office windows.

The 1950s was, perhaps, a unique opportunity for a project with the scope, ambition and cost of the float project. Pilkington were independent of any external review, even from the family shareholders. The industry was as stable as it had ever been, with rapidly growing, profitable markets in which Pilkington was a flourishing participant. The feeling of optimism was high, as there was no perceived end to the growth in the demand for glass. At no other time in the company's history had there been such a happy conjunction of circumstances. The prospect of the float process as a radical, unifying method of production induced a feeling of euphoria. As Dr Johnson said on the sale of Thrales brewery, 'We are here not to sell a parcel of boilers and vats, but the potentiality of growing rich beyond the dreams of avarice.'[32]

CHAPTER THREE

Building the first float plant

D ESPITE THE FACT that the company was actively licensing the Twin
process for making plate glass in the early 1950s, the board recognised
that the Twin process had a finite life and was only the culmination of an
inefficient process that its competitors would be seeking to improve, even
if the competitors were taking licences for Twin in order to preserve their
positions. If the company were to retain its leadership in plate, it would need
to move early to improve upon the Twin, before its competitors did so. As
early as 1950 the board determined that, 'The ultimate objective ... is to
arrive at standards of flatness resembling those of plate without the grinding
and polishing.'[1] The prime motivating factor throughout the early 1950s was
radically to improve on the Twin: 'The most important matter facing the firm,
therefore, is to recapture the commanding position in Plate technically [sic]
that we have held for the last fifty years.'[2]

The first phase of the float project was from the setting of the target,
through the appointment of the project team and the early experimental work,
culminating with the conclusion that the project had real prospects and the
decision to build the first full-scale plant.

The invention of float glass

In July 1949 the Manufacturing Conference, the committee charged with
responsibility for overseeing the technical work of the company, had agreed to
set up two new teams in the works, separate from research and not responsible
to the works, with the object 'to discover a new process or processes which
without grinding and polishing will produce a glass that will rival plate at
a cost comparable with that of sheet ... [The teams are] responsible only to
the board and are to go ahead with all possible speed.'[3] Barradell-Smith,
an engineer, was in charge of one team at Plate Works, Cowley Hill, in
St Helens (the other seems to have come to nothing) with the emphasis on

inventiveness: 'It must not stifle independent developments or discourage individual enthusiasm.'[4]

It is noteworthy that this vital project, reporting to the highest level, was given, not to Research, but to a young team of engineers with works backgrounds. Barradell-Smith was the oldest, 34 at the time of his appointment. Surprisingly, he had only been with the company since 1947, having spent seven years with Rolls Royce, and was being given a great deal of responsibility in a crucial area despite his youth and relative inexperience in glass-making. At this time Research was an analytical service, carrying out experiments at the behest of the works, rather than taking a proactive role in developing new technology. The board seems to have been ambivalent about the role of the Research department. They took great trouble to recruit first-class people to head the function, paid them at the same rate as a works manager (i.e. just below the directors) and then kept them separate from the real development work. One of the key roles of the Manufacturing Conference was to share ideas coming up from the works and to encourage operating managers with bright ideas to try them out in the works and to make something of them. It says much of the role of Research at this time that it is not Lawrence Pilkington, as the head of the technical function, who was the chief protagonist of float and its prospects, but James Watt, the production director.

One of the new team's first projects was to investigate the Bowes process. Bowes was an American inventor who suggested flowing the glass from the tank between two vibrating platens, or plates, rather than rollers, the theory being that the platens would not mark the glass, leaving the ribbon with a smooth finish that would not require polishing. In August 1950 Kenneth Bickerstaff had been recruited into Barradell-Smith's team and was assigned to the Bowes work. A fundamental problem with this technique was transporting the soft ribbon of glass away from the platens until it was cool enough to handle without marking. At some time between August and November 1950 Bickerstaff had the idea of using a liquid as a transport medium, which would provide a level surface and not mark the glass. Molten tin fitted the parameters required for the liquid; Barradell-Smith supported the idea and some drawings were made. It is not clear whether any trials were run, although the General board noted in May 1951 that variations on the Bowes process were being explored, 'and it is hoped shortly to run the ribbon on a bath of molten tin'.[5] Bickerstaff obtained promotion to Assistant Chief Draughtsman later in 1951 (and ceased work in this field until late 1955) but (to his surprise) was credited with his idea by being named co-inventor with Alastair Pilkington when the first float patent was filed in 1953.

At the same time some completely separate work was being done at the company's works at Doncaster, where a layer of molten tin was put in a shallow canal and glass melted over it in order to investigate whether the tin protected

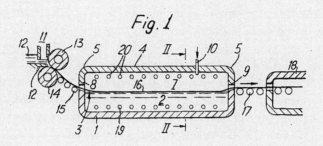

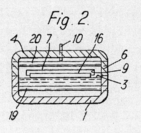

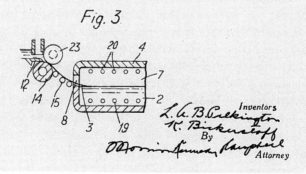

The first US patent application showing the use of rollers and the very simple concept of the float bath.

the refractories (ceramic materials with which all glass melting tanks are lined to protect them from attack by the molten glass) and reduced the amount of seed (particles of eroded refractory) contaminating the glass. This also came within Barradell-Smith's remit. Bickerstaff was probably aware of this work started by J.R. Nuttall in 1950,[6] which had established that glass did float on tin without there being any obvious mixing of, or reaction between, the two materials. It is certain that Alastair Pilkington was aware of this work and had been involved in some of the experiments. He was Production Director at Doncaster, and therefore directly responsible for the experiments and was present at the Manufacturing Conference in January 1951 when the melting work was discussed.[7]

Alastair was also present at the Manufacturing Conference in January 1952, and in a discussion about the Bowes process he 'suggested that this [fire finishing after the ribbon of glass had passed through the platens] might be done by floating the ribbon on a bath of molten tin in a neutral atmosphere. It was decided that it was worth trying this to find out whether it gives a fire finishing effect.'[8] Lawrence Pilkington chaired this meeting as the director responsible for technology and Watt was also present. Both would have been aware of Bickerstaff's work, and it is highly unlikely that Alastair was not aware of it. The key difference between Bickerstaff's idea and Alastair's is that the former only contemplated transporting the glass whereas the latter contemplated exploiting the nature of the molten tin to fire finish the glass. It was the fire finish which was so desired by glass-makers to improve the relatively matt finish of plate. Within days of this meeting Alastair met with Lawrence Pilkington and a number of other key people to discuss this idea. It seems from the tenor of the discussion that it had moved from being an off-the-cuff remark to a fully fledged proposal. Certainly the objects of the experiment were defined and a location to carry it out was being urgently sought.

In interviews with Professor Quinn for a case study[9] Alastair is quoted as saying that the invention took place in June 1952, although in a speech in Toledo in 1963 he says it occurred in October 1952.[10] But the idea proposed at the January Manufacturing Conference and advanced to experimental status a few days later, had already been mentioned to the board in March,[11] so that it appears that the invention was made early in 1952. In the Quinn interview Alastair said that the inventive moment came while he was helping his wife wash the dishes. As this is a mindless task he was mulling over some ideas that he had had about the forming of glass and 'it was one of those moments when your mind is able to think and then it was sort of 'bang' – like that. Indeed the final solution was very similar to the original idea ...' What is not clear is what he thought of and when. If it had been prior to the Conference meeting in January it would not merely have been mentioned as an aside; plans for an experiment would have been made there and then.

It is more likely that the importance of the remark came to Alastair in the hours or days after the Conference meeting and he immediately sought the meeting with Lawrence. Perhaps at the Conference Alastair used the words 'fire finished' to denote the imparting of a shiny finish and it only came to him later, at the sink, that the glass on the molten tin could be sufficiently hot and soft to melt out all of the surface defects so there was no need for the smoothing action of the Bowes platens. Alastair's other critical idea, and arguably the most important breakthrough, was the concept of free fall, where the molten glass was not formed by rollers but was just poured onto the tin and formed a ribbon as it flowed sideways under the influence of gravity. However, this idea is not mentioned until 1956 when it was tested on the third pilot plant. There is no evidence that this is the idea that came at the kitchen sink. Indeed, in November 1952 Alastair wrote to Lawrence, 'Perhaps the most likely way of producing both sheet glass and plate glass in one process is to cast a ribbon say half an inch thick and six inches wide, and produce a ribbon ¼ inch thick and one foot wide by merely allowing the glass to flow out on top of the tin and produce a flat surface by itself.'[12] There is no mention of the concept of free fall here. The original 'kitchen sink' invention must have been only to smooth a pre-formed ribbon, with the next step of flowing a pre-formed ribbon to the desired thickness when it is reheated on the tin and the final step is that of free fall without the need for rollers.

The presence of the kitchen sink became part of the mythology. Alastair never claimed more than he was engaged on a mindless task and his mind was wandering. Claims by later writers who said that the bubbles (or the plates or the grease) on the water gave him the idea* are embellishments that Alastair always rejected. Some were so carried away that they said that he thought of the idea in the bath, but this is surely confusing him with Archimedes. Some sceptics dubbed it the 'sink process' when it was costing the company so much money, but, when it proved to be a success, others claimed he had thought of the idea while walking on water. There is little doubt that the 'kitchen sink' story is true. Alastair was scrupulous about the accounts of the invention and development of float, and would not tolerate any embellishment of the story despite the encouragement of the publicity consultants at the time of the launch in 1959. For those who knew him there is no possibility that Alastair enhanced the inventive moment. His passion was for the truth, both as the purpose of research and in the accounts of it, and he did not have the vanity to see the story as one that might be twisted to enhance his image. Knowing the care Sir Alastair took in getting the story

---

* Such claims were still being repeated in 2007 (24 July) in James May's BBC television programme on twentieth-century cities.

right, it is surprising that there is some lack of clarity about what precisely the initial invention was and the confusion over when it took place.*

The development teams

Glass-making in the 1950s was still something of a black art. Glass-makers knew from many years' experience what made good glass, but they did not necessarily know why. The skills were acquired from a long apprenticeship at the hands of a master without having a theoretical understanding of the process. For example, at about this time a comparison had been made between two glass-making tanks and, although they were thought to be identical, they had had very different performances: 'It is still a mystery why.'[13] During the course of the development of float it gradually became apparent how little was known about the complexities of the behaviour of molten glass. Because glass-making was an art rather than a science the operators and engineers knew what worked rather than why it worked. Once the project team moved away from the tried and tested they realised how little they knew about the fundamentals of the behaviour of molten glass and its sensitivity to minor changes.

Throughout the development period the board and its committees agonised about the difficulty of recruitment of top-quality engineers, but rarely praised the quality of the engineers it did have. From the outset there were a dozen or more young engineers (Barradell-Smith was the oldest) who were supporting Alastair in operating at the forefront of a number of technologies, making original contributions and managing the pilot and full-scale plants. At a later stage they shared their expertise with licensees and helped them overcome a myriad problems as the technology spread out to new physical and technical environments. Unlike some other companies, Pilkington earned and retained the engineers' total loyalty. There was a great deal of money to be made as a consultant to companies who wanted an alternative to Pilkington as a source of float expertise, but none of the Pilkington engineers exploited this opportunity. It was only later that the company began to appreciate the quality of the engineers it had among its staff. Some were promoted to high office, others to less exalted but vital roles in the organisation, particularly in the team who liaised with licensees. But there was a solid core of talented, sometimes brilliant, engineers who came to be regarded by their peers as world leaders in their field.

While qualified and experienced engineers were in charge of the plants the detail of the operation of the plants, especially at night and over the weekends, was left to the shop-floor shift workers. They, too, were very experienced glass-

---

* Theo Barker agreed about the inventive moment but did not discuss precisely what was invented.

makers, many of them from families who had had generations of employment at Pilkington. At the time that Barradell-Smith's development team was set up he recruited not only a small group of engineers but also a group of experienced operators[14] who contributed significantly to the detailed plant operation for the melting and controlling of the glass. The expertise contributed by the operators was evident once the full-scale plant was running, as Tom Grundy, the most senior of the foremen, was a regular attendee at the daily management meetings to discuss progress and work planning. The foremen were not only practical operators but outstanding team leaders and were capable of going into a plant in chaos and quickly restoring order. Indeed, in a later era men with their capabilities would probably have gone to university and become qualified engineers.

Even at the pilot plant stage the experiments ran on a 24-hour basis, and the operators were left on their own at night to manage the plant. From the outset there was a high degree of trust in the workforce, not only on their skills but also in the ability to keep a secret. There was no leak from the factory throughout the seven-year development period. Even the wives did not know the nature of the work their husbands were doing, which could lead to problems if the husband had to work yet another extended shift,[15] although one of the excuses used was that they were growing mushrooms. The project was very popular with the workers as it had almost unlimited overtime and free meals. It was known as the Golden Mile. Barradell-Smith was very supportive of his team; on one hot day he brought in ice cream for the workers and when there was a threat that the free meals might be withdrawn he immediately protested to Alastair to have them reinstated. The company relented but on another occasion the canteen refused to supply any more meals until the dirty plates were returned. A dumper truck loaded with hundreds of plates was promptly sent to the canteen. Generally works managers were very strict and Baradell-Smith was something of a contrast, although there is no evidence that he was taken advantage of. However, he never progressed past this level to works management and retired early in 1960, having suffered a great deal of ill health when younger.

There do not appear to have been any labour disputes during the period of the development; certainly none was reported. The relationship with the unions was good. For example, when Queenborough works had to close in 1952–53 the company was complimented by the trade union for the way in which the company had handled the matter. Grundy[16] attributed the attitude of the workers to the fact that many of them had come out of the services with the discipline to tolerate hard work and the drive to provide for their families in the rebuilding of life after the war. The combination of the company's relatively advanced attitude to the treatment of their workforce and the work ethic of that workforce were material factors in coping with the severe workloads put on the development teams and delivering outcomes in a shorter time than would otherwise have been possible.

Possibly the most critical factor, however, was the role of Alastair himself. Throughout the project, despite his rapid elevation to the board, he remained very close to its progress. This was not just in technical contribution, as his name on a succession of patents attests. As many as three times a day he was on the plant, often until late at night, discussing progress and the programme of work. He was strong in setting goals and introducing new ideas but not to the point of dogmatism. He was prepared to be persuaded by a good argument and was at his best when his exuberance was tempered by hard-headed glass-makers. But above all he was an advocate for the team and the project. At the board level he had to be dispassionate about its prospects and whether it was right to continue to fund it. At the works level he had to persuade often sceptical management that float would work, either to gain their support for the pilot plants, which were run off a commercial plant with occasionally conflicting requirements, or that the project was delivering worthwhile outcomes while draining a great deal of their hard-earned profit. The project lasted for some ten years before it began to make consistent profits, and went through hugely discouraging periods. But Alastair's conviction that the process would work, and his ability to convince others, whether the board or other managers, was central to the morale of the team.

The pilot plants

Once the decision had been taken to investigate Alastair's ideas, no time was lost in drawing plans for the experiments. There were a number of problems to be addressed by the first pilot plant:

- How to contain the molten tin in the bath as it aggressively attacks many materials, such as steel.

- What atmosphere was suitable to put in the enclosure around the bath to prevent oxidation of the tin.*

- How to heat the bath so that the glass is sufficiently molten (between 1000°C and 1100°C) at the hot end to melt out any surface defects but so that the temperature of the ribbon of glass progressively drops to about 600°C at the cold end so that it can be handled without marking the surface of the glass.

- Most importantly, was there any fundamental problem in the relationship between glass and tin which could not be overcome.

---

* Molten tin exposed to the air quickly combines with the oxygen to form solid tin oxides which spoil the ability of the molten tin to transport the glass without marking it.

This became the defining question of the whole project; 'Is there any reason why this won't work?'

The first pilot plant was built by December 1952 on No.2 Rolled Plate Tank (RP2) in St Helens simply by knocking a hole in the side of a glass melting furnace and allowing some of the glass to be diverted from the normal commercial output into the experimental bath. Experiments were conducted until March 1953, the biggest problem being to contain the molten tin in the simple bath (20 foot × 15 inches) that had been constructed. The ribbon was only 12 inches wide, but the team could report to the board that the glass was good for the top surface and the bottom, while good for fire finish was marred by tin oxidation bloom and fine pits thought to be associated with devitrification.* Even at this very early stage the work was sufficiently important that it warranted reporting to the board.[17]

The results were encouraging enough for a second pilot plant to be built, this time at No.1 Rolled Plate Tank (RP1), which started up in February 1954 and had a second run of experiments in July. The bath was now 25 foot long with a ribbon 15 inches wide. There were constant improvements from refining the atmosphere (which was still burnt 'towns gas'† at this stage) to reduce its moisture content and other impurities which contaminated the tin. This was subsequently described as a 'critical stage',[18] as it had to be decided whether the defects were a natural consequence of the tin/glass interface (in which case the process was fundamentally flawed) or only as a result of impurities, which could be cured, at least in theory.

A further run was carried out in September 1954 and the rate of improvement in the quality of the glass was enough to allow support for a larger, third pilot plant, with a 30 foot bath and a 2 ft 6 ins ribbon, to be built, the requisition for £47,560 being approved in October 1954.[19] All the plants to date had received a glass ribbon formed between rollers to determine its thickness and the ribbon then ran over a plate and onto the tin. The new plant eliminated the plate, a cause of marking on the glass, and introduced electrical induction heating of the tin to reduce the need for burning gas in the bath, which caused carbon deposits and other impurities.

This new plant was operational as early as January 1955 and again there was a considerable improvement in the quality of the glass. There was a very high level of optimism at this stage. The Manufacturing Conference in March 1955 recorded 'there now appears no reason why the process should not prove successful. There seem to be no insoluble problems in adapting it to the production scale.'[20] It is worth noting that Douglas Phelps (the CEO) was

---

* Devitrification is a common glass-making problem where stagnant glass in the forming process does not cool properly and crystallises, causing visible defects in the glass.

† Actually coal gas that was made in the company's own gas plant.

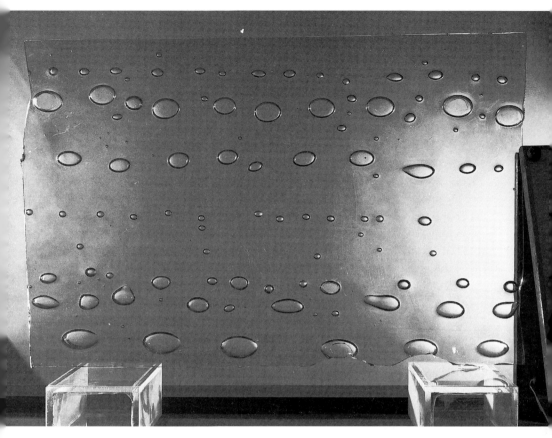

Early piece of float glass showing huge bubbles across the whole of the ribbon
PILKINGTON ARCHIVE

unusually present, as well as Lawrence Pilkington, James Watt and Alastair (who had just been promoted a full member of the board). The Flat Glass Management Committee at its meeting soon thereafter concluded that 'the time had come for a large-scale trial on No.1 Tank, Cowley Hill' (Cowley Hill was the plate glass works in St Helens and No.1 Tank, Cowley Hill (CH1) was at that time mothballed). James Watt and Alastair reported that, 'It appears probable that this process will produce plate glass quality at sheet glass prices. If these hopes are realised its possibilities are unlimited and it is capable of replacing all the existing processes for making transparent flat glass.'[21]

The published accounts of the development of the float process rightly stress the importance of Alastair's technical ability and leadership, his relationship with Sir Harry, and the sponsorship of the latter who was quick to recognise the importance of the idea.[22] But Douglas Phelps, Sir Harry's cousin and

James Watt.
PILKINGTON ARCHIVE

deputy, James Watt and Lawrence Pilkington (the director responsible for technology) were all present at key meetings. Watt, the director in charge of production, may have been a critical factor at this time. He had joined the company in 1914; by 1923 Watt was in charge of the drawn cylinder process, and in 1929 was in charge of the PPG sheet process trials. His technical input to the sheet process and his strong management skills ('He was totally terrifying,' said one of his junior engineers) had resulted in his becoming one of the few non-family managers to have been promoted to the board. Sir Harry, in particular, valued his technical judgement.

The key report on float, prior to the decision to build the first full-scale production plant, was co-authored by Alastair and Watt in about March 1955 and was submitted to the Flat Glass Management Committee, the Group Executive and the board in April and May.[23] It is probable that Watt was asked to provide a wise old head in assessing the prospects for float and to temper the enthusiasm of the inventor and developer, Alastair, who had been described in 1950 as 'lacking a little in moderation and judgement, faults of youth which he will overcome'.[24] In fact this report is the most bullish of all of the float reports during the development period and foresaw the replacement of both plate and sheet by the float process. Certainly Alastair was more cautious in his later reports, and the enthusiasm of Watt as a very experienced glass-maker would have been highly influential in obtaining board support for the project. Despite his title as the director responsible for technology (including Research), Lawrence Pilkington appears to have had no significant technical involvement with the development of float. Although little material survives in the record (it is rumoured that the adverse material was destroyed) Research (and, by implication, Lawrence) were very dubious about the potential of float and were therefore kept remote from the project, certainly in the early years, providing only an analytical service.[25] Members of the project team were very sceptical of the contributions of Research; one recalls that if Research said something would not work it heartened the team who then confidently expected a breakthrough.

The market forecast

Early in 1955 the company carried out a major review of the sheet and plate market forecast for the period up to 1960. The figures in private files,[26] the Group Executive papers[27] and the board papers[28] are difficult to reconcile, but an indicative amalgam of the various figures is shown in Table 3.1. The growth from 1939 to 1954 in plate was attributed in part to expansion of polishing capacity, but three quarters of the four-fold increase was due to improved methods of operation. In sheet the improvements were more modest, but even here there was an 83 per cent increase in output due to improvements in efficiency. After considering a range of possible forecasts the Group Executive recommended to the board that the capacity for plate be raised to 100 million sq. ft by 1960, a doubling of the capacity, to meet the optimistic end of the forecast range, and to increase sheet capacity to 350 million sq. ft, a 40 per cent increase. Much of this increase would come from improvements in efficiency, but some £2 million capital expenditure would be required. Part of the expenditure was to bring CH1 back on stream at this stage to contribute to plate glass output. Only later was it agreed that it would be converted to float. This decision would put extra pressure on the company later in the project. The conversion of CH1 was not just to provide a full-scale pilot plant whose prime role was to develop the process, but also to meet an essential part of the foreseen demand for high-quality glass. This meant that the company was short of plate glass when the project took longer than anyone expected. Once the process started to work the demand for making glass was such that not enough time could be dedicated to development when the final problems of the float process needed to be resolved, thereby prolonging the development period.

Table 3.1   *Pilkington production, actual and forecast (million sq. ft)*

	1939 (actual)	1954 (actual)	1960 (forecast)
Plate	15	48	83
Sheet	122	257	318

Source: Pilkington archives

The board were full of optimism for the future, and confident that improvements in plate and sheet efficiency, at a relatively low cost, could deliver a large proportion of the increased capacity required. The forecast growth in plate, which was a much more profitable product and in which the company had technical leadership and greater control of the market, was particularly encouraging. There was spare sheet capacity at Queenborough in Kent (which it just been agreed would come back on stream[29]) which could be converted to the more productive PPG process if the sheet market grew more than expected. (Pilkington had acquired the Fourcault machines at Queenborough in 1933.)

The rough estimate of manufacturing costs per square foot for float compared with the current process costs were:

⅜ inch sheet   current   3.34*d.*   float   3.25*d.*
¼ inch plate   current   21.25*d.*   float   10*d.*

At these figures float glass would prove to be economical enough to replace both plate and sheet. It had been decided that float, if and when successful, was to replace plate. There was no point in confusing the market with a new quality between sheet and plate, and in the early part of its life float would need to command the prices of plate until the yields became commercial, although it was still anticipated that the cost of producing float would, in the long term, match that of producing sheet. While the above figures were based on a mix of ambitious assumptions and wishful thinking, the cost of producing float did match that of ⅜ inch sheet in the mid-1970s, some 20 years later.

The decision to build

The Watt/Alastair report to both the Group Executive and the board in April and May referred to above concluded, 'It is thought that we are now able to design a production unit which would operate successfully.'[30] Both bodies approved the following expenditure:

May pilot	£9,500 capital	£8,000 special current
		(i.e. running costs)
June pilot	£23,500 capital	£8,000 special current
CH1 rebuild	£210,000 capital	
Bath	£113,500 capital	

The expectation was that CH1 would start up on 1 February 1956. In fact CH1 did not start up until May 1957, and the capital cost was £1.6 million.

A number of specific questions were identified:

- the best method of heat input;

- the type of lehr* rollers to prevent scratching of the ribbon as it emerged from the bath;

- control of the top and bottom cooling of the bath;

- which contaminants affect quality?

Work on these points was to be carried out on the pilot plant in parallel with the construction of the production unit.

The Group Executive injected a note of caution, 'success may be some time off yet … in the meantime plans for future expansion of both Plate and Sheet should go ahead unchanged.'[31] Despite the fact that only two months earlier CH1 had been part of the plate glass expansion and was now to be dedicated to float, the reconstructed glass tank could be used for plate glass production if float did not succeed. The board were, as ever, patrician, 'In view of the probable success of float finish, the congratulations of the board were extended to Mr L.A.B. Pilkington, who had been largely responsible for the original idea and the initial experiments. It was appreciated that the introduction of this process, if successful, would require very careful handling and the greatest care must be taken to ensure secrecy.'[32]

The record of the debate and the decision focuses on the detailed report on the technical progress to date and the technical work to be done. The risk was seen to be containable to the cost of the bath (which was not that great in the context of the capital cost of glass-making plant) and the running costs until the bath produced saleable glass. The rebuild costs of the glass melting tank at CH1 would have to be incurred anyway if the plant was to produce plate in due course. There was no consideration of the effect of a successful float project, or what its sales or profitability would be. It was as if the decision related to an interesting and promising, large-scale experiment which, if it

---

* A lehr is a long chamber at the end of the forming process in which the temperature is carefully controlled so that the glass is gradually cooled (annealed) to minimise the internal stresses in the glass and to make it less fragile.

failed, could be written off to R&D. The project could be stopped at any time if the board considered further costs to be unjustified.

The decision appears to have been an easy one. Approval to build the plant was granted at first hearing at each level of the approval process. The board would not approve the expenditure of £250,000 lightly, but that figure instead of the £2 million required for a new plate plant left considerable room for error. The known factors were clear, even if they were not discussed at the approval meetings. The company needed more capacity for the manufacture of plate-quality glass, and to replace its plate facilities, which were much older than those of its competitors. The pilot plants had revealed no fundamental obstacles, and progress had been so rapid that it engendered an optimism that the outstanding problems could be resolved equally quickly. Pilkington was small in relation to its rivals and the war had given it a position of relative strength and consequent profitability. The company had a brief window of opportunity during which it could exploit its position and fund a major development programme. The company was making record profits in 1955 which influenced its attitude to the affordability of the project. Twin was manifestly inefficient, and rivals were examining a number of technologies to improve the process. Time, therefore, might not be on the company's side. The forecast costs (in as far as guesswork could be called a forecast) looked competitive with sheet, let alone the far more expensive plate, and therefore capable of delivering a high level of profit. The step change in technology would keep Pilkington ahead of its rivals and enhance its leadership in the quality flat glass field.

The relevant company culture was pressing for approval. The company had been the leader in plate technology for fifty years. It was aware others were experimenting with improvements to the plate process, and the company was determined to be first to make a breakthrough. Plate replacement was planned for long before the benefits from licensing Twin were exhausted. Although there was a lot of optimism at this stage, the board were disposed for a long-term project. Their experience told them that major glass developments took time, and their relationship with the shareholders allowed them to take a long-term view in relation to profitability. As the decision was secret there was little pressure from the industry culture, but there was general pressure for plate improvement.

Yet it was a decision made in profound ignorance. As Alastair later remarked, 'Once having set up a production plant the consequences of failure would have been enormous, and in retrospect we were woefully unaware of the magnitude of the problems we were going to face when we reached a mass production scale.'[33] The partial solutions of the technical problems so far were as much a product of trial and error as of understanding the processes at work. There was to be the world of difference between the pilot plant and the full-scale plant. The first 75 per cent of progress was to be far easier than the last 5 per cent. There was no hint that the combined and growing expertise of the project team was to find it so hard to crack critical problems. There was complete ignorance of the eventual cost of the project. There was a gross underestimate of the capital cost of the project, partially because the authors of the requisition did not know what they were costing. Moreover, there was no estimate of the running costs of the new plant before it became commercial. This implies that the existing pilot plant was expected to have solved the problems before the full plant came on-line, and that the latter would require only a conventional commissioning period to iron out snags before it was yielding an acceptable proportion of good glass. There was, conversely, no false estimate of profits from the new process.

The ignorance also imposed another hurdle which nearly killed the project. It was decided at the outset that float glass had to replace plate, i.e. the highest quality glass, and not just create a new standard between sheet and plate. Most new processes are launched with a tolerance for defects and improve with experience. Float glass could only be launched when it could make a perfect product which was at least as good as the best being made. This was an extraordinarily high hurdle, and proved to be nearly impossible to surmount.

Perhaps the ignorance was fortuitous. Alastair later remarked, 'If we had been aware of the horrors which were to come it is unlikely that we would have proceeded with development work.'[34] Possibly not. But Sir Harry, Phelps and Watt had all been with the company long enough to remember how long it had taken to develop both the sheet process and the Twin. Perhaps they anticipated the duration of the struggles to come. With the benefit of hindsight Sir Harry put the project in historical perspective: 'This is really a short period for a modern development of this scale and importance. For instance, the Fourcault process ... took thirteen years to become a commercial possibility and our own Twin-grinding process was almost as long in the development stage.'[35]

While the decision to proceed with the development of float was taken largely in ignorance, it was not a bad decision. The board analysed the known elements and then applied their intuitive judgement, based on considerable experience, to the gaps in their knowledge. To the extent that the board were taking a risk, that risk was limitable. If the grounds for making the decision changed, for example the problems became unsolveable, or the costs became too high, then the project could be stopped at any time. It could be reviewed in detail by the directors at least once a month, and it was only the sunk cost that would ever be at risk.

CHAPTER FOUR

Continuing development work

WITHIN MONTHS of the decision to build CH1, the board were learning of unforeseen problems, all of which were fundamental and seemed bound to undermine the chances of success for the project.

- The process only produced glass ¼ inch thick. In 1955 the majority of the company's market for plate was for ¼ inch (6.75mm) glass, although there was a rapidly growing market for ⅛ inch glass for the laminating of automotive windscreens and there was a general trend towards thinner glass. This was difficult to make with Twin process as the thinner ribbon was more fragile and it was difficult to dissipate the heat generated by the friction in the grinding and polishing. When the first experiments on float were carried out the rolled ribbon fed onto the tin was produced at about ¼ inch as this was close to the major product requirement. It was only when, soon after the 1955 decision, other thicknesses were attempted that a fundamental problem was revealed. Whatever the thickness of the ribbon put into the process, when the ribbon was reheated on the tin it assumed a thickness of ¼ inch and nothing the team could do gave a useable ribbon of a thinner substance.

   Some theoretical work quickly proved that this was an inevitable function of the physics of the process. The surface tension of a liquid under the pull of gravity dictates whether it will form a thick or thin pool when poured onto a surface, and the nature of the surface will affect the thickness as well. The physical properties of molten tin and glass mean that glass will naturally form a ribbon about ¼ inch thick, the so called equilibrium thickness. It proved to be very difficult to change the thickness of the ribbon once it had been formed and it was not until 1962 that a method was devised. It was a matter of great good fortune that the equilibrium thickness of the ribbon was acceptable for the majority of the plate glass market; any other equilibrium thickness might have killed the project.

- The glass showed a tendency to 'bloom' on toughening. Much of the growing market for plate was for the automotive industry where the glass had to be toughened, a process which required reheating the glass and then rapidly cooling it. This process caused the surface of the float glass to develop a bluish haze, or 'bloom', and made the glass unacceptable. Although it was soon established that the problem was caused by tin ions in the surface of the glass only a few microns thick and could be cured by underpolishing, it was the mid-1960s before this problem was completely eliminated in the process and the expensive polishers dispensed with.

- The original patent applications in the USA had been rejected because the idea of floating glass on molten metal had already been patented in the USA in 1902 (Heal) and 1905 (Hitchcock). The search for prior art in the USA is much longer than in the UK and therefore these patents had not come to light earlier. For many months the protection of the process was in doubt as the inability to patent in the USA, a major market and the home of the two biggest competitors, would have substantially weakened the company's intellectual property rights and its control of the process. It took a substantial number of redrafts and a great deal of personal persuasion by both the patent agents and Sir Alastair to obtain what proved to be very robust patent coverage in the US. Despite many protestations by the eventual licensees that the patents were invalid, they were never challenged in court.

No sooner had the board decided to go ahead with the full-scale plant than they were faced with the decision whether these problems were insurmountable. This process was to repeat itself regularly. Every month over the next four years the decision-making bodies were faced with the question 'Should we go ahead?' Or, more accurately, 'Should we stop?' Because the question tended to be phrased in the latter manner, there was never an overwhelming case to stop the project. Alastair could honestly say at each meeting that they had not yet found any fundamental reason why the process was impossible. The board was always prepared to sanction the next step. Each requisition for more funds was palatable in the context of the company's trading and there was no sense of quite how far away success was to act as a brake on the momentum of the project.

The construction of the first production plant

The forecast to the board was that the plant would start up in February 1956 at a cost of £323,000. In fact it started up on 8 May 1957 at a cost of over £1 million.[1] The delays and cost increases were due to the engineering difficulties of increasing the size of the bath from 30 ft long with a ribbon 30 ins wide to a bath 100 ft long with a ribbon 100 ins wide. In addition there was the constant redesigning as new information came in from the pilot plant and new ideas were explored to deal with problems. There was a shortage of skilled engineers and draughtsmen to cope with the flood of detailed design and drawing. There were long delivery periods for critical materials, such as steel, from outside suppliers, particularly when Pilkington was asking many of them to work at the limit of, or outside, their experience.

At this stage the work was being done by Barradell-Smith's experimental engineering team under the overall leadership of Alastair, who would have responsibility for the design, building and initial operation of the plant. It would be handed over to the Cowley Hill works management when they were satisfied that it was a stable process.[2] From the outset 'it was emphasised that the most important development in hand is float Finish and this must therefore have the highest priority'.[3] Frequent meetings of the Design Committee were held,[4] chaired by Alastair whenever he was available, to discuss progress of the design, timing and other problems related to delivery of materials, feedback from the pilot plant, and to make decisions as to future action. This committee was set up in May 1955 and it noted that there was a problem on delivery times (even steel plate for the bath had a three- to twelve-month lead time), and the shortage of staff with design and specialist manufacturing skills. There was no question of contracting out any aspect of the design as the whole project had to maintain the closest possible secrecy. Suppliers were given only the minimum amount of information to enable them to supply the right materials and where their special expertise was required they had to sign confidentiality agreements with the company. Even if help were needed from other works they were not told what was going on in any detail, only what was required of them.

There were constant reminders of the urgency of the work if the start-up date were to be met, even though that date kept being put back, and Alastair was recorded as remarking tersely: 'No work for other parts of the PB organisation should be allowed to stand in the way of this project.'[5]

Nearly every aspect of the design was novel, operating at the limit of known engineering experience and often at the limit of theory. Some of the key subject areas were:

Direct pour

The initial experiments had passed the glass through rollers to form the ribbon, but Alastair at some point before late 1955 had conceived the idea of dispensing with the rollers and pouring the glass directly on to the tin and allowing nature, via gravity and surface tension, to form the equilibrium ribbon. This had the advantage, first, of reducing the amount of heat lost to the rollers which then had to be replaced by the bath heaters to get the glass hot enough to melt out the defects and, second, to avoid the difficulties of contamination introduced by the rollers themselves. Some trials were carried out early in 1956. Initially the spout was dipped into the tin, but this resulted in severe erosion of the refractory lip at the tin/glass/lip interface and consequent marring of the glass. Allowing the glass to fall freely on to the tin produced a great improvement. However, at the time the configuration of the production plant had to be finalised it was decided that there was not enough known about direct pour and that the new plant would be built with rollers. It would be easy to replace the rollers with a spout at a later date.

Atmosphere

It was obvious from the start of the experiments that the atmosphere in the enclosed area of the bath was critical. It gradually became clear that it had to contain, as nearly as possible, no impurities. Oxygen, in particular, was critical as it led to the creation of tin oxide which floated on the surface of the tin as dross and either scratched the glass or was incorporated in the surface of the glass as cold end speck, or condensed out of the atmosphere and dripped on to the glass as one cause of top speck or combined with the glass to cause bloom. Even at the start of CH1 the atmosphere was still burnt coal gas, which contained no oxygen but was full of unwanted impurities, but as the design progressed the concept of using nitrogen with a little hydrogen began to evolve, with the consequent problem of how to get nitrogen and hydrogen in sufficient quantities and of sufficient purity.

Sealing

Oxygen was the biggest single enemy of the process and it was later established that it was sensitive to oxygen levels as low as 5 parts per million. Having provided the right atmosphere, it had to be kept in the bath without any outside air being allowed in. Given that the bath was open at both ends, to allow the glass in and out, proper sealing was to remain a challenge until long after the project became public in 1959.

Heating

The bath temperatures ranged from 1100°C at the hot end to 600°C at the cold end. At the time that the CH1 design started, the team were resigned to having some sort of flame in the bath although this made atmosphere control much more difficult and introduced impurities which contaminated the bath. Some experiments had been done with electrical induction heating of the tin, but this created difficulties with tin flow and instability in the direction of the ribbon ('snaking') and was unlikely to be sufficient. In the course of design an external supplier mentioned a form of electrical resistance heaters which could be built into the roof. These proved promising but within six months a new experimental German resistance heater had been found, tested and ordered, even though 'we are doing all the development work.'[6] It was considered that the two types of heater would provide enough heat in the bath (particularly if the project moved to direct pour, which required less heat) and they had the added benefit of allowing 'zoning' of the heat in the different sections of the bath. This proved to be critical in controlling the process and allowing for the elimination of the heaters in the bath bottom which caused a number of problems.

Construction

The bath had to remain absolutely flat and horizontal during operation despite the high temperatures and the temperature difference between each end. The construction had to be airtight and proof against the aggressive attack of molten tin, well as being able to cope with the differential expansion of the different materials during warm up. While the designers were experienced with the construction of high temperature glass furnaces, the bath involved new and unexplored territory. The method of fixing the heaters through the roof was difficult, and much redesign had to be done so that the detailed fixings could survive in the hostile environment of the bath and provide an adequate seal. In addition the team were not sure whether an arch roof or a suspended roof would be preferable, and both were built.

Refractories

The refractories used to protect the wall of the furnace and any other part of the plant from attack by the molten glass are critical to good glass-making, and the company had a great deal of expertise and had undertaken on-going development in this area. Despite this the material used for the canal leading from the furnace to the bath, the tweel (or movable dam in the canal which controls the flow of glass into the bath) and the spout were to give persistent problems for many years. But there was an extraordinary bit of luck with the choice of the refractories for lining the bath. During the whole development period there is no mention of the refractories in the bath giving trouble because of their composition. This is surprising as it was later established that the composition of the blocks, down to the microscopic level, was fundamental to the successful operation of the bath. When one licensee, LOF, started up, their bath 'boiled' because of microscopic pores in refractories they had already found perfectly acceptable elsewhere.[7] Even as late as the 1980s an approved supplier provided blocks which broke up in operation because the source of the clay had been altered; it was chemically identical, but its grains, which caused the failure, were microscopically more angular than in clay from the previous source. It appears, then, that Pilkington just happened upon a refractory that did not create any problems; if that had not been the case, the defects caused by the blocks might well have been one complexity too many for the project to have succeeded. New techniques for fixing the bath bottom blocks and the design of their shape had to be devised to prevent them from becoming dislodged and floating up; they had to be properly dry to avoid moisture in the bath; and even the cement for grouting the blocks and sealing the bath had to be specifically developed, albeit these were relatively simple problems to solve.

Lehr
The take-out rollers at the end of the bath and the first few rollers in the lehr had to be specially designed and manufactured. They had to remain perfectly cylindrical despite the heat and had to be covered with a material that did not mark the glass and also remain perfectly true through long operation.

Tin
The depth, flow, purity and heating of the tin were critical to the process, and ever more sophisticated methods for controlling these elements were introduced as information was fed back from the pilot plant. Even draining the tin was a problem. A simple valve compromised the integrity of the bath bottom, and devising a method for pumping the liquid tin required completely original work. The use of tin was not taken for granted. Aluminium was tried, but its oxides were rock like and much too aggressive on the glass. Lead was suggested (much to the dismay of Barradell-Smith, who foresaw the health problems of lead vapour), and the other metals with the right range of temperatures at which they were molten and the right vapour pressure were less common and far more expensive.[8] As late as 1958 alternatives to tin were still on the agenda.

Cutting
The expected output of the bath was far higher than existing plants, and the team had to start to devise ways in which the ribbon could be cut and handled into the warehouse at far greater speeds than ever before.

Progress on the design and the work on the pilot plant was regularly reported to the Manufacturing Conference, the Flat Glass Management Committee, the Group Executive and the board. The pilot plant was consistently improving the results of the process. In January 1956 it was reported that the tin contamination causing bloom on toughening was only 10 microns thick and that there were conditions in which it might be reduced, but it was conceded that if it was impossible to prevent on subsequent heating for toughening or bending it would 'severely' limit float's use.[9]

The Group Executive wobbled a bit in October 1956: 'Some members of the board expressed doubt as to the value of float as it could only make equilibrium substances.' The conclusion was that equilibrium was 'probability'. But despite this unusually pessimistic conclusion, 'float development is to be given priority over everything else.'[10]

By January 1957 induction heating of the tin was reasonably successful, but flows in the tin caused the ribbon to snake in a manner that could not yet be controlled. The new roof heaters were successful, and some types of distortion were found to be controllable with a better understanding of temperature control in the bath. In particular, the temperature gradient of the ribbon was not what was required. At the hot end the glass gave up heat to the tin, cooling it too quickly, and at the cold end the tin gave up heat to the glass, making it too hot. This was being regulated by water coolers in the tin, although the problems had not been completely solved. The minute is terse: 'We [the Manufacturing Conference] want a reasonable assurance that they will be solved fairly quickly in the production scale plant.'[11]

By the next meeting of the Manufacturing Conference in March 1957 the team could report that they had gone back to using the rollers and the pilot plant had run for some weeks without trouble. Cowley Hill management (who were to take responsibility for CH1 when it came on stream) were satisfied that the process was a fairly stable one to operate and were prepared to accept it. Snaking of the ribbon had been cured by water-cooled pushers; top specks were apparently related to the atmosphere; and all CO_2 and sulphur needed to be removed. A crucial discovery was that bloom was not caused when a piece of glass was floated on clean tin under laboratory conditions. The cause of bloom, like all the other defects which were rendering the glass unsaleable, was not fundamental to the process. It was just a matter of getting the operating plant to be as perfect as the laboratory.

The problems all appeared to be solveable.[12] The report to the board was rather more bullish; one particularly difficult form of distortion had been cured by the rate of cooling, and the glass 'last week was satisfactory for motor trade. Most samples do not show a great tendency to bloom on toughening,'[13] (an uncharacteristically obscure use of language). The board agreed to the starting up of CH1 in the light of progress on RP1 (the pilot plant), and it also agreed to continue further experiments on RP1 at a cost of £10,000.[14]

The first eighteen months of production

CH1 started up at 1 p.m. on 8 May 1957. Initially the plant was using rollers to form the ribbon and burnt towns gas for the atmosphere. There were plenty of defects, but they had all been seen before and had been controlled to an acceptable level. However, they proved much more intractable to solve on the full-scale plant. Alastair admitted to the Group Executive that conditions on CH1 were quite different from the experimental unit.[15] On 24 June the atmosphere was changed to a nitrogen/hydrogen mixture and there was a 'spectacular improvement for dust and bubble.'[16] Early in September the bath had to shut down for running repairs, and the decision was made by the team to start up again with direct pour. The rollers were causing too many faults, partly because they were relatively cold, and the tin dross was sticking to them and getting on the underside of the glass, and partly because it was very difficult to seal the bath in the area around the rollers to prevent oxygen getting in. By this time a flat ribbon was being made and the Group Executive noted that the glass was very nearly saleable but for an accumulation of defects such as bubble,[17] although the board were warned in the same month, 'It is not possible to say how soon, or how easy, it will be to eliminate these faults, but we still believe that the process will be a success.'[18]

When direct pour started on 19 September 1957 a platinum-coated spout was used. It was 40 inches wide in relation to a ribbon 100 inches wide. Platinum is very resistant to attack by molten glass, and the intention was to reduce the contaminants caused by the erosion of the spout. A few days later platinum coating was used on the tweel, although they were both found to generate an electrostatic charge that had to be earthed as the charge caused bubble. The team had been varying the temperature of the glass flowing into the bath, the speed of the ribbon, the temperature gradient through the bath, the depth of the tin, the electrical flows in the spout and tweel as well as trying to improve the sealing at either end of the bath and the purity of the atmosphere.[19]

The strain on the development team was now far more intense as CH1 was a full-scale plant operating 24 hours a day and capable of producing 1,200 tons of glass a week. Through the whole of the period from May 1957 to October 1958 virtually none of the product was saleable, although there were tantalising patches of good glass by June 1958, which encouraged the team that they were making progress. Apart from a few samples, one of which was made into a mirror and is now at The World of Glass Museum in St Helens, the whole output was broken up for recycling. (The optimum batch for glass-making includes a proportion of broken glass or cullet, and so this glass could be used both on CH1 and other Pilkington plants. However, there were times when the glass was so contaminated with tin that it was discussed how this

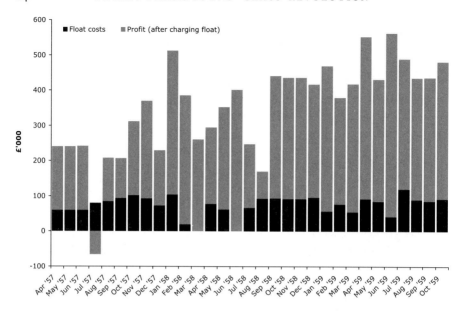

Figure 4.1   UK sheet and plate profits and float costs, April 1957–October 1959.

SOURCE: PILKINGTON ARCHIVES

could be disposed of without breaching security.) The Flat Glass Management Committee had as early as March 1956 agreed the Special Current requisition for £180,000 for three months' operation for CH1.[20] After that period, the plant was expected to be earning its keep and any further operating costs would have to obtain the approval of the Group Executive. Every month Alastair had to report to the Group Executive and receive formal approval of another month's running costs. At this time the costs were about £80,000 per month and were absorbing a high proportion of the monthly profit of the whole of the UK flat glass operations (see Figure 4.1). Indeed, in July 1957, a poor month for trading, the flat glass operations made a loss of £66,000 after charging £80,000 for float.[21]

In November the daily meeting reviewed the ten weeks' experience of direct pour production. There had been steady improvement, but curing one problem only seemed to exacerbate another. The report to the Group Executive said, 'The latest results have been encouraging [even] if, as so often happened in our work on float, the reasons for the improvement are by no means clear.'[22]

The board also received a version of this report, the fullest technical review it had yet considered, and concluded: 'It may be that the process will be proved so difficult to control that it is not economic to use it for production

Part of the float development team, including George Dickinson (third from left), one of the most respected expert engineers and a patent holder in his own right. From left to right: Alastair Pilkington, Ernie Litherland, George Dickinson, J.E.C. Thomas, Jack Topping, Dick Barradell-Smith.

of glass in the 7 mm range.'[23] The report to the board was brutally honest, and set out the individual views of key members of the team, and not just the consensus view or that of Alastair. This style of report was unique as each of the authors had a different view of the difficulties to be faced and the time it would take to overcome them. Within the team views varied as to whether it would take 6 or 12 months to achieve success, and there was 'no evidence to encourage us that it is possible to make glass outside the 6.5–7 mm range'. However, all the authors agreed that the problems were solveable, and that the remaining issues were no more difficult than those that had already been solved. 'Before giving up float it is necessary to consider the alternatives which appear to be heavy expenditure on grinding and polishing equipment and comparatively a back place technically in plate manufacture for some time.'[24] Alastair had seen work being done by Ford on the acid polishing of plate as an alternative to the current polishing with rouge and that done by LOF in the twin grinding of ⅛ inch plate, and the Continentals were also rumoured to be working on the twin grinding of thin plate. The company was now committed to float; if the project were to fail, it was becoming increasingly likely that others companies would gain the upper hand.

A special meeting of the Group Executive was held in January 1958 to review the float project to date, the total costs incurred and the latest cost estimates of float against plate. This showed a difference of 4*d*. per foot (14*d*. for plate against 10*d*. for float). A great number of assumptions were made, not only in relation to the uncertainties of float but also on the costs and efficiencies of future plate, bearing in mind that most of the company's plate assets were pre-war in date.[25]

Despite the difficulties reported, there seems to have been no serious consideration of stopping the project, but, without diluting the effort on float the board knew it ought to explore urgently other means of making thin plate, even if it meant buying in other processes.[26] When CH1 had to stop shortly afterwards for repairs it was decided to restart the plant using the float bath merely as a transporter and not to finish the glass, to make thin rough cast plate, which could then be ground and polished, to cover the repair of another plate tank and to help meet the current high demand for plate generally. This run was from January to July 1958 (with a break for the complete reblocking of the bottom of the bath) and gave the team time to try to consolidate what they had learned and to gather experience of the relatively calm operation of the float bath as a conveyor. Research Department

Sid Robinson.
PILKINGTON ARCHIVE

were also involved, for example doing work on tin alloys as an alternative to tin and to try and alter the equilibrium thickness of the ribbon by changing the composition of the glass. The board minuted that the chances of success for this work were small.[27]

At the same time it was decided to do some parallel experimental work on the Vitrolite plant in Doncaster. Vitrolite was an opaque glass in a variety of colours used as a wall covering, but was only made by a batch process and was proving to be uncompetitive in cost with alternatives. Using the float process to make Vitrolite would reduce costs, give the product a new lease of life and contribute to the float process know-how. As the glass was opaque some of the problems of distortion and the under surface could be ignored and efforts concentrated on the formation and stability of the ribbon.

One of the Vitrolite team was Sid Robinson, who had joined the company in 1949 and who, encouraged by James Watt, had developed methods of modelling flows of glass in the forming process to help identify problems. While at Doncaster he modelled the flow of glass in the crucial area of the spout and explored the effects of the subtle changes to the formation of the ribbon as the configuration of the spout was changed. A great deal was learned from these trials and Vitrolite was successfully made by the float process, despite the fact that some of the colours had glass compositions which were even more sensitive to the forming process than conventional glass. The work proved to be in vain for Vitrolite, which was soon discontinued as uncompetitive, but the work was invaluable for the float development.

Table 4.1   *UK sheet and plate sales and profits, 1949–1959 (£m)*

	1949	1950	1951	1952	1953	1954	1955	1956	1957	1958	1959
Total home sales	8.3	8.6	8.6	9.6	9.3	12.2	14.6	17.0	18.2	22.0	22.0
Total export sales	2.9	3.8	4.3	5.5	3.7	4.6	5.9	7.3	6.8	6.3	6.7
Sheet profit	0.6	0.8	1.0	0.8	0.4	0.9	0.9	0.9	0.7	1.0	1.0
Plate profit	0.2	0.5	0.8	1.0	0.4	1.2	1.8	2.1	1.4	1.3	2.1
Float costs									−0.1	−0.9	−0.9

Source: Pilkington accounts

The uncertainty of the success of float, particularly to make thin glass, was having a material effect on the finances of the company. Although the company was experiencing record demand (see Table 4.1), the costs of float were making significant inroads into the flat glass profits (see Figure 4.1 above) and the company could not rely on float meeting, or helping to meet, the forecast growth in the flat glass markets. Accordingly the Group Executive decided

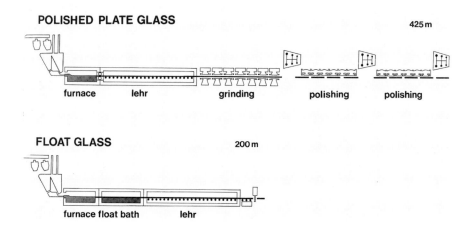

Diagram showing the relative sizes of plate and float plants.
PILKINGTON ARCHIVE

to invest in a new grinder and polisher (capable of producing thin plate) at a cost of £3 million. In his report to the Executive on thin plate demand. even Alastair seemed resigned to the inability of float to make thin glass. The following cost comparisons between plate and float were tabled:

	Twin grinder	Float
Annual output	41.5m sq. ft	44.8m sq. ft
Works operating cost	£2.5m	£1.9m
Manufacturing expenses	£110,000	£110,000
Replacement charges*	£661,000	£252,000
Costs per foot	18s. 7d.	12s. 3d.

* This indicates that the capital cost of the twin was more than two and a half times that of float.[28]

The next campaign on float started in July 1958, and the team were again exploring all the parameters of the process to try to eliminate the persistent faults of cold end speck (tiny particles of tin oxide on the underside of the glass caused by dross arising from oxygen in the bath), hot end speck (tiny particles on the top surface caused by the condensation of tin and sulphur oxides in the hot end of the bath atmosphere), line distortion (caused by lack of homogeneity in the glass and contaminants from the canal, tweel and spout), devitrification (caused by stagnant glass behind the lip of the spout) and bloom (caused by the absorption by the glass of tin ions where there was oxygen contamination of the tin). Even though the causes of most of the faults were now understood, at least in principle, it was proving very difficult to cure them. It must be remembered that the team were trying to produce a near-perfect product. Glass sold to the customer had to be free of faults, and the human eye is capable of detecting flaws only fractions of an inch in diameter, particularly if the glass was used for mirrors. The rate of flaws in the glass had to be such that a high percentage of the glass made could be sold to the customer after allowing for normal losses in the cutting of plates from the ribbon to meet customer requirements.

The float process was proving to be very subtle. Tiny variations in the operating parameters seemed to make a big difference to the type and frequency of faults. It was extremely difficult to monitor inside the float bath key matters such as the temperature of tin, glass and atmosphere and the flows of liquids and gases. The development of new measuring techniques was going hand in hand with other advances. In September 1958 it was realised that some of the equipment for reading temperature was not accurate, and the team could not be sure that the parameters they thought they knew and understood had even been measured and recorded correctly.[29]

Despite these difficulties progress was being made, although there is just a hint that the board were losing patience. In September 1958 it received a report that some glass of motor trade quality had been made but it was only intermittent, in the central part of the ribbon. Generally speaking it had been by far the most encouraging month ever since CH1 was lit, but Alastair was still cautious: 'the float process is quite capable of having kept some difficulties up its sleeve.'[30] The board's response was that in view of the promising state of production a further four months of trials would be funded.[31] The approval for float expenditure given by the Group Executive had been given 'if necessary to the end of January when a special meeting of the Group Executive will be held'.[32] This reads as an ultimatum that if the process were not successful by the end of the four months the future of float would be in question.

The doubts proved to be a momentary lapse. By the next meeting it appeared that there had been a breakthrough, and the board were agreeing to let Triplex (the automotive glass processing customer) have samples of the glass for toughening trials with a view to announcing the process to the world on 20 January 1959.[33]

The precise nature of the breakthrough was unclear at the time. The team thought that bloom had been reduced to a level which was acceptable on their tests. Cold end speck could be dealt with by under-cleaning the glass with conventional polishers; while not ideal, this would produce saleable glass until the problem was finally solved, and would also get rid of the layer of contaminated glass which caused bloom. The gas curtains at either end of the bath were controlling the atmosphere better, and oxygen ingress was at a tolerable level. Stirrers in the canal had improved the homogeneity of the glass and therefore reduced the distortion. Occasional refining of the tin to remove oxides and residual oxygen in the tin had had beneficial results, and the key remaining problem was top speck, and even that was at a level where the yields into the warehouse were acceptable. However, there was still too high a proportion of unacceptable glass for the process to be commercial. The fault density was too high to put more than 40 per cent of the glass into the warehouse, and the yield had to be more than 50 per cent if it was to be commercial.

The daily meeting of the project team recorded that the spout was sagging (7 October), and that on the following day it had been jacked up. The next note of import was the report on 4 November that 600,000 sq. ft were now in stock.[34] Suddenly the plant was making saleable glass in significant, if not yet commercial, quantities. Although the team were unaware of it, the deformation of the spout was altering the flow of the glass so that impurities and bubbles from the refractories of the canal and spout were being carried to the edge of the glass,[35] and the glass quality and consistency of much of the ribbon were suddenly showing a viable process. The change was too subtle for a breakthrough to be recognised, let alone announced; the threshold of viability had been crept over rather than being crossed with a flourish. As Sid Robinson said: 'There were no eureka moments with float; we just struggled from crisis to crisis.'[36] At its meeting in November 1958 the board were informed, 'the bubble at present is good and appears to be under control although we do not yet know exactly what we are doing or why we are doing it.'[37]

There is a disarming honesty about Alastair's reports to the board throughout the development period. Later accounts of the float saga emphasised Alastair's advocacy with the board to persuade them to continue with funding at the rate of £80,000–100,000 per month. Yet the papers and the minutes show a self-deprecating style that is in contrast to the current vogue for unremitting optimism in problem solving, especially its public face. After the initial enthusiasm engendered by the possibility of float replacing both plate and sheet, the hard reality of the drawn-out development process required a different style. The audience was not a group of economic analysts who were only concerned with impact on short-term profits and who wanted to see progress every half year to comment to arm's-length investors. The board were all experienced glass-makers who knew how difficult any forming process was to control. They would not be persuaded by false optimism and unsupportable claims. They lived with the fact that much of glass-making was an art and therefore the subject of trial and error. Alastair later said that the most he could say at each meeting was that the team had not discovered a fundamental problem, one that was scientifically incapable of being solved. The problems were difficult, and solving one often seemed to lead to others, but there was nothing to indicate that, given time and continued support, the team would not succeed. One suspects that Alastair allowed himself to be critical, but woe betide anybody else who criticised the lack of progress being made.

The long agreed policy was that when the company was confident that the float process was viable they would first have the glass trialled at Triplex, a major UK customer (in which Pilkington had a large shareholding) who produced toughened glass for all of the British automotive industry. Only the Chairman of Triplex was taken into the company's confidence that the glass to be tested was made by a novel process, and glass was sent to Triplex without revealing that it was anything extraordinary. Experts from the company were to be on hand to witness the trials. If the trials were successful a public announcement would be made as soon as possible to minimise the risk of a leak.

The trials with Triplex were not a total triumph. Some glass still bloomed on toughening, probably because Triplex reheated the glass for certain designs of windscreen to a higher temperature than that used in Pilkington's tests.[38] However under-cleaning would eliminate the problem, at least as an interim measure, and Triplex decided that the glass was acceptable. The board were told that the team were very hopeful that they had found a way to control bloom: 'if we can do this then float is a success, unless some new and unknown problem arises.'[39]

The final hurdle

The public announcement of float was made to an astonished glass-making world on 20 January 1959, despite reservations from Alastair of announcing a process which turned out to be a 'fiasco',[40] but the board were anxious to announce before there were any damaging leaks. After the first patent applications were public in May 1955 there were worries of a leak when Sir Harry had been told soon thereafter that PPG and LOF were repeating a general rumour that Pilkington were working on a process which would completely upset Twin.[41] A statement was devised to be given to those who raised the matter: 'Float Finish is an interesting development which is being followed up by us.'[42] In 1957 Alastair reported that in meetings with both PPG and LOF 'float was continually being brought into the discussion,'[43] but after the announcement that the company was investing in another grinder and polisher the rumours appear to have diminished.[44]

Despite the knowledge that Pilkington were working on something interesting, the extent of the revolution and the quality of the product samples sent to the competitors were a surprise to all. There was industry-wide endorsement of Sir Harry's claim at the press conference that, 'float [is] the most fundamental, revolutionary and important of all the advances in glass-making of the present century'.[45] PPG decided to delay any further commitment to upgrading its facilities until more information was available about Pilkington's process.[46] The head of St Gobain had even thought that the announcement was a ruse to aid the company's negotiations in relation to a licence to St Gobain for Twin in the USA.[47] General interest was so high that the PR Department asked for 20,000 extra copies of the brochure announcing float.[48]

CH1 had to be shut down for repairs in January 1959, and at that time the broken spout was replaced. The plant reverted to poor yields. It was to be another ten months before the plant was consistently making acceptable glass. The manner in which the final hurdle to commercial production was overcome, and tracing it back to the sagging spout in October 1958, has become part of the mythology of float. Even Sir Alastair made much of the lucky accident of the broken spout in his story of float to the Royal Society in his fellowship address in 1969,[49] a version over which he took particular pains to be accurate.* However, there is some question as to how vital the broken spout was; certainly it was not so obvious to the team in 1959.

What is certain is that the team realised that the configuration of the forming area of the ribbon was crucial, and had to be understood. By this time Sid Robinson had returned to the pilot plant from Doncaster and in the middle months of 1959 was running a set of experiments with models. He constructed a ¼ scale bath from perspex and substituted concentrated lead nitrate solution for the molten tin and silicone fluid for the glass. Traces of dye could be added to the silicone to observe clearly the precise nature of the flow of the glass. It was quickly established that the glass flowing from the tank and in contact with the canal and spout was slightly contaminated and slightly cooler than the glass above it. If the glass falling from the spout to the tin were allowed to flow sideways freely then the cooler, contaminated glass naturally flowed to the edge of the ribbon, leaving the centre fault free. In addition the precise height of the spout discouraged the glass from becoming stagnant under the lip, a primary cause of devitrification distortion. It was also noted that a faster flow of glass down the centre of the spout affected the flow of defects from centre to edge of the ribbon, and it was probably this effect caused by the previous October's sagging of the spout that had tipped the yields to a near acceptable level. Sid Robinson did an extended series of experiments over a number of months to explore the parameters of

---

* Despite the fact that in 1969 float was an undeniable triumph and Sir Alastair had given innumerable presentations about its development, he confessed to be extremely nervous about his inaugural address to the Fellows of the Royal Society.

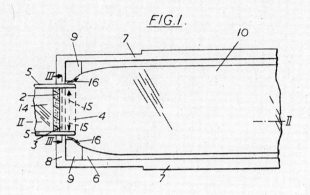

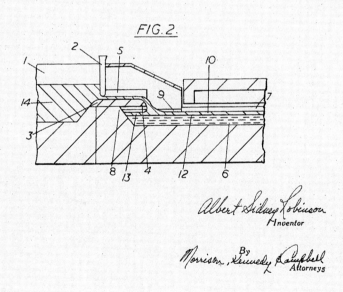

US patent application for the detailed layout around the spout invented by Sid
Robinson.

these effects. The range of success was tiny. A hollowing of the 40 inch spout by 1 inch produced the right effects. More hollowing created a different set of problems and the amount of lateral flow in the 100 inch wide ribbon was optimum at about 4 inches. The precision of the set-up of the spout and the area around it, differing with different loads, was critical to the success of float and its patent protection. Licensees were happy to pay royalty for the product of this work and other equally rigorous experiments, rather than conduct expensive development of their own with the risk that it might not avoid the Pilkington patents.

The results of these experiments could not be installed immediately, and there was a succession of other problems with the plant. At the same time work was being done on purifying the atmosphere further, purifying the tin and experimenting with the depth of the tin (which also had a fundamental impact on distortion) and the speed of the ribbon. In each run some saleable glass was made (see Figure 4.2), but the yields were poor, and the team did not think that they had the process under control. The daily meeting on 23 July 1959 was despondent enough to describe the problems as 'intractable'.[50] But the new spout embodying the work on the precise interactions on the flow of glass around and behind the spout produced a good ribbon. Another major step forward was made when experiments with the heating and recirculation

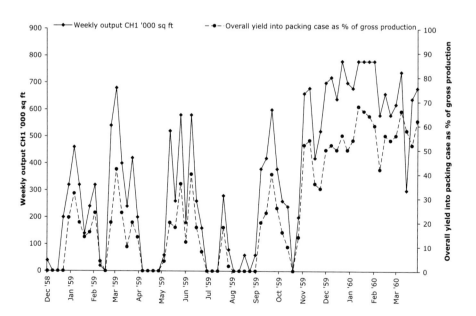

Figure 4.2   Float glass – production report No.2
SOURCE: PILKINGTON ARCHIVES

of the atmosphere at last offered hope for the elimination of top speck, or at least reduction to a level which allowed economic yields.

The pressure on the team had been intense. The process had been announced. Competitors were clamouring for samples and a chance to inspect the process with a view to seeking a licence. The plant was costing £100,000 a month to run, with hardly any glass going into the warehouse, and the company's shortfall in production was such that it had to buy in 2 million sq. ft of plate in order to meet the demands of customers.[51] But by the middle of September the plant was consistently producing good glass with high yields, and thereafter the ribbon was speeded up to 110 inches per minute without problems. Figure 4.2 shows the output yields into packing case (i.e. the saleable product) in 1959. There was a series of problems causing stoppages, but the gradual introduction of ideas from other experiments was producing improvements and after a final, minor stoppage in October 1959 the plant began to produce saleable glass at a rate that the team were confident was viable in the long term.

Although there were many problems yet to be solved, November 1959 was the real turning point in the commercial success of the process. It was to be many months before float recorded a profit (mainly because the plant was frequently being used as an experimental unit to try to produce other thicknesses of glass), but when it was operating the plant produced glass economically from this date onwards. The company was now so confident of the long-term viability of the process that it made plans to build a second float plant at Cowley Hill.[52]

The papers and minutes do not show any criticism or reservations of the project by any individual, other than Sir Alastair himself, who is on more than one occasion recorded as warning that the process was capable of throwing up new surprises. As late as 1960 he was saying, 'There is no doubt that float will run into difficulties in the future'.[53] There was a tradition in the company that decisions were arrived at by consensus; the matter would be discussed until a decision emerged that everybody supported. There was no question of voting or majority verdicts.[54] Although Sir Alastair subsequently referred to plenty of people who were doubtful about the success of the project, this is not reflected to any marked degree in the papers. Sir Alastair could express caveats, but Sir Harry was 'unwavering',[55] and the published view was unanimously in support of the project. The development of float so far had taken seven years and £4 million.[56] The team later established that there were 18 ways in which the float process itself produces bubble, 16 ways of producing distortion and 12 ways of making top speck, all of which were interrelated,[57] but, as Sir Harry said, 'We have willingly paid the heavy price, because we know that the one thing that is more expensive than to lead in industry, is to be led.'[58]

The decisions to continue

The progress of the float project was reviewed by the directors in formal meetings two or three times a month, and probably daily in the directors' lunch room. Throughout the building of CH1 there was a continual upgrading of the original requisition for capital and updates on progress (or lack of it). After the first three months of operating CH1 the project team had to ask for every month's additional funding. Yet despite the constant refrain of frustration and setback the board or the relevant committee approved the continuation of the project. What were the reasons for this continued optimism?

Sir Alastair later said that one of the keys to the success of the project was that there was never a time when he had to say to the board, 'We have hit a fundamental problem'. The team never found a reason why the process would not work, even though they struggled long and hard to find the precise ways in which it could be made to work satisfactorily. In the absence of a categorical barrier, the board was always prepared to fund the next month. After the initial euphoria, Sir Alastair is the only one reported to be critical of the progress and this realism, even pessimism, was in keeping with the experience of all the earlier glass developments. Drawn cylinder, sheet and continuous grinding had all taken years to perfect; there was no reason why float should be different.

The fact that approvals were monthly was also crucial. Although there were months when there was no apparent progress, the team were only asking for one more month's spending. Each month the sum could be looked at in the context of that month's profits, and each month it was affordable. The only time, at the end of 1958, that the board consciously looked further ahead was the one time that the project was given a written ultimatum. If funding had been sought for six months or a year at a time the sheer scale of the proposed expenditure might have been too much to bear.

Vitally, too, there were no onlookers. The family shareholders had truly delegated their stewardship to the board. While Sir Harry had to be conscious of their long-term interests, he did not have to tell them what was being done, let alone explain it to them. He later admitted that he did not know whether the project would have come to fruition if the company had been in public ownership, and that was in 1973 when the nature of surveillance by public shareholders and their advisors was very much less stringent than it was even ten years later. It would be difficult to sustain a five-year experiment, absorbing a quarter of the main division's profits, in the face of commentators who were measuring success by the size of the half-year dividend.

The culture of the company was also supporting the project. As noted, everybody knew that glass development took a long time, but that the rewards would be worth it. Every major invention had eventually reaped great rewards

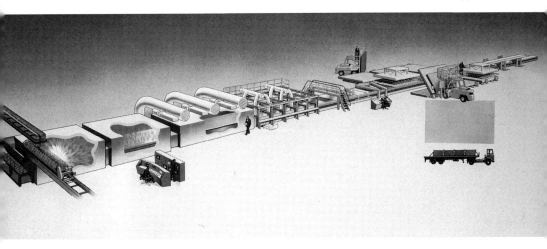

Diagram of a float plant.
PILKINGTON ARCHIVE

for the developer. The company already held the view that it wanted to be among the world leaders in everything it did. It had to make the next plate breakthrough if it was to sustain leadership in its major market. There was a large measure of trust among the members of the board that they would do so. Even though Alastair was a newcomer, he had the support of Sir Harry and Watt, and that was enough for the other directors, even if Lawrence was equivocal about the chance of success. They must have worried about the outcome, but not to the extent that they were going to rock the boat. More surprisingly, in an era which lauded experience and sagacity, youth was given its head. The original remit of the investigation was expressly not to stifle ideas, and the project was manned by enthusiastic, optimistic engineers in their thirties. They didn't know what they couldn't do.

In the same way the industry culture was driving them forward. All the plate manufacturers were working on plate improvements, although none as radical as float. The industry was searching for, and expecting, the next breakthrough. There was also the expectation that the one who announced something valuable could expect the rest of the industry to be banging on its door, as had always been the case in the past.

All of these circumstances were supporting the float project in the 1950s. The individuals had the talents and the leaders had the experience to give talent its head. The company had the resources, the freedom and the ambition. The industry had the expectation. It was perhaps the only time in Pilkington's history that a project with the audacity and radicalism of float could have been contemplated and seen through development to eventual success.

CHAPTER FIVE

The decision to license
float glass technology

O N 19 JANUARY 1959 Pilkington announced the successful development of their float glass process. A few days later the relevant sub-committee of the board discussed the terms on which licences could be granted.[1] However, the principle of licensing had never been discussed by the board or any of its sub-committees. From the earliest days of the float glass project it had simply been assumed that the technology would be licensed, and the only discussion was of the terms and the timing. Elementary business practice would indicate that such a fundamental matter of strategy should have been analysed in depth, and that to make a decision off the cuff was irrational. However, examining the background makes it clear that the strategy of licensing the technology was not only quite rational but probably inevitable.

The recorded decision

The decision to license the float glass technology was perhaps the biggest strategic decision the company had ever taken. To external reviewers whether to license or not was by no means obvious. As late as 1986 the question 'Why did Pilkington license the float glass process?' was still being publicly debated. In making their takeover bid for Pilkington (see Chapter 11) BTR Industries plc raised as a major criticism of the company's management that they had licensed the float glass process and thereby created competitors when they could have kept the process to themselves, relied on the protection of their patents and created a world-wide monopoly. In the *Financial Times* of 5 December 1986, the Lombard columnist Christopher Lorenz answered that it would have been politically suicidal and economically 'more than stupid'. A leading student textbook contains a case study of the exploitation of float glass, and a key debating point for students is how Pilkington should exploit the process once it had been announced.[2]

It is therefore extraordinary that there is no record of the decision to license being taken. At that time even the minutiae of the business, such as the purchase of inexpensive office equipment, had to be approved formally by the directors and minuted, and it is extremely unlikely that a decision was taken without being recorded. The assumption must be that no express decision to license was ever made. It appears from early in the development of float glass that licensing was simply assumed to be part of the exploitation strategy. As early as May 1955, when the Flat Glass Management Committee (FGMC) were considering the decision to build CH1, they said:

> Very careful thought must be given to the whole future policy for
> manufacturing by, and licensing of, this process, including such
> things as obligations to flat glass manufacturers under existing
> agreements, freedom to manufacture in countries abroad and to which
> manufacturers we might license the process.[3]

In January 1956 the Group Executive had agreed to set up a sub-committee to work out 'with the greatest urgency' the general and commercial picture for approval by the board.[4] There is no record of their deliberations, but it is reasonable to assume that this group discussion led to the notes for licensing prepared by Sir Harry. These are dated March 1956 and set out possible terms for licences, the overall policy being for the company to extend manufacture in the UK, to increase its share of world glass sales, to make money out of licensing and 'to shape the glass industry as we desire, particularly so in Europe'.[5] These outline terms were given general approval by the board, but there is no mention of any discussion as to whether licensing was the right policy. In October 1958 the concept of a small committee to concentrate on major policy issues was formalised by the setting up of the Directors' Flat Glass Committee (DFGC) whose terms of reference included, 'broad questions of policy in the flat glass field, both present and in the future, say, up to ten years ahead'.[6] Even though the proceedings of this committee were minuted, and the papers submitted to it are preserved, there is no record at all of any discussion on the question of whether to license or not, only the terms on which licences should be granted. Indeed, they took as their starting point the notes which Sir Harry had prepared in March 1956. The same is true for all the other bodies that carried policy making responsibilities.

Only in his report to shareholders in 1963, when the first licences had already been granted, did Sir Harry feel the need to justify licensing. He said that the company should not be too greedy and should concentrate its efforts in countries where it was already strong and in a position to extend manufacture. To invade the territories of other manufacturers would risk weakening the company in the inevitable fight. Instead, competitors should be encouraged to develop and use float glass as the main glass of the future.[7]

There were many well-understood, but unspoken, commercial reasons why it was not in the company's interests to try to maintain monopoly of manufacture. The real reasons for licensing were deeply ingrained in the business experience of the directors and formed the basis of their intuitive decision process. In addition, many of the factors taken into account were shared across the industry and formed part of the crucial common understandings for its stability. The culture of the company and the industry, therefore, was a major factor in the decision.

Financial capability

As was explored in detail in Chapter 2, the company was financially strong throughout the 1950s. In both 1955 and 1959 performance was particularly good as the company had significant exports to the USA to cover shortfalls in production at PPG and LOF. At the time when the company was committing to significant expenditure or concerned about the continued funding of the float project, profitable sales to PPG and LOF were giving the board the financial confidence to continue with the project.

When the time came to consider licensing there was no issue in the board's mind about whether the company's financial position had been weakened by the float glass project. While the company had spent a large proportion of their flat glass profits on the project (see Figure 4.1), the company was in a stronger financial position at the end of the 1950s than it had been at the beginning of the decade, despite the costs of float and a very ambitious capital programme on plant, R&D facilities and offices. At some point it has become enshrined in the legend that the cost of float had nearly bankrupted Pilkington, or at least severely weakened it, to the extent that it had no option but to license the technology. This idea was so firmly entrenched that it was even on Pilkington's own website as late as 2007. It was simply not true. The expenditure on the development of float was about a quarter of flat glass profits over the first eight years, but those profits had been very high and had been more than adequate to reward the shareholders, expand the business and still allow the growth of cash in the bank by £7 million.

It was not that Pilkington had been weakened by the float glass project (although it had cost £4 million to this point), it was simply that they were not big enough, either in absolute terms, or in comparison with their competitors, to contemplate exploiting float glass on their own. Pilkington were powerful in commercial terms but, despite being the fifth largest glass producer in the world, as a family company it did not have the financial weight of its major competitors, who were all quoted, in the event of a full-scale commercial war.

Pilkington did not have access to enough money to fund the scale of plant building that sole exploitation would require. While profitable and with very little borrowing, its resources were stretched by the float glass plants required in the UK and later in Canada as well as their other capital expenditure. When Henry Benson (later Lord Benson, senior partner at Cooper Brothers, the company's auditors) expressed anxiety about the cash position in view of the heavy capital expenditure over the next few years he had to be reassured by Sir Harry that if profits were more or less as budgeted up to 1960 then the programme could be managed without recourse to borrowing except at peaks.[8] It is difficult to see how the company could have funded the number of plants in the USA and Europe required to make float glass the universal plate glass replacement during the life of the patents, let alone the replacement for sheet glass that was hoped for. It cost Pilkington just under £4 million to convert CH3 to float glass in 1959–60, at a time when it was estimated that it would cost £5 million for a greenfield plant. It cost over £8 million to build the first Canadian plant in 1966. In 1969 there were 22 float glass plants in operation, mainly to replace plate glass, and 12 or more were in the advanced stage of planning as manufacturers anticipated the replacement of sheet glass. The capital expenditure by the whole glass industry on float glass over its first ten years far exceeded £100 million, a sum that would have been far beyond the resources of Pilkington on its own, bearing in mind its sales in 1969 were £113 million and its profits £19.8 million, £5.8 million of which derived from royalties from float glass. By 1974, as the early patents began to expire, the total investment in float glass plants was over £400 million.[9]

The scale of the potential expenditure and Pilkington's own capacity to raise funds were so obvious to the board that they did not need repeating. The company's financial standing was not expressly shared with the rest of the industry (as no accounts were published), but, as a private company, its funding capabilities would have been well understood by its competitors.

Technical considerations

Pilkington thought that the float glass patents were robust. But they were under no illusions that if competitors, all of whom had strong technical resources, were denied licences then they would use those resources to challenge the validity of the patents, or to invent around the patents, with the consequent prolonged and expensive legal battles. As Sir Alastair said, 'the greatest secret about a new process is not how to do it, but that it can be done',[10] and there is usually more than one way to do it. Indeed, the company expected challenges even after licences had been granted. PPG's parting words, having completed negotiations for a licence, were that they could now do work to get around the patents.[11] The fact that this comment was recorded indicates that it was not taken as a joke, even if it was said in jest. The patent monopoly was available only as long as the competitors chose to sustain the illusion, that is, when it was cheaper for them to take a licence and support the patents rather than risk the cost of developing their own technical solutions with the possibility of failure and consequent exclusion from a profitable market. In addition, withholding the technology increased the possibility of theft of technical documents or the poaching of key employees which would quickly reduce the secrecy of the technology. A liberal policy of licensing would reduce the risk of competitors taking such steps. The Guardian case (see Chapter 6) illustrates the risk of poaching and misappropriation.

Some people thought that the company would need the help of the licensees to develop a complete process. As Chapters 3 and 4 revealed, the history of the development of float glass had been extremely fraught. The early promise of a revolutionary technology had become a war of attrition as the development struggled at the frontier of engineering and glass-making science to get the process under control. After over 18 months of full-scale plant trials, at a cost of nearly £100,000 per month, the process had only made a small quantity of saleable glass which still required some treatment before it was suitable for toughening. Sir Alastair thought the announcement in 1959 was being rushed; he would rather have waited until better glass was being made as he did not want to launch an incomplete process; [12] after all, the float glass plant would only make ¼ inch thick (or equilibrium thickness) glass. There are hints in the papers that some directors considered that the input of other glass experts would be necessary to get over the apparent impasse faced by the development team. In fact, as will be seen in Chapter 6, all the major problems were resolved by the Pilkington team rather than the competitors over the next three to four years.

Between the 1959 announcement and the signing of the first licence in 1962 it was vital to keep any doubts within the company, as any lack of confidence on the part of Pilkington would have encouraged the potential licensees to explore non-licence routes. It was considered that the promise of a licence would deter the competitors from doing too much work to circumvent the patents while buying time for the company to perfect the process before they were actually obliged to hand over the technology. This tactical thinking was reflected in the behaviour of the competitors. PPG, St Gobain and Ford did do their own research on float glass to see whether they could circumvent the patents and brought claimed improvements to the negotiating table when discussing licences. But the expense and uncertainty of success deterred a full-scale attack. Ford was later thought to have been very close to developing an independent process when they decided to sign their licence.[13] However, they had lost confidence in their ability to bring their process from promise to fruition, particularly as they saw that Pilkington seemed to have been through that final phase only at great cost. Ford concluded that it would be very difficult to get around one key patent. The risk of expensive development work and not having a competitive product was not acceptable to the competitors when Pilkington were offering a technology which they claimed would work. Despite the competitors' initial expressed enthusiasm, they also had a hard-headed realism as they considered the possibility of licensing, with the cost of royalties and the consequent status as a mere follower. Only when PPG had explored the commercial consequences exhaustively and satisfied themselves that the patents were not breakable (at least in the short term) did they commit themselves to serious negotiations.[14] As the Pilkington board hoped, the company did have a more reliable process, also capable of making thinner, ⅛ inch glass, with a stronger patent position when the licence negotiations eventually took place in seriousness in 1962–64.

In addition, the company did not have the technical management to plan, build and operate a large number of plants. Throughout the decade from 1955 to 1965 there were problems with a lack of design staff and experienced high-quality engineers to build and operate the plants that the company required to replace its own plate glass capacity, to expand its market share and to support its obligations to help design and oversee the building and early operation of the licensees' plants. There would have been even greater problems in trying to recruit adequate management and operators in overseas markets where the company had no infrastructure for the score or more new float glass plants the company would have to build if it were to sustain a monopoly. Any temptation to recruit expertise from competitors would be regarded as a breach of the industry-wide commandment 'Thou shalt not poach my employees' which dated back to the early days of glass manufacturing.[15]

An industrial culture of licensing

If culture is 'collective programming of the mind',[16] then there was certainly a culture of licensing major technology developments in the glass industry stretching back to the early twentieth century. Both PPG and LOF had licensed out their sheet glass processes extensively, and Pilkington had licensed out its continuous grinder for plate glass in the 1920s and its twin grinding technology in the 1930s and 1950s. Pilkington also had experience as a licensee. It had licensed in the sheet glass process from PPG, TV tube technology from Corning and reinforcement fibreglass technology from Owens Corning Fibreglass, all American companies. Pilkington understood well the relative merits of both positions and the degree of control that could be exercised through a licence, particularly if the territory within which a licensee was granted manufacturing rights was limited to one country or group of countries, or even to one plant. No glass company had sought world domination of manufacture by retaining sole access to their technology, but through the licences they could exercise some control over the overall level of production and the location of that production and therefore the degree of competition they would face. In addition a licensor could balance the sources of its income, choosing whether to make profits from manufacture or from the licensing royalties. As Sir Harry made clear in his float glass announcement in January 1959, the company's preference was to be the controller of the technology.[17]

Pilkington's assumptions about the licensing of float glass were part of an industry-wide collective understanding. There was an expectation in the glass industry that Pilkington would license the float glass process. Even before float glass was announced, the publication of the early patents had led to much speculation as to the research that the company was undertaking. For example, Alastair reported to the Group Executive in November 1957 that at a recent meeting with LOF 'float was continually being brought into the discussion'.[18] The American competitors in particular did not want to be left behind if there was a radical new technology. Within a few days of the process being announced the Group Executive were discussing the terms of the potential licences as a matter of urgency, partly because competitors were anxious to discuss the grant of licences which they assumed would be available.[19] The competitors would have been aggrieved, and much more aggressive, if they were denied the possibility of a licence.

The final technical consideration in the offering of licences was the potential of reciprocity. Offering to license float glass meant that if a competitor in the future made a major technical development that was valuable to Pilkington then at least there was some moral obligation to be granted a licence by that company. During most of the period when the licensing policy was being developed (1955–63) the company was concerned that float glass would not be able to meet the increasingly crucial market for ⅛ inch plate glass. LOF, PPG, Ford, Boussois and St Gobain all claimed to be making progress in this field, either by improved grinding or chemical polishing, and Pilkingtons were anxious not to prejudice the possibility of having to license a competitor's technology.

An orderly market

Perhaps an overriding consideration for the board arose from the work that the company, and in particular Sir Harry, had done since the war to create healthy competition (as he defined it, competition where the manufacturers remained healthy) rather than destructive war. The main principle was to maintain the *status quo* in market shares. There was plenty of growth in each producer's existing markets and there was no need to poach in the market of another. Sir Harry set out his view to the management at their first Group Conference in 1969: 'I want everybody to accept that peace among the very big manufacturers, of whom we are not the biggest, can only be obtained by a spirit of mutual sacrifice and mutual trust.'[20] The share of each manufacturer's home market was established, and in the home markets the principle of price leadership was respected; importers would follow the lead of the home producer in setting prices. In export markets there might not be specific market sharing, but there were agreed overall world shares so that each producer could benefit from the growth of the world's markets. The Americans could not, overtly, take part in such arrangements because of antitrust laws, although they were quick to complain if a European undercut their home market prices. The Europeans, who prior to 1965 had no European equivalent of the antitrust laws, reduced some of these arrangements to writing, and they were the subject of monthly meetings, often at the highest level, to police them. Once the Japanese companies started to export significant amounts of glass in the mid-1960s, efforts were made to bring them into the fold. As the European competition rules set out in the Treaty of Rome in 1965 came into force, and their scope was clarified, these arrangements were progressively abandoned.

The reduction of price wars, particularly at times of over-capacity, sustained the profitability of the industry, and the exchange of market data meant that it was easier to plan production expansion and avoid over-capacity. The price of glass is very sensitive to over-capacity. Firstly, manufacture is a continuous process, expensive to stop and restart, and it is more economic to sell glass at low prices for a short time than to shut down the plant. Secondly, glass is a commodity product. One piece of glass is exactly like another (within a given quality band), and the only way for a customer to differentiate between suppliers is on service and, above all in the glass market, price. If one manufacturer adopts low pricing in a time of surplus then very quickly customers will force down the price of competing glass.

One of the major understandings was that no manufacturer would build a factory in the territory of another. St Gobain caused a furore in 1958 when it announced that it was going to put down a plate glass plant in the USA. As the head of LOF said to Sir Harry, 'Imports are fortunes of war, they come and go with the economy, but manufacturing is another thing, it will be resisted tooth and nail by the US manufacturers.'[21] To try to maintain a monopoly in float glass, and therefore to build plants in the USA and Europe in the territories of its competitors, would go against all that the company had been trying to do to stabilise markets and allow for healthy competitors.

Sir Harry is later quoted as saying that

A great deal was said [in the internal debate] about ethics: that it was not our job to deliberately deny any existing glass company the opportunity of living in competition with us ... There was a great deal of investment world-wide in plate, and people needed to have time to write off this plant or convert over.[22]

Similarly Sir Alastair stated that the company had a moral obligation not to disrupt an established industry. This reference to ethics is unconvincing: while the company's charity was widely known, it did not extend to its competitors, nor to a field that was obviously fundamental to the company's future prosperity. Much might have been said about ethics, although there is no record of such discussions, and it sounds more like a lunch-time discussion than one emanating from the boardroom. But Pilkington had been claiming to work for an environment that was healthy for both its competitors and itself, and it would now be somewhat hypocritical to adopt a licensing policy in conflict with the diplomatic efforts of the post-war years. It is easier to be ethical when such behaviour is consistent with one's commercial interests.

At the November board meeting in 1959 Sir Harry tabled a paper prepared in anticipation of a meeting with St Gobain which set out his views on the relationship with the major competitors:

> It is desirable that the main manufacturers in the Western world
> should work in harmony as good club members, having a respect
> for one another's natural interests and ambitions ... Such harmony
> involves full and mutual cooperation on the technical and commercial
> fields alike. In both fields it must necessarily involve a certain sacrifice
> of individual decision ... The creation of such a club and of a suitable
> spirit involves long-term working agreements covering both plate glass
> and sheet glass.[23]

In his view the club should comprise PPG, LOF, St Gobain (including Sambre), the Boussois/Glaver/Delog group, Univerbel, Detag (both later part of Boussois), and Pilkington. At this time St Gobain were the only rebels and were making it worse by insisting on putting down a plate glass plant in the USA. The club did not yet include Ford, although they made plate glass, as they were regarded as outsiders by the rest of the plate glass manufacturers. After all, they had only started making glass in the 1920s whereas some of the others could claim their antecedents back to the mid-1600s. The concept of the club and its reinforcement were at the core of Pilkington's early licensing policy.

If float glass were widely adopted Pilkington could, if it chose, reinforce the *status quo* via its licensing policy. Float glass technology would give Pilkington a legitimate measure of control over the location of the manufacture of float glass for at least the life of the patents. Licences could be granted for manufacture in one country only, reducing the risk, for example, of the Americans moving into Europe with the possibility of over-capacity and consequent pressure on prices. The licensing policy would ensure that Pilkington's exports to its sphere of influence, the British Commonwealth and Argentina, would not be threatened and would allow for an expansion of company-controlled manufacture to those countries when the local market warranted it. Exports could be inhibited, if not controlled, by granting a licensee selling rights only in its home market or a restricted number of countries. It was recognised that the prohibition only worked in countries where there was an enforceable patent system, but the company's policy was to take out patents in all the world's industrialised countries, even those, such as Russia, where the enforceability of patents was somewhat uncertain.

The relative complexity in the early 1960s of the industry's ownership in Europe made rationalisation of production more difficult. If the negotiating strength of float glass could be used to bring various companies closer together then the planning of the growth of capacity could be simplified. This was not a purely anti-competitive stance by the company. Sir Harry was very concerned about the threat from the communist countries and was promoting the idea of close co-operation between the European glass manufacturers in a similar way to that being developed in the European iron and steel industry. Ideally he would have liked to have brought in the US manufacturers, but the antitrust consent decree of 1948, and the antitrust law in general, prohibited production planning between competitors, even if the US manufacturers wanted to follow that route. At this time, outside the USA, the concept of legislation to promote competition was in its infancy, and the prevailing culture within European manufacturing industry as a whole was towards some level of collusion to maintain profits. This was regarded as a natural product of industry: Kynaston[24] reports that by the mid-1950s cartel agreements affected some 50–60 per cent of gross manufacturing output in the UK. But a similar pattern of behaviour on the part of a number of competitors does not inevitably prove collusion.

> Common understandings about how competition operated were crucial
> for [business] conduct and the resulting stability of industries ... But
> it was especially important in oligopolistic markets where stability
> depended on perceptions based on experience about the response of
> competitors to strategy and tactics.[25]

For example, changes in pricing policy will quickly be copied by competitors without any need for an agreement.

The licensing policy could also influence other economic goals. First, and ultimately most important, there was the possibility for the company to take shares in a licensee in lieu of royalties, extending the company's sphere of influence and substituting permanent dividends for short-term royalties. Second, there were tactical pricing issues. At the time of the float glass announcement ¼ inch plate glass was the highest volume product of the plate glass plants. Within Pilkington the other plate glass product prices were to some extent subsidised by ¼ inch sales. If the ¼ inch market was lost to float glass, and competitors did not allow other plate glass prices to rise, then plate glass as a whole within Pilkington would be less profitable. There was a similar situation in sheet glass. Thick-drawn sheet glass was improving in quality and was now acceptable for some plate glass applications, such as car sidelights. As it was marketed more like a second-quality plate glass it could command a high price, which was very profitable in the context of a sheet glass works. Float glass would threaten to replace thick-drawn sheet glass, or at least reduce its price, thereby affecting the profitability of sheet glass as a whole. The introduction of float glass across the industry would allow the prices for plate glass and thick-drawn sheet glass to adjust to allow room for float glass sales to grow without price wars disrupting sheet glass and plate glass profits in the meantime. There would be a mutual interest for prices to be adjusted uniformly, even if there was no agreement, and thereby maintain the company's overall profitability until such time as float glass replaced all sheet glass and plate glass. This was a company-specific argument based on the economics of its plants and its markets, although the price conformity among the producers indicates that they had similar internal economics.

For float glass to become universal it had to have the support of most or all of the manufacturers. If the competitors' positions were threatened, they would fight to retain their markets, as was the case with Glaverbel later in the cycle (see Chapter 8). There was a risk that float glass could be killed in its infancy, even if it was a better technology. The competitors could retaliate to jeopardise the precarious state of float glass at the time of its launch. As one example, the competitors could reduce the price of plate glass to undercut float glass. At the time of its launch the price of float glass was set at just under that of plate glass and was only making a small profit at this level. Although, in theory, float glass would be far cheaper than plate glass once the process was stable, a new float glass plant would not be able to guarantee profits if the competition put pressure on prices, which, given the margins on plate glass, they would be able to do without prejudicing their own viability. For example, in 1960 Pilkington made profits of £9 million on a turnover of £59 million; LOF were making profits of £41.5 million on a turnover of £109 million.[26] In addition any campaign by the competitors to say that float glass was inferior to plate glass (and there were technical differences in the products which could have been exaggerated in a conservative market which was afraid of change) could have a devastating effect in gaining customer acceptance in markets where Pilkington had only a limited presence and would have been at a distinct disadvantage to the established network of home sales teams.

The company had to take into account the pace at which competitors could adopt the new technology. A prospective licensee would also have to allow for the cost of accelerating the writing off any investment in plate glass if float glass were to replace the plate glass capacity. Plate glass plants were extremely expensive, costing approximately £10 million each in 1955. The company, conservatively, wrote off their cost over twelve years, although the plants could be expected to operate for twenty years or more. In addition replacement of plate glass by float glass inevitably put jobs at risk, with associated social and financial implications. All of the plate glass manufacturers had invested in new plant relatively recently (St Gobain was committed to build its new plate glass plant in the USA even after float glass had rendered it obsolete) which would have to be closed prematurely. Later, towards the end of the 1960s, Sir Harry was complaining that the Continentals were not exploiting float glass rapidly enough as they were running down their old plate glass plants (see Chapter 8). The company had to recognise that licensees did not wish, or could not afford, to switch to float glass too rapidly. If the company had been too aggressive in promoting float glass, either on its own or in seeking the over-rapid adoption of the technology, the competitors would have reacted to protect their plate glass investment, to the detriment of float.

Conclusions

There was no express decision to license float glass technology, yet there was, apparently, a complete meeting of minds among the directors that the technology would be licensed. Despite the extensive and exhaustive discussion of the implementation of the licensing policy, the decision to license was a wholly intuitive decision. The over-arching plan was set out as early as late 1955, when the Group Executive stated that,

> While we are under some obligation to our plate glass friends, LOF, PPG, St Gobain, Glaver etc., we must allow sufficient time to get well ahead of them on conversion of plant, particularly so when we want to increase our share of the world market. The longer we wait to license, the longer for them to experiment and break the patents, but if we could have a 5 year gap between commercial production and licensing, so much the better.[27]

In the event the company was in commercial production in late 1958, and the first licensed plant, that of PPG, came on stream in December 1963.

The cultural factors in making the decision, summarised below, can be grouped into those which were shared across the industry and company-specific issues.

Industry

- The concept of constructing new plants in the territory of overseas competitors ran counter to the whole of the company's post-war commercial strategy of preserving the *status quo* in the market shares in the home territories of the plate glass manufacturers, a strategy that was matched by that of the competitors.

- There was a long-standing practice of licensing in the glass industry, and the company had benefited from both inward and outward licensing over the previous forty years. The last two major inventions in the flat glass field, PPG's sheet glass process and Pilkington's Twin process, had been shared around the world.

- If the technology was not shared, then competitors would attack the patents or try to invent around them. Paying royalty was a low-risk and a cheaper option for them. The expense of defending patents in many countries was not an attractive option for the company, particularly as the board had considerable respect for the technical ability of the competitors to invent around the patents.

- Competitors could severely prejudice or defeat the launch of float glass if they chose to compete on price while float glass was still in the early, inefficient stages. They could undermine confidence in float glass among their customers, a significant proportion of whom would have to convert to float glass if it were to succeed, and all this in markets where Pilkington had little or no infrastructure.

- By licensing, the company could expect to exert a degree of control over the world's glass market, in particular in the new markets opening up to high-quality glass, a change that would be accelerated as float glass became ever cheaper in relation to plate glass. Pilkington could expect to regulate, to some extent, the speed with which float glass was adopted in the existing plate glass markets, and to hold for itself all or part of the new markets as they became ready for plants of their own. The plate glass manufacturers would probably be content to exploit their own markets for some years to come and the potentially high profits of the new manufacturing markets could be shared among them depending on their ambitions at the relevant time.

Company

- While the company was financially strong, it did not have the internal resources or access to the level of borrowing or share-issuing necessary to fund the rapid construction of float glass plants overseas.

- The company was stretched to recruit and train the engineers, draughtsmen and skilled operators to man its own plants and to provide start-up teams for its licensees. It would have been very difficult to manage the recruitment of suitable personnel in the numbers required, and in new overseas markets, to operate overseas plants.

- The company had the experience of controlling a licensing programme, and particularly the legal skills for creating the contractual framework to give some certainty that there would be an adequate return on the technology.

- At this time there was a nervousness shared by some of the directors that Pilkington would need the help of licensees to enable the float glass process to make all thicknesses of glass.

There is evidence for all of these issues being in the minds of the directors prior to, or immediately after, the launch of float glass in January 1959, even if they were not all discussed at one time. They would have formed part of the unspoken but shared expertise of the board. Those directors, such as Hudson-Davies and McOnie, who were not directly responsible for flat glass, would have been aware of the issues, even if they were not everyday matters for them.

The absence of any recorded decision of the principle of licensing implies that the decision was obvious, that there was only one logical alternative. However, an outsider faced with the same situation might find the decision complex. For example, Mintzberg and Quinn (two leading academics in the field of strategic decision-making) think it is sufficiently complex to use the decision to license float glass as a case study.[28] Any attempted rational analysis of whether to license or not in 1959 would have faced too many gaps in the available knowledge, both as to the current circumstances and to future consequences, particularly in relation to the competitors' reactions. Those gaps were bridged by the expertise of the directors, whether gathered at first hand in business dealings or as part of the training and sharing of experience within a close-knit group of colleagues. The solutions to the questions were founded in the intuitive knowledge of the directors, which was so thoroughly adopted that it did not require repeating.

The decision was also reinforced by the sharing of the intuitions at the industrial level. Many of the underlying assumptions were shared by the other plate glass makers. Any decision not to license would have run counter not only to the internally shared assumptions but also to those shared across the industry. 'If a basic assumption comes to be strongly held in a group, members will find behaviour based on any other premise inconceivable.'[29] In this sense, not to license the float glass technology was inconceivable.

The decision appeared easy, in the sense that it required no overt discussion. In fact, the decision was very complex and far-reaching, but there were numerous reasons, strongly held at the intuitive level and shared both within and outside the company, which made granting licences the only conceivable outcome.

Postscript

The consequences of the policy of licensing created a fundamental shift in the nature of the high-quality glass industry. The availability of consistently high-quality glass at low prices has affected the design criteria of both the automotive industry and, perhaps even more significantly, the architecture of commercial buildings. The consequences are still being felt, fifty years later, as relatively cheap glass is available world-wide, especially in countries which could formerly only afford sheet glass. In addition, the float glass process enables value to be added easily for more sophisticated markets, for example coatings for low heat emissivity and self cleaning. Enumerating the outcomes that occurred during only the first ten years produces the following list:

- The policy ensured a rapid diffusion of the process.[30] Although plate glass plants continued to operate for some time, they were replaced with float glass plants at a pace dictated by the availability of capital and manpower for the construction of new plants rather than the normal life of the plate glass plants. By the end of 1970, 29 new float glass plants had been built, compared to the 22 plate glass plants still in operation in 1969 (see Appendix 2.E).

- There was a more rapid development of the float glass technology as all of the leading glass technologists worked on the process. Although all the major developments in this period were made by Pilkington, there were many operating refinements in different environments using subtly different raw materials and equipment which fed their way to the licensees, either formally through the improvement exchange, or informally through the open communication between plant engineers.

- Failure to license would have led to a number of 'invent around' varieties of float glass. As there was only one new process there was a concerted effort by all the licensees to ensure all their customers bought the 'new' product. Although a piece of float glass or a piece of plate glass were just two sheets of glass, there was customer resistance to the new product on the basis of the (near invisible) distortion and the nature of the cut edges of the two products. The automotive and construction industry were conservative in relation to new products and conflicting claims with a variety of new products would have slowed the replacement of plate glass.

- The growing inflow of royalties to Pilkington was a significant contributor to profits. In 1969 licence royalties, at £5.8 million, were the same as the total profit of the company had been a decade earlier, in 1959. In 1959 Pilkington could foresee at least twenty years of high royalties and could plan its expansion with a high degree of confidence that it was, to a significant extent, insulated from the dependence on cyclical trading patterns and profits.

CHAPTER SIX

The 1960s: decade of revolution

As the 1960s opened Pilkington at last saw the float process operating at commercial yields. The cost of production was, as hoped, very competitive with the plate process and soon proved to be versatile when the techniques of making non-equilibrium glass had been developed. With competitors queuing for licences, despite some initial bashfulness, the impact of float was beginning to live up to the dreams of the 1950s. However, it was not all plain sailing. There was a need for a radical change to the company's organisation in order to cope with the growth of the business. The float technology posed challenges throughout the decade before it was accepted as the universal process for making flat glass. The transition to float created structural challenges for the whole industry, especially in Europe. Growth in the markets world-wide was tempered in the UK by the stop–go of the home economy and its decline relative to the home markets of the company's competitors.

The development of the float process

By the end of 1959 the development team were beginning to think that they had at last solved the basic problems of the process, and in November float had achieved its first monthly trading profit. In June 1959 it was decided to convert CH3 to float which, given the problems being experienced on CH1 at the time, was a triumph of optimism as there was still no sign that the process would be able to make non-equilibrium glass or be able to dispense with under-cleaning to remove the effects of bloom and bottom speck. However, by February 1960 CH1 was producing 450,000 sq. ft per week and 70 per cent was being packed as saleable quality.*

---

* The 'CH' number related to the original plate plants and the sequence in which they had been built, not the order they were converted to float. So the float plants were converted in the order CH1, CH3, CH4, CH2.

Royal visit, 1961.
PILKINGTON ARCHIVE

Through most of 1960 float was making a trading profit. and the quality of the glass was improving steadily. CH3 came on stream in February 1962 and later in the same year the board were confident enough with the process to approve the conversion of CH4 to float, and this came on stream in July 1963. From the outset CH1 was regarded as a development plant on which to perfect, at full scale, the ideas developed on the pilot plant. In fact it had to both act as a development plant and as a commercial plant. Generally the company was now short of capacity and was trying to reconcile development with producing saleable glass. Development work on CH1 was interrupted by the need to make saleable product at a time when CH3 and CH4 had production problems. In addition, CH3 and CH4 had the latest equipment

Sir Harry starts up the second float glass plant, CH3, February 1962.

and were therefore required to do development work that could not be done on CH1.

Over the next ten years – and it was only in 1971 that the board was finally confident enough to plan to substitute all flat glass, both sheet and plate, with float – the company spent over £3 million developing the process to the point where it could make all substances from 1.5 mm to 15 mm both in clear glass or body-tinted glass and with surface modification for reducing solar gain. There were a whole series of interrelated problems to be solved, and the following is a brief summary of each of the issues.

1. Thin float

No sooner had the process been announced than customers and prospective licensees were asking for thinner glass. The UK motor manufacturers were determined to reduce weight in their cars and reduce the thickness of the glass used from the standard ¼ inch (6.75 mm). In the USA motor manufacturers had for many years specified laminated windscreens, and therefore used ⅛ inch glass to keep the net thickness approximately the same; consequently the US glass-makers saw float as a replacement for plate only if the process could be applied to make thinner substances. In both the USA and Europe the quality of thick-drawn sheet was good enough to replace plate for applications such as car sidelights, and the manufacturers were reluctant to spend the premium for float. In 1959 and early 1960 Pilkington had been totally committed to making a good equilibrium ribbon, had done little practical work to try to reduce the thickness of the ribbon commercially, and had no indication that it would be able to do so. The new pilot plant came on stream in October 1960 and within three months had made 6.1 mm and 5.7 mm glass of sufficient quality to send to the USA as samples to show that float was not a one-product process.

The story of the final breakthrough on thin glass typifies the inventive process, where the inventive step is the conjunction of many factors. The team had despaired of making thin glass. Trials in speeding up the pull at the cold end of the ribbon had only succeeded in making a very narrow ribbon which was still ¼ inch thick. However, some experiments had shown that if one pulled a ribbon which was only just malleable (rather than the treacly liquid coming out of the spout) then you could control the 'waisting in' of the ribbon with edge rollers and make thinner glass. Alastair was discussing this phenomenon with another senior manager who said, 'What we need is two baths, one to form the ribbon and let it cool with another to reheat the ribbon just enough to reform it.' Alastair's immediate solution was to use the one float bath but to control the temperature down the length of the bath to allow the equilibrium thickness ribbon to cool so that it was stiff and then reheat it just enough for it to be stretched thinner.[1] This was the breakthrough that was to give the float process the versatility to replace both plate and sheet.

However, there were major problems in transferring these ideas to a full-scale plant. The thinner the glass, the longer the bath had to be to have the temperature regime to allow for the process of thinning. The extra speed of the ribbon created rapid flows in the tin, which in turn caused distortion in the glass. This was eventually controlled (in 1965) by using linear motors in the bath to control the flow of the tin. After a rebuild in late 1965 CH1 came back on stream to produce the first really good run on 3 mm (approximately ⅛ inch). Prior to this the plants were capable of making 3 mm, but the yields were far from commercial. Table 6.1 shows the substantial improvement in yields at this time.

Table 6.1   *Float yield (% of production available for sale)*

	3 mm	*5 mm*	*6 mm*
1964	17%	19%	49%
1965	19%	60%	63%
1966	37%	67%	64%
1968	60%	68%	65%

Source: Pilkington Archives

Much development time was lost in trying to make a thinner substance without edge rolls as these left marks in the edge of the ribbon; the edges had to be cut off and discarded, resulting in a loss of around 15 per cent. This problem was never solved for 3 mm and below, although 5 mm and 4 mm could be made by the direct stretch method, without edge rolls. However, the percentage loss was reduced after the move to wider ribbons which resulted in the narrowing of the affected edge, while the overall efficiency of the process meant that losses of this magnitude could be absorbed.

2. Bloom

Although the team thought that bloom had been solved by the time that float was announced, there was still enough oxygen contamination of the tin to require some under-cleaning of the glass to ensure that none of the glass bloomed on toughening. The first under-cleaner on CH1 had 17 polishing heads, which added materially to the cost of the glass. Step by step the sealing of the bath was improved to limit the amount of oxygen in it; at the same time, the quality of the bath atmosphere supplied was improved to levels where the oxygen was measured in single figure parts per million; and, finally, additives were introduced to the tin to remove any oxygen that was dissolved in the tin. Even this latter route was complex. Additives had worked very well on the pilot plant, and bloom was cured overnight when the techniques were tried on CH3. But within weeks there were problems caused by the oxidised additive forming a hard dross in the bath which marked the glass. This was solved in late 1963 by introducing the additives electrolytically and therefore in much smaller quantities, which meant that the dross was manageable. At about the same time it was discovered that the correct proportion of hydrogen in the atmosphere was an aid to controlling bloom, and additives were discontinued in late 1965. Bloom was only an intermittent problem after this, and there was a gradual reduction in the need for under-cleaners, although as an insurance they were not abandoned until late 1966.

The need for under-cleaners to deal with bloom and other defects in the bottom of the ribbon was debated at each plant conversion and delays in delivery and operational problems with them meant that production was frequently disrupted. Once bloom had been solved, a plant operating properly did not need its glass to be cleaned, but it was only after 1965 that the plants were operating at a consistently good level. For six months in 1964 some 3 million square feet of ¼ inch glass was transported across the Pennines to Doncaster for under-cleaning as the cleaners in St Helens were not adequate.

3. Melting

The melting technology of the company was found to be inadequate for two main reasons. First, it was discovered that making good ⅛ inch required a much more homogenous metal coming from the tank into the bath. Some of the techniques for doing this were developed from work done on the sheet plants to improve the quality and speed of draw of their glass to match that of the competition. The increasing throughput on thinner substances also required repeated development and redesign of the canal which delivered the glass from the tank to the bath. The combination of techniques to improve the homogeneity of the glass delivered to the bath, which was outside the field of the float technology licence, was novel enough for the company to offer it (in mid-1965) under a separate licence to the float licensees, and a number of them took it up. Despite the considerable efforts of the licensees, the company was maintaining its lead in the technology and enhancing the dependence of the licensees to it.

Second, the tank designs of the time had difficulty in delivering glass at the rates that the float process required to be economic. CH1 was originally designed to make 1,000 tons per week and was increased in size on each rebuild until it was up to 2,000 tons. CH3 and CH4 both started at 2,000 tons and were up-rated to over 3,000 tons; at the end of this period CH2 was being planned to make 4,500 tons per week. Other than CH2, these plants were conversions from earlier plate plants and the glass melting tanks were rebuilds of existing plate tanks with lower designed outputs. It was found that the tanks wore very quickly as the output increased and therefore introduced impurities into the glass. Often the bath was working perfectly but had to be shut down because the tank was in urgent need of repair. By the end of the 1960s improvements in melting technology were at the top of the company's R&D list.

Even the sand, which came from sand fields just to the north of St Helens, was proving to be inadequate as it contained impurities that were not melted out at the new rates of production, and work had to be done to clean the sand more thoroughly.

4. Top speck

Top speck was the generic name for tiny particles of various contaminants that settled on the hot glass ribbon and marred its surface. At the time the process was launched top speck had been reduced to a level where there was a high proportion of uncontaminated glass and the contaminated portions could be cut out as the ribbon was divided into the relatively small plates required by Triplex. However a major consumer of high-quality glass was the mirror industry. Glass for silvering has to be of the highest quality as it is intended to be looked at, rather than through, and the reflection of any defect multiplies its impact. At the same time the company was trying to get its customers to accept lehr end sizes, large plates of glass cut at the end of the lehr and then shipped to customers rather than first being moved to the warehouse and then cut into a multitude of different sized plates as required by the different customers. While the latter method meant that any defects could be cut out and rejected it was very labour-intensive and required large numbers of highly skilled cutters, one of the highest paid classes of worker. The move to lehr end sizes would move this labour intensity to the customer and would also mean that the customer carried the loss entailed in cutting out any defects and creating the cut sizes. However, the fault density of the large plates had to be at a level at which the customer would accept the loss in exchange for the lower price (about 2.5*d.* per foot on a sale price of 35*d.*) for the large plates).

The battle against top speck did not involve any major technical breakthrough, rather the constant improvement of operating procedures and the chemical purity of the process. The near elimination of oxygen and other contaminants in the bath atmosphere required new developments in the purification of the hydrogen and nitrogen supplied to the bath; the interior of the bath was continually redesigned to reduce the number of places on which any contaminant could condense and drip onto the glass; and cleaning the inside of the bath and regular purging of the atmosphere also helped. Over this period the ribbon speed increased radically, from 100 inches per minute at the time of the announcement to 360 inches per minute during trials on 3 mm glass a decade later, in 1969. This increase in throughput also increased the rate at which any remaining contaminants were introduced into the bath and the consequent housekeeping requirements.

5. Thick glass

Plate glass was also made in thicknesses greater than ¼ inch, and if float was to replace plate it had to be capable of making these substances too. The size of the markets for thick glass were relatively modest, and as the Doncaster plate plant had considerable life in it, the development of techniques for producing thick plate was not given much urgency at the time when the company was concentrating on producing thinner float.

The pilot plant produced some thick in 1960, although only of a quality suitable for grinding, but it had at least been established that the process could be adapted. By 1964 the pilot plant was making very good thick glass, but Doncaster was making stocks of thick glass sufficient to last for some time and even then was only able to operate intermittently on this relatively small load. Short runs on the float plants showed that thick was not too difficult to make, and by early 1966 the company was confident that the float process could be regarded as universal at 4 mm and above. In late 1967 the pilot plant was making good yields on 10 mm and 12 mm glass. Because of lack of pressure and a greater understanding of the process by the time it had to make thick glass, these substances were developed relatively easily and, as the following table shows, the costs were highly competitive with plate:

Table 6.2   *Relative costs of making thick glass, 1965 (pence per foot)*

	⅜ inch	½ inch	¼ inch
CH1 @ 1300 tpw	33.3	41.8	–
CH3 @ 2500 tpw	24.5	30.5	16.2
Plate	42.7	59.7	30.2

Source: Pilkington Archives

6. Warehousing

The ribbon speed of float had the potential to put pressure on the technology downstream of the float bath. The lehr had to be able to anneal the glass properly at the greater speeds than in plate manufacturing, although there is no mention of this ever causing problems; lehr development seems to have kept pace with float. However, the warehouse did present a real problem. As noted above, the company wanted to introduce cutting at the lehr end to simplify the warehousing, and this was part of a general drive to automation to cope with higher speeds and the reduction of the reliance on expensive, manual glass cutters.

Progress was not acceptable in the first few years of float; the new process was making good glass, only to find that the warehouse yields were low because of downstream problems caused either by the lack of cutters or because the new equipment itself was breaking down, or, worse, breaking or marking the glass. The company decided to take advantage of the good relationship with PPG and in late 1963 sent George Dickinson to Pittsburgh to investigate the progress there. His report was robust: it was estimated that PPG were ten years ahead of Pilkingtons, and as a result the company quickly negotiated a warehouse agreement with PPG (signed in early 1965) to share their technology at a cost of $1 m over three years. Within months housekeeping techniques were improving results, while a commitment to substantial investment in automation equipment steadily brought the warehouse yields up and allowed the warehouse to cope with the rapidly increasing speed of the ribbon, so that when it reached 360 inches per minute in 1969 the automated machinery was equal to the task.

7. New developments

Despite the fact that the company was building three new plants in the period to July 1963, and the baths were modified regularly, there was a concern

CH3 warehouse, 1963.

PILKINGTON ARCHIVE

that the company was falling behind its licensees in its technology. Each new licensee built a plant with all the latest technology and also introduced improvements as their glass-makers applied their own expertise to the new technology. There was a continual flow of improvements being sent to St Helens under the provisions of the licences. In particular, PPG, LOF and Ford were doing much development work on the manufacture of ⅛ inch, creating the concern that the company was falling behind, let alone maintaining the lead over the licensees that they had planned for.

As a result of their pre-licence research, Ford from the outset had decided to put a carbon lining in their bath which they claimed reduced the contamination in the tin. When CH3 bath was being rebuilt in 1967 it was decided, after some pressure from PPG who wanted the company to evaluate the technology, to put a carbon lining in the bath. This caused near disaster at a time when the company needed the output from the plant. Although the bath eventually was made to work, at the cost of some £1.5 million, it illustrated the difficulty of adopting major changes from other glass-makers who had different glass-making techniques. It appears Ford had solved the problems of the carbon lining through practices in glass melting, and the company was very reluctant to start receiving melting technology from a third party, particularly Ford.

In general the company does not appear to have adopted any other major improvements from its licensees. The real value of the improvements clause came from the operating techniques and minor engineering refinements which pooled the ideas of all of the world's leading glass technologists. The technical relationship with competitors at this time was very close. Pilkington provided the designs for each bath, was closely involved in the sourcing of materials, had teams present at the start-up of new plants and during their early operation, and provided a trouble-shooting service throughout the licence period. Until licensees built their expertise and confidence, this latter service was often intensive. As a result Pilkington's engineers built an unrivalled expertise in the operation of float plants, not only from the three plants operated by Pilkington, but also from the 22 licensed plants that were in operation by the end of the 1960s.

Pilkington worked on two other major developments of its own which had a mixed outcome. First, the company appreciated at an early stage that the high output from a float plant would not suit all markets, and that it would be better for smaller markets if a melting tank could feed both a float bath and conventional sheet equipment so that the output could be tailored to smaller markets currently fed by exports. Although they were confident enough of success to announce the compatible tank in 1964 there were complaints from the plate manufacturers who were concerned that this would enable countries which relied on plate imports to become independent. Although the company contemplated using the technology on its new plant in Canada, it was decided to make this a pure float plant, and it appears that a compatible tank was only ever used in Mexico; there is no record of the flood of new licence applications which the company anticipated.

Second, there was an increasing demand for glass which reduced solar gain (i.e. the greenhouse effect) in both cars and high-rise buildings with large expanses of glass. It was established early on that the float process could make body tinted glass, but this required a different batch from clear glass, and the transition time between batches was lengthy and expensive. It was known that solar gain could be reduced by applying very thin coatings to the glass, but the coatings were soft (i.e. were easily scratched) and were difficult to apply evenly.

The company developed a coating process which exploited the bloom phenomenon. Bloom was caused by tin ions migrating into the surface of the glass, and by manipulating other molten metals on the surface of the ribbon within the bath they could be introduced in microscopically thin layers within the surface of the glass. Choice of the right metal altered the colour and the light and heat transmission properties of the glass, while the coating was as hard as any other glass. The new process, which was technically brilliant, could simply be switched on and off, with very little loss of production in between. It was announced in 1967 with great optimism, but was found to be very difficult to control at a commercial output to get the required consistency of colour. Customers were not prepared to accept colour variation on the face of a prestigious new building. A later development on this process used gas containing the relevant metals and this produced a much more consistent product. But it was still not consistent enough, and by the early 1970s it was considered that the process was too difficult to control. It was to be another twenty years before on-line coatings could finally be applied on a consistently successful basis.

8. The simple solutions

Through the final development period it became apparent that often the simple solutions were the best. It was as if the laws of physics and chemistry wanted to make good glass if only the operators could get rid of nature's dirt. All you had to do was to deliver perfectly melted glass at an homogenous temperature into a bath with pure tin and an atmosphere of nitrogen with precisely the right amount of hydrogen and virtually no oxygen, and physics would produce a perfect ribbon of glass at just the right thickness to make large windows. But it took over fifteen years and £7 million to discover the need for simplicity and the ability to achieve it. A major contributor to success in reducing surface defects was the running time of the bath. It was found that the float process as a whole seemed to settle down and improve quality if it were allowed to run for some time without interruption. Every time the bath was opened for repairs or alterations air got in and it took time before the bath atmosphere was back to operating cleanliness. Changes of thickness or the speed of the ribbon unsettled the process and tended to cause higher than acceptable levels of defect. As the various operating problems were solved, and the plants were able to settle down to better production planning and long runs on the same substance without interruption, so the consistency of the product quality improved. In many respects the float process is simpler now than in the early days when ever more complex solutions only seemed to introduce more problems.

A crisis of confidence

Once the float process began making commercial yields at the end of 1959, it was hoped that the remaining problems would be solved quickly, especially with the new pilot plant due on stream in October 1960. But, while the float process made steady improvement over the next three years, it was not at the rate the board had hoped. Two new float plants, CH3 and CH4, had been brought on stream, but far from solving problems they seemed to be introducing new ones. In July 1963 the Directors' Flat Glass Committee complained that, 'the position in float generally at the present time is very disappointing'.[2] There were continual problems in meeting the expectations of the licensees and the customers, and this was typified by the series of problems that faced the company in the summer and autumn of 1963. The glass market was in a boom phase, and the company could not meet the demand for glass, let alone expand its market share.

CH1 was inconsistent in its output and could not produce ³⁄₁₆ inch or ⅛ inch at commercial yields. CH3 was finding problems with the cleaning additives in the tin as they were causing dross scars on the glass. CH4 had had a dreadful start-up because of problems with the refurbished glass melting tank, and eventually had to close for a repair at the end of the year. The automatic warehouse was encountering teething problems, and the underpolishers (an old technology which Pilkington thought it had perfected on its plate plants) were introducing faults which were eventually cured with help from PPG. St Roch, the Belgian plate associate company of St Gobain, had placed a big order for 6 million sq. ft of ³⁄₁₆ inch float to prepare its market for the introduction of its own float plant and the company was facing difficulties in making the glass with the possibility of spoiling the reputation of the process. The new grinding and polishing plant at Doncaster was operating poorly, and could not produce enough ⅛ inch to cover for the problems with float in this substance: Triplex was having to buy half of its requirements for ⅛ inch from the Continent. Glass was being shipped to and from Doncaster because of the inadequacy of the underpolishers in St Helens.

Start-up of CH4 in 1963: waiting for the glass to come through. Note the temporary sealing between the end of the melting tank and the entry to the bath.

The Amalgamated Engineering Union (AEU) were operating a long-term overtime ban, which was inhibiting the introduction of new plant and there were difficulties with the shortage of cutters. The company was unwilling to train new cutters as this would only create redundancy when new automated equipment came on line, and the unions were reluctant to allow the company to use 'dilutees', relatively unskilled cutters, to do the simpler work of splitting the ribbon. Management in the plants were overloaded, and new managers were brought in urgently to bring more resources to bear on solving the problems.

Finally, the constant optimism prior to the opening of each new plant had led to the sales department generating new orders to meet the anticipated output, only for the customers to be let down when the plants failed to meet their forecast outputs. In the six months of June to November 1963 float made a trading loss of over £300,000, not including development costs of over £150,000, the last time (apart from the strike in 1970) that float made a loss.

The board were losing patience: 'float in particular was very disappointing at a time when, as the only manufacturer in the world, we should have been earning large profits. This week PPG had commenced manufacture, so in a short time we would have competition.'[3] Although profits were being made in early 1964, Alastair 'warned [the Group Executive] that the float process was as yet far from being 'tamed', much development work still needed to be done, and problems not experienced before were still being thrown up, with consequent adverse effects on production.'[4] As had been the case with the sheet process and the company's development of continuous grinding, the

Start-up of CH4 in 1963: 'rowing' the glass ribbon through the float bath until it is picked up by the take-out rollers.

PILKINGTON ARCHIVE

float process had a significant period of refinement as the engineers gained understanding of the subtleties of the process and made it more versatile and reliable. It took most of the 1960s for the process to develop from a temperamental newcomer with promise to being a totally reliable replacement for all of the existing processes.

The financial environment

Throughout the 1960s Pilkington continued to be profitable despite the heavy costs of float development and the recurrent recessions in the glass market. The monthly report to the board set out the rolling annual sales of the previous 12 months, and almost every month in this decade showed an increase in the total until the strike (see Chapter 8) in 1970. Growth was rapid. The company achieved annual sales of £50 million in 1959 and this had doubled to £100 million in June 1968.

Figure 6.1 shows the monthly trading profit from float and the costs of float development over the ten-year period and, while float could fully fund the development by mid-1962, the cumulative totals (Figure 6.2) show that

The last plate of glass lifted from Cowley Hill plate works on 3 November 1962, after 85 years of production.

that float trading did not break even over the total development costs until July 1965, 13 years after the initial invention. If licence income is included, the break-even was achieved in March 1964. In the early period the profits from plate were still significant (Figure 6.3), but as ¼ inch float replaced this profitable plate substance the profits rapidly reduced. CH4 plate was closed in 1962, the last plant to make plate in St Helens.

The future for Doncaster, the other UK site which made plate, was in doubt once the initial decision to make float at CH1 was taken. As each new float plant was debated, Doncaster was considered as a potential site, but the economies of running all of the float plants on one site always outweighed the possibility of building a plant in Doncaster. The company had agreed to build a new plate grinder and polisher at Doncaster in 1958, when it was not certain that float would be a success, but the plant took a long time to build and was very disappointing in performance when it did finally come on stream, despite the fact that it was based on old technology. As float plants began to manufacture thinner substances Doncaster was only partly loaded and operated intermittently from 1965, making stocks of thick glass and other special glasses that float could not yet make. Glass-making in Doncaster ceased in 1966 and thereafter the grinder and polisher was the only part of the factory to operate, finishing the lucrative polished wired glass which was cast in St Helens. The rundown of Doncaster was expensive, not only because the plant was being

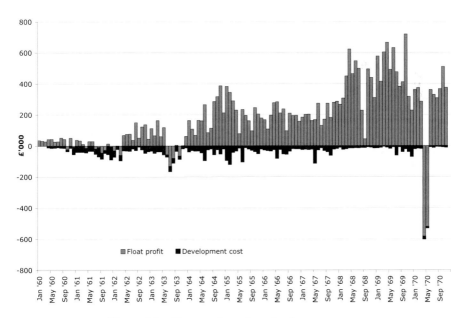

Figure 6.1   Float profit against development cost.

SOURCE: PILKINGTON ACCOUNTS

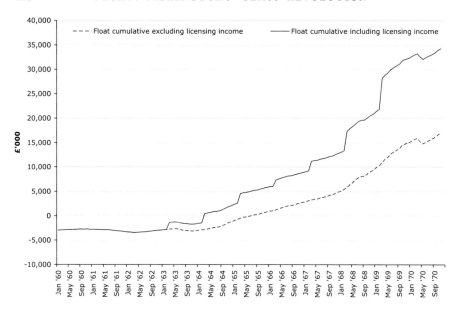

Figure 6.2   Cumulative profit from float to 1970.

SOURCE: PILKINGTON ACCOUNTS

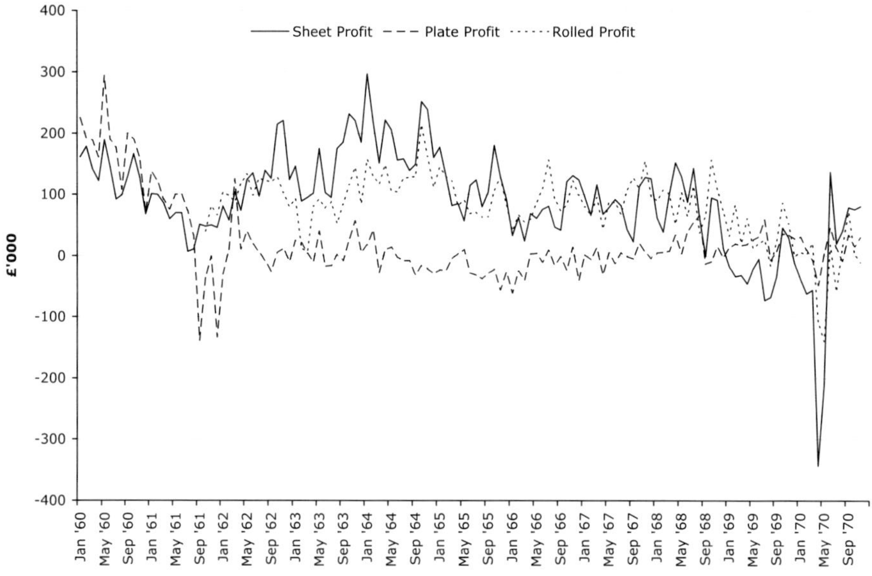

Figure 6.3   Sheet, plate and rolled profit, 1960–1970.

SOURCE: PILKINGTON ACCOUNTS

run inefficiently, but also because the plant was written off over five years rather than the customary twelve, thereby reducing the profits.

Through the period to 1969 sheet continued to make good profits (see Figure 6.3), despite the price freeze in the UK, the pressure from imports over the period (reducing the company's market share in the UK by 10 per cent) and the competition in export markets as the working of the 'club' arrangements broke down at the end of the decade. A product area not much discussed in the company through the 1960s was rolled glass, making a range of surface textured glasses mainly for the building market. The profits from this division were consistent, substantial and made a significant contribution to the results of the Flat Glass Division. The other Pilkington divisions, Fibreglass, Pressed Glass, Safety Glass and Optical generally made significant contributions to profit in this period, as Table 6.3 shows.

Table 6.3   *Profitability of Pilkington divisions*
(£000s)

	Average of the five years to 1964	*1965*	*1966*	*1967*	*1968*	*1969*
Flat Glass	3,828	6,523	3,213	4,202	5,687	10,325
Pressed	375	342	133	−162	−7	35
Safety	1,260	2,386	2,143	2,499	2,623	2,525
Optical	131	171	275	−6	−112	−32
Fibres	927	1,221	1,161	1,221	1,520	1,521

Source: Pilkington accounts

The world markets for glass showed a rapid increase in the period from 1957 to 1967, the period in which the float process moved from full-scale trials to a commercial process. Not only was float trying to replace plate, but the plate market was growing at a rapid pace, particularly in Europe (see Table 6.4). The company had lost some of its home market share in sheet (down from 95 per cent to 88 per cent) but had increased its share of the plate/float market (up from 88 per cent to 90 per cent) despite all the problems with the float plants and the competition from Continental sheet.

The annual accounts (summarised in Table 6.5) show consistent growth in financial strength over the period 1957–69, despite the recessions of 1961–62 and 1965–66.

Table 6.4 Market increase, 1957–1967 (000 square feet)

| | | 1957 | | 1967 | | | |
		Sheet	Float/plate	Sheet	% increase	Float/plate	% increase
UK	Home	216,117	27,108	253,940		74,352	
	Imports	11,305	3,661	35,715		7,663	
	Total UK	227,422	30,769	289,655	27	82,015	166
France	Market	184,000	57,000	245,000	32	116,000	100
West Germany	Market	299,000	49,000	413,000	38	161,000	229
USA	Market	1,181,000	662,000	1,490,000	26	884,000	34

Source: Pilkington Archives

Table 6.5   Annual results, 1957–1969 (£ million)

Years to 31 March	1957	1958	1959	1960	1961	1962	1963	1964	1965	1966	1967	1968	1969
Share capital	6.0	6.0	6.0	6.0	5.8	5.8	5.5	13.8	13.8	13.5	13.5	13.5	13.5
Reserves	21.6	24.5	28.1	33.8	38.3	41.5	45.6	42.2	49.9	52.4	56.7	63.3	69.8
Fixed assets	17.2	19.4	20.3	23.9	28.8	34.8	37.7	39.8	49.0	51.0	63.3	67.5	73.0
Turnover	44.1	49.1	51.2	58.9	57.9	56.6	60.9	67.3	79.6	84.8	86.3	97.5	113.9
Profit before tax	4.3	4.1	5.6	8.6	7.2	3.0	6.6	6.7	10.5	7.9	9.5	13.2	19.8
Dividend	0.5	0.5	0.6	0.7	0.7	0.6	0.7	0.8	1.4	1.9	1.9	1.9	1.9
Retained profit	1.2	1.1	1.8	3.4	2.5	0.7	1.4	1.4	2.2	2.0	1.9	3.0	6.7
Cash	4.3	4.3	7.0	9.7	7.9	0.6	2.0	0.5	1.7	3.4	-3.0	0.2	0.9
Royalties							1.4	1.9	1.7	1.1	1.8	3.6	5.8

Source: Pilkington accounts

The European environment

For years St Gobain had been difficult to deal with at the diplomatic level, perhaps because they thought they, as the largest producer in Europe by some margin, should be the leaders of the club. Sir Harry had concerns about the personal antipathy towards him felt by Grandegeorge (the head of St Gobain), who initially thought that the announcement of float was merely a ruse to avoid the grant to St Gobain of a Twin licence for the USA. Grandegeorge insisted on completing the negotiations for the plate plant, which was obsolete before it was built and was a burden on St Gobain throughout its relatively short life. Sir Harry used the Twin negotiations to improve relationships with St Gobain, and in 1960 an agreement with St Gobain setting out the general terms of an accord was signed. Although it appears that the formal accord was cancelled soon thereafter, the company sought to operate within its spirit. The relationship for the next ten years was distant (or as distant as it could be when the manufacturers were meeting regularly to discuss matters of joint interest), but relatively cordial. St Gobain did not take the lead in float that Pilkington hoped they would as market leaders in much of Europe: they were not the first to sign a European float licence, and they irritated Pilkington by being slow to exploit the process, as they wanted to get as much production value as possible from their substantial investment in plate.

Relationships with Boussois were much closer. As early as 1959 the Pilkington board approved the principle of investing in the capital of Boussois, and the company finally bought 8 per cent in 1963 as part of the negotiations for the float licence. Boussois merged with Souchon-Neuvesel (a bottle maker) in 1965 to become BSN (although it was normally referred to as Boussois). The merger brought Antoine Riboud into Boussois, who was appointed the following year to be the head of that company and whose ambition was to lead Boussois to be one of the leading companies in Europe. His personal relationship with successive heads of Pilkington was to have a major impact on the company. The fact that Pilkington had taken a small share in Boussois was not well received by St Gobain, but the regular meetings on trading matters kept open the lines of communication, and there were regular discussions on the restructuring of the Scandinavian glass industry and similar discussions on the shaping of the glass industry in South America, including the possibility of jointly owned float plants.

Pilkington had promised the Europeans in 1962 that it would not seek to undermine the plate and sheet markets in Europe, and that its float prices in Europe would relate to those of plate. In due course, however, the pricing of float would have to be based on its cost, and in the meantime Pilkington reserved the right to price float in its own markets as it chose. In 1966 the European licensees, led by St Gobain, protested strongly that Pilkington were selling 'float B' in the UK at prices to compete with thick-drawn sheet. This was a ruse devised by Terry Bird, the head of the Flat Glass Division. At this stage the company did not want to lower its float prices generally to the level of sheet, and had designated float sold in competition to thick-drawn sheet for the motor industry as 'B', implying it was second quality and could therefore be sold at a discount. Actually it was the same quality (although with different fault characteristics which justified the designation), and St Gobain had written to say that this 'was an act of inadmissible hostility to all [Pilkington's] licensees'.[5] They were reminded that Pilkington would sell at the prices it chose in its markets, but it would extend its support of the European pricing structure until 1969, as long as the European companies increased their exploitation of float and did not undermine the position of float in the UK by the importing of cheap thick-drawn sheet. All except Glaverbel, with their heavy commitment to sheet and their reliance on exports, thought this constructive.[6]

One key customer in the UK for Glaverbel was British Indestructo Glass (BIG), owned by a consortium of car manufacturers to provide competition for Triplex, the only other UK automotive glass processor, partially owned by Pilkington but at this time fiercely independent. BIG exploited the motor manufacturers' enthusiasm for thinner substances by utilising thick-drawn sheet and imported 10 million sq. ft from the Continent, a substantial part of the then current total sheet glass imports of 15 million sq. ft. However, BIG was making losses, and in 1967 the owners decided to sell BIG to Triplex, who promptly closed it down. Glaverbel were furious at the loss of this market and became much more aggressive, particularly in selling thick-drawn sheet into the general UK market.

In October 1967 it was reported to the board that the quality of the relationship between the Europeans was at the lowest for a long time.[7] Boussois and Glaverbel had both shut down plate plants, but there was still a great deal of over-capacity and Glaverbel and St Gobain had fallen out. In 1968 Glaverbel were no longer prepared to support Centraver, a company set up by the Continental manufacturers to co-ordinate the export sales of their glass, and it was feared that the entente had irretrievably broken down in Europe. At the same time Pilkington decided to set up a small selling office in Europe to counteract the rise of imports into the UK.

Threats of breach of the manufacturing understandings were dealt with robustly. In 1966 St Gobain were rumoured to be planning a safety glass operation in Canada, and the DFGC reviewed the methods of retaliation, including exporting to France and allowing float licensees to export to France. The DFGC minuted, 'The time has come to remind St Gobain of possible repercussions'.[8] St Gobain did not build the Canadian safety glass plant. Later, in 1970, the company became aware that Glaverbel were planning to set up operations in Canada, Australia and South Africa. This was tantamount to a declaration of war as it breached the fundamental premise that club members would not manufacture in the territory of another, and the company said that it might have to reconsider its policy not to manufacture in Europe.[9] St Gobain were appalled when they heard about this as, in their view, it would be immoral to grant a licence at a royalty and then manufacture in the same territory.

Although the relationship with Boussois was much more open as a consequence of the company's investment in it, it was perhaps only open when it suited Boussois. As Boussois owned 25 per cent of Glaverbel, it was assumed at the time of purchase of the shares in Boussois that this entailed some degree of control. A report to the board in 1965 made it clear that this was not the case.[10] There was very little communication between the two, and there was no question of Boussois exercising any control over Glaverbel. In addition, there was strife within Glaverbel. The Glaver part of the organisation was in favour of supporting float, with the constraints that entailed, whereas the Univerbel part of the merged company still believed that Belgium had a right to export anywhere in the world and their heavy commitment to sheet meant that they were reluctant to move to float.

It appeared to be a surprise to the company when, in early 1969, Boussois launched a bid for control of St Gobain, to consolidate and strengthen the French glass industry; there is no indication that there was any prior consultation between Boussois and Pilkington. The bid was seen as outrageous in France, given the relative sizes of the two companies, and it failed. Almost immediately thereafter Riboud announced that Boussois was going downstream, to fill the bottles that it made, by buying mineral water and brewing companies. The resulting issue of shares for the acquisitions took Pilkington's holding below 3.5 per cent. Despite the bid, the market relationship between Boussois and St Gobain did not appear to have been prejudiced.

While still smaller than its major competitors, Pilkingtons was now exerting a measure of control over them and was confident that it was shaping the industry as it had planned. This was reciprocal in the sense that the competitors expected something in return for their technical subservience. The licensees had accepted the elements of territoriality contained in the licences. If they were paying Pilkington for technology, they expected Pilkington to protect the value of that technology, including the policing of the territoriality contained in the licences. Whatever the company might have felt about any competition for float, there were strong views among the licensees about what steps needed to be taken. At this stage the *status quo* in terms of market shares was breaking down. Pilkington had hoped that float would uniformly replace plate and preserve the balance between the manufacturers. This was largely true in the USA where the plate manufacturers had built new plants in line with their market shares. But in Europe the imbalance between Glaverbel and St Gobain as they moved to float and tried to protect sheet, had led to a breakdown in the delicate market accord. Although Sir Harry tried to hold the entente together, he was now seen as having a special role in promoting float to the prospective detriment of sheet, and Glaverbel could not face the consequences of that shift. Float glass prices were not as high as had been expected at the time of the launch of the process. The price had not stayed close to that of plate, but had been forced down closer to that of sheet. Although this entailed a healthy rather than extravagant level of profit, it also accelerated the reduction in float manufacturing cost and resulted in an earlier replacement of sheet. By using thick-drawn sheet to force down the price of float, Glaverbel hastened their own decline as float costs were reduced to enable it to compete with thick-drawn sheet and ultimately replace the whole of the sheet market.

The shareholders

Throughout the decade Pilkington remained a private limited company with fewer than fifty shareholders, all of whom were descendants of the founders. During the 1960s it was decided that the company would have to go public. The discussion of this major change is not revealed in the papers or the minutes of the board or the bodies charged with policy making. The debate must have been substantial as it would radically affect the shareholders and the style of management of the company, but, perhaps for confidentiality reasons, it was first explicit only a few months before the formal decision was taken in early 1970. The reasons can therefore only be inferred from the papers.

As in 1962 the company lost its exempt private company status and would from that time have to lodge its accounts at Companies House, there could no longer be any secrecy as to its overall profitability. (In fact, the lodging was delayed as long as possible because the figures revealed a drop in profit as a result of the recession of that year, and the company did not want potential licensees to think that the drop in profit reflected the poor performance of float.) If there was no secrecy then one of the main commercial reasons for remaining private had gone.

The shareholders were also under financial pressure. The price for the transfer of shares had to be cleared with the Inland Revenue and, as the company increased in profitability with little scope to increase the share capital, the value of each share rose rapidly. As the number of shareholders was limited by statute, there were real problems each time a shareholder died. On death, the estate had to raise the death duties partly, if not wholly, by the sale of Pilkington shares and this inevitably meant that the remaining members of the family had to find the cash to buy them. A number of the shareholders were now of an age when the burden on the rest of the family in the near future would be unsustainable and a public market for the shares was the only realistic way out.

Up to this point there had been no real difficulty in funding the company's capital expenditure. All of the UK expansion had been funded from retained cash and the Canadian subsidiary had been able to borrow the capital required for its float plants. However, the ambitions for expansion with new, and more expensive, plants overseas meant that the company would need to find new sources of finance and being a public company would facilitate this. In the early 1960s the decision had been taken that the company would have to become a public company in about 1970, after the full potential of float as a universal process for glass-making was established, but before the profitability of the company was distorted by the royalty receipts.[11]

Plans were well established for flotation in September 1970 and the management changes and reporting structures were already in place. While there was no obvious change in the board's attitude, there must have been some thinking about the new regime of accountability to outside shareholders. The board would have been receiving advice about the content of the offer document and the need to disclose any significant litigation and any consequent threat to royalties. No longer could the board expect the shareholders simply to trust the board. Convincing explanations for major decisions would have to be given to investors and their advisors, most of whom would know nothing of the subtleties of the glass industry.

The board and management

The structure adopted in 1958 (Chapter 2) lasted until the middle of 1967 when it was refashioned, with advice from the company's auditors, Cooper Brothers, with the prospect of going public. Again, the intention was to free the directors to spend more time on policy and the development of relationships with other manufacturers, and, more importantly, to create product divisions as profit centres with a greater degree of autonomy from the centre. The work of the Group Executive was split into the policy making and long-term planning of the Chairman's Consultative Committee (CCC) and the resource allocation and monthly review of figures carried out by the Co-ordinating Committee. The DFGC was disbanded, as the CCC now carried out this role, and the Flat Glass Divisional board (FGDB) took over the role of the Flat Glass Management Committee with enhanced delegated powers (see Figure 6.5).

The board in 1970 had fifteen members and now included three non-executive directors who had no previous experience of the glass industry: Sir Humphrey Mynors, Sir Norman Kipping and Ted Judge (see Appendix 1).

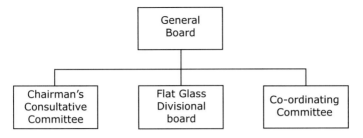

Figure 6.5 Organisation chart, 1970 (part only).

Although there were a number of relatively recent executive appointees, it is noticeable that they had all spent a long period with the company, normally their whole careers. The principle of developing managers as candidates for the board resulted in the promotion of two individuals who were to have a major impact on the future of the company, Terry Bird and Leslie Wall, both of whom came from beyond the public school, Oxbridge mould.

Terry Bird, a locally educated graduate of Imperial College, London, had joined the company in 1935. After a series of works-based roles he was

Terry Bird.
PILKINGTON ARCHIVE

promoted to production manager in Sheet Works in 1954, his first senior management post, and took over the role of works manager in 1956. In 1960 he was appointed a local director, a titular role and regarded as a sort of probation for full membership of the board, although in this case he was also appointed to the Group Executive. Bird was very much a protégé of James Watt. Neither was a member of the family. They both made progress through the works environment with a combination of strong personality and intellectual rigour. They could both be 'totally terrifying' and had a presence which reduced a room to silence. Despite the difference in their ages, one ex-colleague described them as 'thick as thieves', and Watt saw Bird as his natural successor. As Watt had played a crucial role in the pursuit of float technology, so Bird played a crucial role in the widening of licensing policy which was to change the shape of the glass industry.

There was some disquiet at the time of his promotion to the board about Bird's 'character', as he was reported as having been severe with subordinate managers in a meeting, not the manner expected of a director. It is worth recalling that most of the directors, as members of the family, had had a rapid rise through the ranks in a variety of posts and had spent relatively little time in the works, and even then they had the authority that came naturally from being members of the family. Terry Bird had spent a long time in the more

Leslie Wall.

CH3, 1962, showing the relative peace and cleanliness of the bath in operation.

assertive, less diplomatic environment of the works and had had to rely on force of character to make progress. He was not someone to suffer fools gladly, and his forthright manner with subordinates was not diminished when, despite six months' delay, he was appointed to the board as a sub-director in 1960 and as a full member in 1962. From then on Terry Bird's contribution was immense, particularly after he was appointed chairman of the FGDB on its formation in 1966. Many of the key policy papers were written by him, often challenging the established practices; he was not content with the ingrained, intuitive answers. Clear thinking and forceful, his contribution was critical in rationalising the change of policy which led to the licensing of Guardian and averting a litigation crisis (Chapter 7).

Leslie Wall had entered legal articles directly from grammar school. He joined the company in 1956 as an assistant solicitor, but when the head of the Legal Department resigned as a result of ill-health in 1957 he was not an automatic choice to succeed. Some felt he would 'never be big enough'.[12] After some months of fruitless searching for an external candidate (the location of the head office in St Helens was held to be a major handicap to recruitment of urbane lawyers), the board decided to appoint Wall, and he took over the senior legal role in December 1958, just as the development of the float licensing was beginning to be discussed. His papers to the various boards on licensing matters were complimented as being clear and concise, and he was soon involved with Sir Alastair in the early licence negotiations. He obviously had a rapport with Sir Alastair and was not afraid to debate the policy or tactics being followed, and quickly became both highly trusted and indispensable in negotiations. Indeed colleagues recall blazing rows between Sir Alastair and Wall on matters of policy which blew over and left no rancour. He was also trusted by the negotiators on the opposing teams as he was capable of seeing their point of view and offering concessions which met their aims without impinging on the company's objectives. I recall a meeting with senior LOF negotiators in the mid-1970s, when Leslie Wall introduced a point by saying, 'I want to be fair,' and was interrupted by his opposite number exclaiming, 'Oh no Leslie, we can't afford you to be fair!' Wall was an ardent supporter of the company's policy of reasonableness in negotiation. Even if the company was in a position of strength it was not part of the culture to bully the other party. As he said, it didn't do to kick a competitor when he was down; he might get up. Wall was promoted to the board in 1970, soon after the Guardian decision, but was clearly influential as a trusted adviser in the board decision process prior to that appointment.

The building of new float plants for the company, their operation and the provision of design and operating assistance to the licensees resulted in the rapid development of a team of experienced engineers. Because they were involved with all of the plants, either directly or through the pooling of information within Pilkington, they were gathering information about float in different geographic climates, using different raw materials and different plant configurations and operating techniques. They drew on their own experiences and those of the other skilled glass-makers around the world and had a level of expertise unmatched by any other producer even though the latter were entitled to improvements. Generally their relationships with the other engineers was excellent. There was a world-wide fraternity of float engineers during the licensing period and beyond. Even if relationships at the board level were fraught, there was often a friendly exchange of ideas at the plant level.[13]

Many of the skilled tradesmen were also regular travellers to the licensees, particularly the bricklayers who were expert in the critical task of installing the refractory blocks lining the float bath. At the commissioning of each new licensee plant, Pilkington would send a complete start-up team – management, foreman and tradesmen – to both train and supervise the licensee's workforce. Once the plant was operating properly the team was reduced for the remainder of the start-up period and often left under the control of a senior foreman. There was considerable respect between the different levels within these teams, each recognising the others' expertise and trusting them to carry out their roles with the minimum of supervision.[14]

Conclusions

Paradoxically, the very success of float glass technology and its exploitation was leading to stresses that would lead to the break-up of the old plate glass oligopoly.

Float glass was now a proven success and had all but replaced plate. The last of the plate plants were working out their time. The market for high-quality glass was burgeoning. The traditional Western markets were booming and new markets were expanding throughout the world. Outsiders were looking on enviously at this profitable arena, which seemed to be closed to non members.

Expertise in float technology was now widely disseminated. Hundreds of engineers around the world had access to the drawings and manuals and carried much of the detail, and their own refinements, in their heads. Although they were all obliged to keep the technology confidential, the prize for breaking the ranks was considerable. It was only a matter of time before an engineer was tempted to risk a breach of confidentiality lawsuit and try to profit from operating outside the club.

By the end of the 1960s it was recognised that float glass could be made as cheaply as sheet glass. (Table 6.4 is indicative of the relative sizes of the sheet and plate glass markets.) This was a significant step-change in the potential market, and sustaining the oligopoly into the new market would inevitably create dissatisfaction among existing sheet producers, their customers (who saw a potential narrowing of their suppliers) and those who viewed glass as an exciting new area for manufacture. The big customers could blame all of their ills on the perceived lack of competition between the suppliers, and wonder if they would be better off moving upstream into glass manufacture themselves.

Pressures were building for a change in the structure of the industry, and the next chapter examines how the change took place. The challenge for Pilkington was to manage any change so that they retained control of their technology without a total free-for-all.

CHAPTER SEVEN

The Guardian controversy

G UARDIAN INDUSTRIES INC. (GUARDIAN) was a US-based, privately owned processor of flat glass for the automotive and architectural markets. As its demand for glass grew through the 1960s, Guardian decided to manufacture its own glass. In order to do so it both recruited engineering expertise from Ford and applied to Pilkington for a licence for float technology. In January 1969 the Flat Glass Divisional board (FGDB) noted that Guardian had been refused a licence, but in December the same year the board were resolving to amend the float licensing policy to include as potential licensees companies which had not previously made glass but which had a high internal demand. This new policy might include companies such as Guardian. There had been a series of papers leading to this significant change of policy, but there were also, possibly more important, reasons which were not discussed openly but which weighed heavily in the minds of the directors when they made this decision. The decision was not only a major change of direction in the company's strategy, but also a change to the company and industry culture that was highly significant in shaping the future structure of the whole of the world's glass industry. It was a major strategic decision, perhaps the most fundamental decision in the whole of the float exploitation, but it was made *sotto voce* and with great difficulty. The decision to license float technology in effect maintained the *status quo*. The decision explored in this chapter lead to a complete reshaping of the 300-year-old glass industry.

Licensing policy

Sir Harry's 1956 notes on the possible terms of a licence were tabled at the fifth meeting of the Directors' Flat Glass Committee (DFGC) in February 1959, just days after the public announcement of the float process. Despite the anticipated requests for licences, it was agreed that there would be no grant of licences until the company was in full commercial production, selling on a substantial scale, and with the ability to manufacture in all thicknesses. There would be no commitment to prefer or exclude anybody, and the company would consider a shareholding in the licensee in lieu of royalty. By the next meeting of the DFGC in March 1959 some of the principles were already being questioned. Sir Harry noted that the European manufacturers were already consolidating into two main groups, St Gobain and Glaverbel/ Boussois and, if the company were to obtain a share of ownership in either of these groupings, it would need to move quickly before positions became entrenched. He was even prepared to contemplate some reduction of royalty until the process was perfected, although this was later rejected by the Group Executive. Sir Alastair was more cautious, as he wanted to wait until the major technical problems were solved before licensing was pursued.

It was decided to develop the licence agreement piecemeal with the main prospective licensees, PPG, LOF, St Gobain, Detag (later merged with Boussois), Glaverbel and Boussois together with Sambre (later merged with St Gobain) and UVMB (later merged with Glaverbel). These were all of the plate manufacturers, except Ford and the Japanese 'who may still be important eventually'.[1]

There was already some jockeying for position as to who was to be first. From their previous experience with the Twin technology, members of the board were well aware of the responsibilities and pitfalls of licensing. The board had quickly realised that the obligation of providing design assistance and help in starting up plants would place a heavy demand on the company's resources and that there would have to be some careful planning of the timing of the granting of licences. In any event the board did not want a rapid increase in glass output ahead of the demand for the product, especially if the licensees built new capacity rather than replacing existing plate plant. Sir Harry had met both PPG and LOF and felt that PPG had claims to be first as

> Hill [the head of PPG] is undoubtedly the most attractive and forceful personality in the glass industry in the United States at the present time, and that his company is still really the biggest; and secondly, that I believe that they are the ones most likely to put their backs into it and to invent or develop improvements.[2]

There followed two years of intermittent negotiations, with PPG, LOF, St Gobain and Boussois alternately showing great enthusiasm and indifference. This was in part due to the prospective licensees evaluating the published information about the process, mainly in the patents, and waiting to see if float glass could be made in non-equilibrium substances.

PPG in particular had an extended internal debate about the adoption of float.[3] They had spent a considerable amount of time and money over a period of ten years trying to perfect a technique of chemically polishing

Bath control room, UK5, St Helens, 1986.
PILKINGTON ARCHIVE

glass to reduce the cost of mechanical polishing. In this light of this, it is not surprising that there was some resistance to abandoning all this work and adopting an incomplete process from a third party. They already felt they had been subservient to Pilkington for long enough, with licences for the grinding and Twin technologies going back to the 1920s. PPG carried out, in the period 1959 to 1962, more than twenty analyses of the economics of float, its impact on PPG, and assessments of how PPG's own technical teams could improve upon, or invent around, the Pilkington technology. The conclusion was that the polishing research should be stopped and the Pilkington technology should be licensed. PPG was anxious to regain its lead over the other US plate producers, a lead which it had lost over the years spent deferring investment decisions while they attempted to improve polishing technology to a commercial level. PPG believed that LOF and Ford would delay taking a licence for some time and that a combination of the Pilkington technology and their own developments of it would give them a lead of some seven years over the other US producers.

Despite the concerns expressed within Pilkington about the versatility of the float process they proved to be unfounded. The new float pilot plant, started in 1960, quickly discovered methods for producing thinner glass and reducing the surface defects; samples of high-quality thin glass and a plant visit to see the new ideas in operation on CH1 were enough to convince PPG that float was the process of the future. They were the first to sign a licence, after hard negotiations, on 27 July 1962, and although concessions had to be made on the rate of royalty (in part recognising that they were the first to sign up for what was still then an incomplete process), and the duration of the licence, the principles were otherwise close to the ideas first tabled in 1956. There was no exchange of improvements at this time, probably because PPG thought they would be able to invent their way around the patents and did not want to be committed to share improvements with Pilkington, let alone the other licensees.

As a result of the PPG negotiations new draft licences were sent to the

Signature of the first float glass technology licence, with PPG, July 1962. Sitting, R.F.Barker (PPG) and Sir Harry Pilkington with Alastair Pilkington between. Standing, J.B.Bowden (Pilkington), L.N.Wall (Pilkington), G.McOnie (Pilkington), J.T.Owens (PPG), R.H.Mitchel (PPG), O.L.Spencer (PPG), L.H.A.Pilkinton, D.V.Phelps (Pilkington) and A.C.Pilkington.

PILKINGTON ARCHIVE

other prospective licensees, and the fact that the world's largest plate producer had signed, combined with a feeling of not wanting to be left behind, induced a flurry of signings over the next nine months (see Appendix 2.A), with Glaverbel, Boussois, St Gobain (separately for France, Italy, Germany and later Spain), St Roch (a Belgian associate of St Gobain) and LOF all taking licences on terms broadly similar to those accepted by PPG, with the exception of the improvements exchange which was accepted by all the other licensees. The licensees had covered their positions. They now had rights to use float, but were not committing themselves to adopting the process, and a number of them seemed very cautious about it, judging by the time that elapsed before they built their first float plants. They could afford to take their time to assess the process and only move to manufacture when they determined the time was right, either because the process was proven to be adequate, or the market had grown, requiring new capacity, or because their plate plants were written off. St Gobain did not put down a float plant in France, its home market, for nearly ten years.

While Pilkington were concentrating on the primary list of licensees they had also had pressing enquiries from Asahi and Nippon in Japan and Ford in the USA. There had been success in general negotiations (in conjunction with the Europeans) with Asahi and Nippon in gaining agreement that they would respect the principle of the established markets of the other plate producers, and in particular Pilkington's primacy in the British Commonwealth. Partly because of this, and in recognition that Japan had a large home market to absorb the output of new float plants, licences were quickly granted in 1964 to both of the Japanese companies, who had agreed between themselves who was to build the first plant (Asahi) as well as the timing of the second. There was astonishment at the speed with which the first plant was built, only twelve months from the time the licence was signed.

Ford was more problematic. Despite the fact that Ford (in conjunction with Pilkington) had been the first to develop continuous glass-making in the 1920s, Pilkington in 1960 did not regard Ford as a major glass-maker and they were not on the initial list of licensees. Some years earlier, in 1952, Ford had asked for a licence for Twin and the Executive Committee stated, rather archly, 'We have always been against motor car manufacturers dabbling in glass-making at all.'[4] Discussions took place with PPG and LOF before any decision was made about a Twin licence to Ford. They were both uncomfortable with Ford as it made most of the glass for its own use, and if it had a surplus it would sell it in the open market at prices of which PPG and LOF did not approve. Having granted Twin licences to both LOF (1951) and PPG (1954), a licence to Ford was declined in 1955 on the grounds that 'we have no interest in facilitating a further increase in production of plate, particularly by a motor manufacturer'.[5]

Ford enquired after a float licence soon after the announcement of float in 1959, but it was decided to decline one. By mid-1962 the attitude was mellowing a little, and on receiving a further enquiry from Ford it was agreed that, as long as PPG and LOF took licences, Ford could receive one, but not for a considerable period of time.[6] Despite this Ford were permitted to see the plant soon thereafter and when they asked for a draft licence in early 1963 it was considered that they could not be denied as negotiations had, in effect, already commenced. Anyway, this could now be used to put pressure on LOF, who were still not committed. PPG were not happy with this step as they did not trust Ford, on the grounds that they had a reputation of being cavalier with other people's technology and did not treat it with the same degree of secrecy as other manufacturers. The board stated that it was 'of the opinion that it was preferable to have Ford licensed and paying a royalty rather than enticing staff from PPG and LOF and infringing our process'.[7] Ford were advised that they were in the second group of licensees with the Japanese and Detag (of Germany). There were rumours that Ford were making float in April 1964, but they still professed that they wanted to negotiate, although they had qualms over the inability to make ⅛ inch float, as this was 60 per cent of their requirement. It was later discovered that, after reading the early Pilkington patent, Ford had built a pilot plant and spent $1 million on research and were within six months of making float.[8] However, with the issue of later patents and the announcement that Pilkington had made good ⅛ inch float, Ford had decided that it would be difficult to invent around the Pilkington technology and it would be cheaper and less risky to take a licence.[9] Despite difficult negotiations over a refusal to grant rights for them to export, and the method of calculating royalties, the licence with Ford was signed in July 1964, at which PPG expressed their extreme displeasure.

The ambition to commute some part of the licence income in exchange for equity in the licensee had little success. Only Boussois was interested in the concept, and it was eventually agreed that Pilkington would take an 8 per cent share in the capital of Boussois, although the idea of commuting some of the royalties was abandoned. The attractions of a 20 per cent share of the Mexican glass industry was enough to entice the company to grant a licence to Vidrio Plano de Mexico in 1965 (despite the fact they did not make plate), although no plant was built for four years.

In spite of Sir Harry's concerns about the West keeping ahead of Communist Bloc technology, the company was eager to grant licences to the Communist countries in order to increase the revenue from royalties and to get some measure of control over exports from that area. Russia had expressed interest in licensing Twin as early as 1954, but the interest was sporadic and did not come to fruition. They made their first enquiries for float in 1964, but there were long intervals of silence between each communication and it was not until March 1967 that a licence was finally signed; it was claimed to be the first licence of Western technology to Communist USSR. Despite extensive objections by the Russians, the terms were similar to the existing licences, and exports were limited to a short list of territories which were of little interest to the established majors. This followed the pattern that had been established by Sklo Union, a Czechoslovakian company who had signed their licence in December 1966, who had argued, reasonably, that they needed to export to earn hard currency to pay the royalties.

East Germany had also been anxious to get a licence and had been the first eastern European country to apply, in 1963. However, St Gobain objected strongly to the proposal as the site for the plant had been sequestered from St Gobain, without compensation, by the East German government, and they did not want the East German's position legitimated by the grant of a licence. The company was not sure whether to accede to St Gobain's wishes, but some legal research revealed that East Germany had never been recognised by the UK and that therefore any dispute with them could not be resolved in an English court. This provided an adequate reason to end discussion until the mid-1970s.

The only plate manufacturer not now licensed was Central Glass of Japan which had been set up by the Japanese government to counter the oligopoly of Asahi and Nippon. The company was reluctant to grant Central a licence as there was a risk that it would lead to over-production in Japan and a further rise in damaging exports: in the five years 1962–66 Japanese exports of plate (with some float) rose from 2 million sq. ft to 25.5 million, the main exporter being Central. There were already concerns about imports into Western USA and Australia, although it was hoped that the latter would be limited by the entente with the Japanese referred to above relating to the protection of the home markets of the majors. However, the float licence could be used as a vehicle to inhibit exports of glass and insist that Central use float only to replace plate. The licence was signed in February 1968.

The company's licensing policy had been tested by two other applications in 1965, from Corning Glass and Owens Illinois, both US-based companies. Corning was interested in the float process to make the raw material for a new chemically toughened glass that they had developed. It does not appear that they intended this to compete immediately with the conventional thermally toughened glass as used by the motor industry, but there were fears that if the motor industry decided to specify thinner toughened glass (which could not at that time be produced by thermal toughening) a major raw material market could be lost to Corning. The general policy was not to create new flat glass manufacturers and Corning was not in this field, but was the world leader in speciality glass such as Pyrex and television tubes. It was agreed that Corning be offered a licence, but only for experimental purposes and with grant back rights in toughening technology if the experiments came to anything. A number of the other major manufacturers were doing work on chemical toughening at this time, and the company was concerned that it was being left behind. An association with Corning would be useful insurance as they had a very powerful research capability and would be financially strong enough to compete with PPG and LOF if they wanted to enter the traditional markets. Owens Illinois was interested in making flat glass for cooker tops and it prompted some urgent research work in Pilkington to explore what other glass compositions were practical on the float process. In the event both enquiries faded away, possibly because an economic float plant would need to produce very high tonnages (at this time over 2,000 tons per week), and this was far too much for either of the proposed markets.

There were regular reviews of the licensing policy and some fine tuning to the terms of some of the licences to keep them all consistent. While the company kept the terms of the licences confidential it was assumed that licensees and potential licensees were in touch with each other and would know the terms of the licences. Accordingly, it was important that all the terms were generally consistent and any differences were defensible if one of the licensees choose to argue that they were being treated unfairly.

PPG were given a royalty discount for the problems they had encountered in the first year of float, although they did not offer an increase when the second and third years were better than they expected. It is interesting to compare the two internal reasons for the early difficulties. PPG thought that Pilkington were holding back key information in order to maintain their lead (not recognising that Pilkington may well not have had the information), and had oversold the completeness of the process in the licence negotiations. Pilkington, on the other hand, felt that they had not been stern enough with PPG when PPG wanted to make changes to the Pilkington procedures and had been drawn into development work with PPG when the company's responsibility was to deliver a process that worked. PPG and LOF were both given some rebate on their royalties for the work they had to do on tuning the process to make ⅛ inch, despite the fact that they had both argued to reduce the original royalty rate on the grounds that the process was at that time incomplete.

Leslie Wall was also concerned about the terms of the letters that were sent to companies enquiring about float licences, and on two occasions in the mid-1960s tried to insist on standard form letters which had been approved by the lawyers. It was legally reasonable for the company to decline an application because it was too busy with other applicants, or because the immediate market to be served by the prospective plant was too small or because Pilkington would not deal through third parties. But the wording of the letter, particularly if the applicant was in the USA, could not imply that the company was in any way rationing its licences or discriminating among applicants. Ken Borrows, the most senior lawyer under Leslie Wall, wrote a paper to the FGBD in July 1967 setting out explicitly the prohibitions of the antitrust law and the need to refer all replies to legal department to ensure they complied with the law. There was an early warning when an applicant from Puerto Rico was turned down and promptly replied that it was going to sue for breach of the antitrust laws (it didn't). When Fourco, a US sheet manufacturer, applied for a licence for the second time in 1968 they were declined, but no reasons were to be given in the correspondence in case they were capable of misinterpretation.

With the last of the plate manufacturers now in negotiation, the company turned to review its overall licensing policy in relation to float. Sir Harry tabled a lengthy draft for comment at the meeting of the CCC in July 1967. His overall policy remained that of a benevolent oligopolist:

> The glass industry is essentially a large scale continuous process industry; this forces the main responsibility into the hands of a few very large groups. These groups have most at stake in times of competitive trouble; they are the best custodian of the industry's wider interests. These groups should, therefore, aim to strengthen each other in their own geographical or manufacturing spheres rather than encourage or assist new uncontrolled manufacturers to disturb the market ... [although he recognised that this was a time of change and] ... We must comply with the letter and the spirit of the Law.[10]

He went on to say that the best hope for the European groups was to retain technical and production leadership and keep ahead of the outsiders by exchanging licences on new technology. Float was the only fundamental process protected by patents and its development should therefore be speeded up to obtain cost advantages 'to secure its position for the future as well as, or in priority over, immediate profit'. Manufacturers should recognise the leadership of one company in any given country, and should follow that leader. Each glass-maker should stick to its existing glass-making territory unless there is an extreme emergency involving outside manufacturers.

The most expansive comments tabled were those from Terry Bird, who was anxious that new productivity should lead to plant closure and not to over-production, reduced prices (and profits) and a mad scramble for exports. He produced figures to show that the company had made only £600,000 profit on exports of 460 million sq. ft of plate and float over the previous six years. Over the same period its share of the float/plate market had not increased, and it had not got sufficient return on its investment. The revised paper was put to the board in October, proposing circulation to all the European companies.

It is not clear whether Sir Harry's paper was in fact circulated; certainly it was not mentioned again. It is inconsistent with Pilkington's actions. Pilkington had done the most to exacerbate the competitive race for new production capacity by building a float plant in Canada which did not replace plate, licensing float, encouraging the construction of new float plants (and complaining when the Europeans were slow to put down new plants). Pilkingtons tended to forget the fact that the licensees had highly profitable, relatively new plate plants whose closure would result in huge write-offs and potentially expensive problems with redundant labour.

By the end of the 1960s, 20 float plants had been built by licensees, but they were still operating 22 plate plants (see Appendix 2.E). In less than ten years more than half of the world's booming market for high-quality glass had been captured by float. In addition it was Pilkington who had licensed the Russians and Eastern Europeans. They would only be confined to their territory for a limited time and in any event had no restrictions on exporting from sheet plants that would have spare capacity once float came on stream. It is not clear who the 'outsiders' were: there were very few independent sheet manufacturers in Western Europe to be afraid of, and Pilkington were not at this time under any great pressure to license any newcomer.

Certainly relations between the Europeans in the late 1960s were very strained. Glaverbel was annoyed at the closure of British Indestructo Glass (see page 115), and all the Europeans were annoyed at the competition between float 'B' and thick-drawn sheet (see page 115). Relations between St Gobain and Glaverbel were reported to have broken down. Perhaps Sir Harry's July 1967 paper was intended to be a rallying cry to try to avert an all-out price war. A comment indicative of Pilkington's perception of its leadership role in the industry at that time was contained in the papers of the same meeting. Sir Harry was reporting on the new head of LOF, Wingerter, and wrote, 'It is of great importance that we teach him something about international policy and must bring him to rely on our judgement.'[11]

There was an unprecedently public (in the sense that it appeared in the minutes) conflict of opinions within the board over the next twelve months. In July 1968, possibly prompted by the new application for a float licence from Fourco in the USA, a paper to the FGDB (probably by Terry Bird) said that licensees were now more convinced that float would predominate in sheet as well as plate, and that Ford were planning to make only float in the early 1970s.[12] This raised the possibility that the company would have to consider seriously moving away from the policy of only licensing plate manufacturers within the next few years. The opposite point of view was tabled at the August 1968 meeting of the same body. Antony Pilkington (the future Chairman, but then the 33-year-old head of the new Flat Glass Marketing Planning Department) wrote a paper stating:

It is in all our interests to operate a co-ordinated policy to discourage the future setting up of new glass manufacturers and to limit the expansion of those already in existence (other than the three major groups in Europe, Japan and the USA).[13]

As Antony Pilkington reported indirectly to Terry Bird, it is interesting to speculate who was sponsoring this view, especially as Arthur, Antony's father, was Chairman of the Co-ordinating Committee and second only to Sir Harry in the hierarchy. The minute of the August meeting did not disagree with this statement; nor did it state other views, but at the next meeting it was minuted that 'Mr Bird said that in the near future the board would have to examine whether the present float licensing policy needed to be revised. There could be a case for greater exploitation of the float process through the grant of licences.'[14] It is apparent that there were two factions in the board, but there was no question of stifling the debate.

In November 1968 the FGDB approved a paper by Terry Bird to be put before the board in December. It stated that the overall objectives were:

- To manufacture all flat glass by the lower cost float process and to market it in order to maximise profits over the next decade.

- To protect, by strengthening relative to all others, the members of the Pilkington Group.

- To shape the world of flat glass manufacture around our float licensees by encouraging their parallel exploitation of float, thereby suppressing the 'pirate' sheet manufacturers who threaten the position of the established companies.

- To achieve a larger share of the total world market for the group and in particular for the UK.[15]

So far the policy seems unchanged, but the paper goes on to suggest the need to alter licences to allow licensees to expand into those territories where they make sheet and to consider new licences to large sheet glass makers or groupings (but does not go so far as to suggest large customers) to make sure they do not go the float route without a licence. This paper expressly contemplates setting up new manufacturers outside the existing majors, in contradiction to Sir Harry's and Antony's papers. The minute does not disagree with the paper, but equally does not accept it as a redefinition of policy.

At the January 1969 meeting of the Flat Glass Divisional board Antony tabled another draft, this time a prospective agreement between the Europeans and the Japanese on general policy which stated:

There are dangers to long-term stability from the uncoordinated setting up of too many new independent manufacturers. Within the broad sphere of his own markets and his own leadership, each member [of the club] should in his own long-term interest try to forestall the establishment of uneconomic domestic manufacturers, if necessary by the initiation of manufacture himself, possibly ahead of the true economic time.[16]

Upon seeing this draft, Ken Borrows sent Antony a sharp note pointing out that this was anti-competitive and should not be published. The draft was never used, but it shows the conflict of ideas at this time, and the uncertainty whether the glass industry should be kept within the club or not, or whether the club should admit new members. The openness of the debate says much about Pilkington's attitude towards decision-making. Despite the fact it was still a family-controlled company, there was no question that the family directors would suppress Terry Bird, a non-family director. It is even more surprising that Bird allowed papers contradicting his views, ostensibly prepared by a subordinate, to be tabled at the board. The debate in the boardroom must have indicated which directors supported which point of view, but the minutes are neutral and do not attribute views, despite the fact that the editor of the minutes, Sir Harry, was obviously partisan.

Whatever the outcome of the debate might have been, the intervention of a third party sharpened the question. The same 31 January 1969 meeting also minuted:

On 20th January representatives of Guardian Industries Corporation had visited Pilkington for the purpose of asking whether we would be willing to grant a licence under our float patents in the USA. We had replied on 28th January that we would not be willing to grant the licence they had requested.[17]

It is surprising that the response was not delayed for two days so that it could be discussed by the Divisional board.

As a result of the Guardian threat (for a detailed account see below, pages 137–41) there was a rapid reappraisal of the float licensing policy, and there was a campaign for change centred on a series of papers by Terry Bird. First, in a pair of papers to the FGDB in May 1969 he set out the future of float and sheet (by now the total replacement of plate by float was only a matter of time as manufacturers phased out their plate plants). Both the company and some leading licensees were planning to replace all sheet down to 3 mm thickness with float, and technical work had shown that float down to 2 mm, and even thinner, was possible.[18]

In October 1969 the CCC minuted that the company was 'now reaching a new stage in its licensing, particularly as we were contemplating putting down a float tank to replace sheet'.[19] At the following CCC meeting Terry Bird set out the arguments for changing the policy, and asked whether the company was prepared to create new flat glass manufacturers provided they have an adequate market. If float were to replace sheet, there must be greater float capacity. It was agreed that the objectives were:

- getting float established as the main flat glass process;
- protecting areas where the company had or wanted an interest; and
- the establishment of a stable world market, with prosperous competitors.

The company would consider new manufacturers but not where they were big consumers of glass (e.g. the motor manufacturers) on whom the existing licensees relied, but they would consider Guardian. (This is a contradiction as Guardian was a processor of glass for the automotive industry and a major customer of the US licensees.)

At the board in December 1969 a further paper reiterated the objectives and set out new market data compiled by Terry Bird showing the consumption of float as a ratio with Gross National Income, which indicated that float was under-exploited in the USA. It also said:

> Float is now entering a new phase wherein it will challenge sheet on the basis of cost; the number of potential licensees is as a consequence greatly increased and we should exploit the opportunity thus presented … We are prepared to create new clear flat glass companies where they have a tied market of adequate size although this would exclude big consumers such as the motor car manufacturers … Large safety glass groups such as Guardian … we would consider as possible new licensees.[20]

The minutes confirmed the proposals and said that the recent purchase by Guardian of Permaglass (another US-based glass processor) 'gives them a large tied outlet for glass and brings them within our amended policy criteria'. At the January 1970 meeting of the CCC it was agreed to write to Guardian, together with Fourco and Combustion Engineering (both US sheet manufacturers) and offer them licences as a consequence of the review of policy.[21] There was a case to justify a licence to Guardian which was strong enough to persuade members of the board and, perhaps more importantly, the existing licensees.

It was not just the threat from Guardian that prompted a change of attitude. The company now felt confident that float could, in the near future, be competitive with all sheet substances and this meant that any sheet producer with an adequate market was a potential float licensee. The patents would begin to run out in key countries in the near future, and the sooner the company could get new licences, the longer the stream of royalties would flow. Royalties were payable for as long as the licensee used Pilkington technology, unpatented or not, for the 16-year duration of the licence (at which point the licensee had paid-up rights for the territory of the original licence) and, as long as the proprietary nature of the Pilkington know-how could be sustained, royalties would flow and Pilkington could limit the territories in which manufacture could take place (see pages 185–9). In addition new licensees might be prepared to allow Pilkington some form of ownership so that it could extend its sphere of influence. The opportunities for ownership were limited and should be grasped quickly.

There was an intuitive concern to admitting new members to the club. The Pilkington directors (and the plate glass industry as a whole) had been brought up to believe in the membership of the plate fraternity. There had been arrangements among them since 1904 (see below, pages 29–30). The reasons (logical or not) had become part of the industrial culture. This encultured reaction was very difficult to change, despite the manifest commercial logic of doing so. It required a change, not only to the company's intuitive base, but also to that of the industry as a whole. Such a change of culture is thought to be difficult, if not impossible,[22] but in this case there was a mutual external threat to the key players, Pilkington and the US licensees. Although the change of policy was rational without the threat from Guardian, Guardian's actions galvanised the acceptance of a more rapid change of policy, not just among the directors of the company but also among the licensees.

The Guardian debate

Guardian Industries Inc. had been founded in the USA in the 1930s as glass processors. In the late 1950s it was effectively bankrupt, but William (Bill) Davidson, a family member, became its head in 1959, nursed it back to health and by 1969 Guardian were large-scale producers of toughened and laminated glass for the automotive original equipment and replacement market. Guardian had had dealings with the company before. In 1964 the company had struggled to meet a large order from Guardian for ⅛ inch float as a means of expanding their sales overseas and getting into the lucrative US motor equipment market. In November 1968 it was reported that a Mr Sczesny had left Ford the previous month, and it later transpired that he and two other Ford engineers had moved to Guardian. Sczesny had been a senior engineer at Ford, well known to the Pilkington engineers as he was the regular contact on float matters and was highly regarded as one of the most competent people in the field, not least because he had been responsible for the Ford experiments that so nearly circumvented the Pilkington patents.[23] The news prompted a paper to the FGDB examining whether someone could set up a rival plant without a licence in the light of the fact that there may be knowledgeable engineers in the market. The paper said that there were still patents that were essential for a float plant and that therefore it would be some years before a non-infringing plant could be built. It was assumed that the company would take legal action for any infringement of the patents. Despite the rumours about Sczesny, there had been no application for a float licence from Guardian or any other indication that they were contemplating making glass, float or otherwise.

When the Flat Glass Division was set up in 1966 one of the responsibilities devolved to it from the Group Executive was the review of float licence applications; only if they recommended a grant would it need to be referred to the CCC or the board. In practice the applications were referred to Terry Bird as Chairman of the FGDB and he made any decision to refuse, it being merely noted at the next FGDB meeting. The refusal to license Guardian, despite the review of policy going on at that time, was only mentioned at the FGDB on 31 January 1969, after the letter refusing a licence had been sent out on 28 January. Although this has the appearance of being a routine, rule-following decision, it was not likely that the decision was made by Terry Bird alone. Sir Harry had received a call on 9 January from the Canadian plant manager reporting that they had heard that Guardian were going into glass melting with a tin bath. On 10 January Arthur Pilkington wrote to Sir Harry:

> There is great anxiety over this as Sczesny knows everything about float and Wall is nervous that if they applied to the courts there is a chance that our patents in the States could be invalidated if they were successful in proving we were discriminating among manufacturers ... Alastair is afraid they will try and blackmail us.[24]

On the same day Sir Harry wrote to Wingerter at LOF: 'You and the other licensees have every right to expect us to do all we can to protect your rights and our own and we, for our part, certainly intend to do this.' Sir Harry met with Barker of PPG on 18 January, whose comment was that 'they [Guardian] would be about the worst people in the world to get a licence ... he was sure it would not be to anybody's advantage.'[25] The possibility of bringing a new member into the club radically challenged the culture at both the company and the industry level and triggered a powerful automatic response.

After this flurry the negotiating team of Bird, Wall and Roberson (another director) were non-committal at a meeting on 20 January 1969 with Davidson and Feldman of Guardian. (This may appear to be a relatively junior team, but it gave room for an appeal to the top team of Sir Harry and Sir Alastair.) Davidson had trained as a lawyer, and Feldman was his external legal adviser, although also a member of the board. Leslie Wall's notes of the meeting are very brief,[26] Guardian were committed to building a glass-making plant and asked if the company was prepared to license them. The response was only that Pilkington would consider it. It is possible, from later references, that Guardian hinted at an antitrust defence even at this stage and left the implication that they had their own technology and they only wanted a licence to avoid a dispute.

Guardian issued a press release on 20 March 1969 saying they were going to build a plant at Carleton, Michigan, and would be floating glass on molten metal; that approaches to Pilkington for a licence had thus far been unsuccessful; and that Pilkington 'had advised' Guardian that any use of float technology would involve infringement of its patents and breach of confidentiality. Guardian's lawyers had advised that any such claims 'would be without merit'.[27] Immediately after this Sir Harry wrote to Sir Alastair, 'As far as I am concerned I am still dead against giving up without a fight.' In a more Churchillian vein he wrote to Sir Norman Kipping, a non-executive director, 'There should be absolutely no talk of any kind of defeatism but we must fight to the utmost.'[28] It was some months before Pilkington changed their licensing policy and wrote to Guardian in January 1970 offering them a licence. What had happened in the intervening months, in addition to the review of policy, to make the company change its mind?

As early as April 1969 Miles Kirkpatrick, the company's antitrust lawyer from Morgan Lewis and Bockius in Washington, had flown to England and given the directors two papers, setting out the advantages and disadvantages of instituting proceedings against Guardian.[29] There could be no action for patent infringement until the plant was in commercial production, as until that point there was no infringement. The company had been told that Ford drawings had been used by Guardian in placing orders for equipment, and the drawings would have incorporated Pilkington know-how. It was probable, therefore, that Sczesny and two other ex-Ford employees at Guardian had passed over Pilkington-owned information in breach of their confidentiality agreement with Ford and consequently they could be sued for breach of confidence, although there was some nice debate as to whether it should be Ford or Pilkington who brought the proceedings. An action for breach of confidentiality would mean proving that the know-how (i.e. the unpatented proprietary information) was still not in the public domain and entailed some risk. If an unsympathetic American court found that the know-how *was* in the public domain then Pilkington would lose control of the technology as soon as the patents ran out. Know-how, unlike patents, had no time limit, and the company could retain control of float, via the know-how, for as long as there was no successful challenge to its continuing confidentiality. However, there should not be too much emphasis on know-how as US patent law required disclosure of sufficient information to work the patents, and if the value of know-how was over-emphasised then the patents might be declared invalid.

The biggest risk, however, was that Guardian would raise an antitrust defence, claiming that Pilkington had worked with the licensees to limit access to the technology and unfairly preclude potential competition.[30] If, for example, Pilkington had discussed with PPG or LOF the exclusion of Ford then the company could be accused of improper behaviour. It is likely that Sczesny would have known that Ford believed they were being excluded,[31] and suspected collusion. Kirkpatrick spelt out in detail the problems of an antitrust action; the wide-ranging discovery process (i.e. the requirement to review a huge number of files to find anything relevant and potentially damaging), the risk of triple and punitive damages, the huge commitment of senior management time and the possibility that the patents would be declared invalid. Unwritten, but undoubtedly referred to, was the possibility of finding evidence of arrangements between Pilkington and its competitors in the USA to fix prices. Any such evidence could lead to huge damages, not only payable to Guardian, but potentially to all of the commercial glass consumers in the USA via a class action. The US government could also institute criminal proceedings, with wide-ranging powers to impose a variety of sanctions.

The directors would not have been easily persuaded that they were in the wrong. As recently as 1966 an extensive investigation by the Monopolies Commission in the UK had concluded that there was no improper activity as far as the supply of glass in the UK was concerned.[32] Kirkpatrick organised a trial search of Pilkington files to establish if there was any damaging evidence, and, given the continual discussions between Pilkington and PPG and LOF, it is probable that damaging evidence, even if it was only circumstantial, was found. For example the Group Executive in April 1963 had minuted: 'Despite PPG's feelings on a licence to Ford, there is no reason to suppose that giving Ford a licence will lose our friendship with PPG' and PPG would see reason.[33] An internal memorandum records that; 'Files which came to light pose almost insuperable difficulties.'[34]

Notwithstanding Sir Harry's determination to fight, the risks to the company would be too great. A claim against the three engineers who had moved to Guardian was drafted, but it is not clear if it was ever lodged in the US court, although there is a hint that it had been lodged and that the initial response made it clear that antitrust would be raised. In March 1970 the CCC resolved that 'we must do everything possible to come to terms with Guardian',[35] a view that was reinforced by the report at the same meeting that PPG hoped that Guardian would get away without a licence as that would be the day that PPG stopped paying royalty. It was also relevant that the company was planning to go public in 1970, and it would not want to have to reveal to potential shareholders that it was engaged in an expensive antitrust action carrying the risk of large financial penalties and the potential destruction of the licensing value of its float technology.

The letter offering a licence to Guardian in January 1970 produced an immediate response, and a meeting was held in Montreal on 19 February. Guardian, at this meeting and at the three subsequent meetings (one of which was held in the bridal suite of a Bermuda hotel under the banner 'Love conquers all'[36]) vacillated between wanting a full licence of patents and know-how and a bare patents licence, claiming that they had their own technology sufficient to operate the process. In the event the memorandum of understanding of November 1970 and the final licence, which was signed on 18 May 1971, were for patents only. The CCC recorded that as Guardian had their own technology; Pilkington had lost control of float know-how, and implied that there was now a potential competitor in the field of float licensing.[37]

This conclusion (only partially justified and rather dramatic) was to affect the whole of Pilkington's licensing strategy over the ensuing years. On many occasions the company was driven to negotiate with a licence applicant, however undesirable, if they threatened to collaborate with Guardian (see Chapter 10). For example, in April 1971 it was rumoured that Vernante, an Italian applicant for a licence whom the company was reluctant to bring into the club, were in talks with Guardian to get float technology. In subsequent negotiations Vernante threatened to go ahead with their own version of float without a licence. Leslie Wall told the board that he was in favour of granting a licence whenever asked by a sheet manufacturer, if we could not persuade them that a plant was not viable, to avoid the risk of unlicensed producers.[38] A float licence was signed with Vernante a year later. It was vital that there were no unlicensed plants that could operate unchallenged as this would collapse the whole basis on which control of the float technology and the royalty income was founded.

Conclusions

There are three elements to the Guardian decision: the initial refusal of a licence; the revision of the licensing policy; and the decision to grant a licence, clearly illustrating the impact of culture on a decision.

Initial decision
There were many licence applications at the end of the 1960s from non-glass-makers and glass-makers with inadequate markets. Refusals were a matter of routine and merited little thought. Although the initial refusal to Guardian was within policy, the explicit involvement of Sir Harry and Arthur Pilkington with LOF and PPG meant it was more than mere rule-following, and indicates

that Guardian was never regarded as a routine application from a non-glass-maker. There was an immediate lobby, both within Pilkington and externally, seeking to ensure there was no disturbance to the *status quo*. Nevertheless, what thought there was tended to reinforce the intuitive decision to sustain the culture of the plate club.

The change of policy

The change of policy required altering the culture at the company level and, in this case, changes to the more intractable industry-wide culture. The cultural factors can be divided into 'industry' and 'company', as follows:

Industry

- The club expected a refusal. There had been a persistent diplomatic round of discussion, often led by Sir Harry, to keep the substitution of plate glass by float within a narrow group of manufacturers. This is to some extent justified by the 'ethics' (see Chapter 5) of not damaging the businesses of the plate glass manufacturers, which could be regarded as altruistic behaviour on the part of the company. However, it is questionable whether Pilkington would have had regard to the ethics if its competitors had not been in a position to retaliate.

- Creating over-capacity of flat glass would hurt both Pilkington and its licensees. Equally not having enough capacity would not optimise the licensing return and would frustrate customers.

- Newcomers to the industry would not have the same historical appreciation of the structure of the industry nor the need to preserve the *status quo*, threatening the institution itself.

- There were moral if not legal obligations not to allow the undermining of the fledgling float businesses of licensees by granting new licences before the market was ready for the extra capacity. But if there was an unlicensed producer the licensee would have an excuse to stop paying royalties.

- There was an industry-wide recognition that the development of float to cover all thicknesses of glass at prices to compete with sheet glass made it more difficult to justify the plate oligopoly. New licences would have to be granted.

Company

- The company had limited resources to supply training and support to experienced glass-makers, let alone companies with no glass-making expertise.

- Initially the process was difficult to operate and required experienced glass-makers.

The process of changing the policy was drawn out over many months, with a series of papers exploring the economics of a change of policy. The repetitive process was neither iterative (in the sense that it moved forward a little with each discussion) nor incremental (in that it moved forward in small logical steps). It was more that sheer repetition and embellishment of the argument wore down any opposition. The minutes remained terse and dispassionate. However, the board and committee papers showed that Terry Bird had a very different view of the commercial need of wider licensing from the views of Sir Harry and Antony Pilkington. But it may be that the argument had to be developed both to persuade the board and the US licensees. Granting a licence to Guardian in direct contravention to the licensees' wishes would invite a hostile reaction. The 12-month-long debate reflects a need to change not only the company's cultural position but the culture of the industry as a whole. The commercial logic for the company, to extend the royalty return and its potential power base by further licensing, appears enough to sway the internal culture; certainly Terry Bird was persuaded, and it is unlikely that he was alone. But it was Sir Harry who would have to face the licensees, and there was not a strong commercial case for the US licensees to accept a change in the face of widely held, ingrained views.

But despite the inhibiting factors of culture there was a special factor in the debate; the threat that Pilkington and all the US licensees would be implicated in an antitrust action if Pilkington sued Guardian. Whether or not any of the parties had a guilty conscience, the disruption costs of such an action and the uncertainty of the outcome were enough to sway the debate in favour of change.

Although the policy review was under way before the request from Guardian, it might well have taken much longer to agree a new policy without the pressure from Guardian. In the face of the Guardian announcement doing nothing was not an option for the company, as licensees would cease paying royalties and the technology would be deemed to be in the public domain. Suing Guardian was high risk because of antitrust counter-claims, involving the US licensees. There was also the problem of having to disclose such litigation, and the consequent risk to royalties, in the company's 1970 share offer document, prejudicing the offer price. The litigation risk was probably the major single reason for the change of policy, but the economic case had to be built in the boardroom for public consumption. Once this had been done then Guardian could be offered a licence even though they did not actually fit the new criteria.

Final decision

Having made a new policy, it was just a question of following the new rules to grant a licence to Guardian without the need for much debate. This is not likely to have been an intuitive decision as all the reasons for the offer will have been familiar to the directors (Sir Harry must have had to explain in detail to the non-executives why he was retreating from his Churchillian resistance), and in the forefront of their minds as they heaved a sigh of relief at having the prospect of steering a course between Scylla and Charybdis.

The final decision was easy, but the process had been very difficult. The matter was debated repeatedly without progress, atypical for this board, as the rational model for choice (with the economic advantages of giving Guardian a licence and changing the policy) fought against the intuitive maintenance of the *status quo*. The difficulty was exacerbated by the fact that the culture was shared at both the company and the industrial level.

Postscript

Although a change in policy might have come in due course, it is unlikely to have included non-glass-makers. Guardian were the only non-glass-maker to be granted a licence up to 1987. The addition of Guardian made a radical change to the shape of the glass world.

Guardian were not part of the club, and did not want to be bound by its rules. Despite the protestations of friendship, they did what they wanted. Although they did not create over-capacity in the USA, there was never a further debate about under-capacity; either an existing licensee would build or Guardian would exploit the shortfall in capacity. Despite their hostile reception, new plants in Europe were successful for Guardian, forcing down the prices of the entrenched majors with workforces to protect, and opening up new markets in eastern Europe and the Far East. Henceforth, Pilkington technology was now available for any viable project at a fair market price and there was no inhibition on plant building, even at the risk of over-capacity, which the majors had been very anxious to avoid. Consumers benefited from plenty of glass at low prices, and Guardian benefited to the extent that it is now one of the top four producers in the world (see Appendix 2F).

Pilkington also profited, despite their misgivings, as the range of licensees became broader, preserving the flow of royalties for much longer than if they had only licensed the plate producers and avoiding the risk of compulsory licensing or even more blatant piracy.

CHAPTER EIGHT

Turmoil and consolidation,
1970–1985

T HE FINAL PERIOD covered by this story, 1970–85, was a period of
drastic change in almost all aspects of Pilkington's business. After more
than twenty years as Chairman Sir Harry made way for Sir Alastair and then
Sir Antony. The company had gone public and the board had to reconcile
its past, secretive, behaviour with the openness required by the external
shareholders and their advisers. The ownership of the glass industry in Europe
was consolidating, and the relationships which Sir Harry had fostered were
breaking down. The markets were having to adjust to the demise of plate glass,
the potential demise of the sheet glass industry, and the premature closing of
expensive, labour-intensive factories.

Although markets still grew over the period, there was not the continuous
growth of the golden era of 1950–70. Severe recessions compounded the
inevitable structural changes in a time of labour unrest and militancy, as well
as a relative decline in the British industrial base. Yet, with the strength of
the royalty income, Pilkington not only survived these changes but ended
the period stronger than ever and had consolidated its position as the largest,
most widely spread glass-maker in the world.

The shareholders

Only about a third of Pilkington's share capital was placed on the market
in 1970 when it went public. Over the succeeding years the family steadily
released its holdings into the market so that by the mid-1970s it controlled
about a third of the capital and by the mid-1980s the family holdings had
fallen to less than 10 per cent (see Figure 8.1).

Over the same period the total number of shareholders rose to almost
30,000, but the major holdings were concentrated in a relatively small number
of insurance companies and fund managers. Nearly 30 per cent of the capital
was held by little more than a dozen firms. As the practical definition of

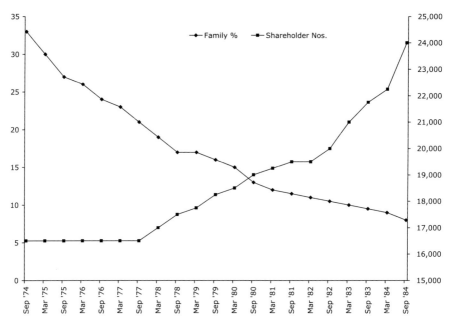

Figure 8.1   Share register, 1974–1985

SOURCE: PILKINGTON ARCHIVE

control of a public company is set at 30 per cent, in many ways the company was more tightly controlled in 1985 than before it went public.*

In the first ten years of public ownership the company's relationship with the City was still relatively comfortable. Outside analysts were not over-aggressive, and the company's profitability and reputation for sound strategy were not being questioned. As the extent of the family ownership was not public knowledge there may have been a feeling that the family were more powerful than they were, and still had effective control. The rights issue in the early 1980s to raise the cash required for the Flachglas acquisition was not overtly criticised, but by the time of the LOF acquisition the position was beginning to change. While the Flachglas acquisition was widely praised the *Financial Times* described the LOF acquisition as 'very, very brave', and the analysts were concerned that Pilkington were over-stretching themselves at a time when the European glass market was in recession. No longer could the board simply assume that the shareholders would trust them, and there

---

* A holding of 30 per cent is not technical control, which is 50 per cent, but, given the diffusion and apathy of a considerable proportion of shareholders, a holding of 30 per cent gives the owner(s) effective control.

was a growing frustration that the expertise and judgement of the board were being second-guessed by a group of theoreticians who knew little or nothing about the glass industry.

In general the analysts were becoming more vociferous in their views as corporate takeovers increased and perceived weaknesses were exposed.[1] Money managers had become preoccupied with short-term financial return. It was about this time that the board (prompted by its American advisers) began to look at the company through the eyes of a putative predator: how could the company be aggressively criticised for its actions and how should it amend its behaviour? This change in emphasis, from the confident control of its own long-term future to the conscious, and rather defensive, application of the short-term fashions of the analysts, underpinned a number of the company's later (and arguably less successful) strategic decisions, with the decision to acquire LOF perhaps the last of the 'free' decisions.

The board and management

By 1979, when the decisions about Flachglas were being made, the number of directors had risen to 21; 12 executive, 4 retired executive and 5 non-executive

General Board, 1974. Left to right; John Leighton-Boyce, Leslie Wall, Ted Judge, David Pilkington, Lawrence Pilkington, Arthur Pilkington, Ben Tyler (standing, secretary), Douglas Phelps, Harry Pilkington, Alastair Pilkington, Terry Bird, Arnold France, Norman Kipping, Barrie Heath, Sol Kay, Antony Pilkington.

PILKINGTON ARCHIVE

(see Appendix 1). With three exceptions the executives had still spent most, or all, of their careers with the company, and those three had spent ten years or more with the organisation in senior roles. The board's committees had been reorganised. The Chairman's Consultative Committee had been replaced with the Chairman's Committee (CC), the Coordinating Committee had been replaced by the Central Resources Committee (CRC) and a new body, the Organisation and Senior Management Committee, had been set up. These committees each comprised the Executive Directors, and the CRC was chaired by the Vice Chairman of the company who was effectively the Chief Operating Officer, concentrating on the review of the monthly results and the day-to-day management of the company. At the meetings of the General board there was a leaning to the past. Sir Harry was still on the board until after the Flachglas purchase, and the influence of Sir Harry, Lawrence, Arthur and Terry Bird was very heavy, even if they said nothing. Sir Alastair was committed to the principle of consultation with his colleagues, and the sheer size of the board at this time could have made decisions ponderous if consultation was full. By the time of the Flachglas decision Sir Antony Pilkington had been identified as Sir Alastair's successor as Chairman of the company and he had a major role in the conduct of the negotiations.

Through the 1950s and 1960s there had been a feeling among management that industrial relations generally were very good. The company had a reputation of being an innovator in matters such as pensions and extended leave, and were competitive in the rates of pay. However, the conversion of the float plants reduced the number of employees at the Cowley Hill works as the plate plants were superseded, and it was clear that sheet would also be replaced, with the loss of many jobs, leading to considerable insecurity. There was growing dissatisfaction at sheet works as the workers felt they were not being treated as well as those at the new float works, and it was increasingly difficult to recruit long-term workers for some of the more dangerous and unpleasant work. There were minor disputes reported in the 1960s but it came as a complete surprise to the board when a major strike erupted in St Helens in April 1970. It lasted for seven weeks, cost the company £6 million, and lost parts of the UK market that were never recovered, as customers felt they could no longer trust the company and chose to second source.

There was a growing militancy in St Helens at this time but there was a sense in the company that it was immune because of the close relationship with the unions and the long service and loyalty of the workforce. The trigger point was the short-term employees at sheet works and a militant group which set up a new union to respond to the shop-floor feeling that the existing unions were too cosy with the company. The company had nobody to negotiate with in the first few weeks of the strike as it could not give recognition to the new union and the recognised unions had lost control over, and contact with, their members. The lack of progress in negotiation and the chaotic public meetings of the workers led to increased bitterness as positions became entrenched, and it was weeks before an orderly secret ballot could be organised and the strike petered out.[2]

The cost was high, not only in lost profit, but in loss of trust between the parties. For many years the relationship between the company and the employees was uncomfortable, even aggressive. Communication was via relatively hostile union representatives who were concerned they would be bypassed again if they were not seen to fight for their members and who reflected the general dominance of the trade unions in the period before the mid-1980s. The rapport of working together in the common cause of float had gone, even though this had only ever really applied to a small section of the workforce. The company became defensive about the creation of new capacity overseas. The workforce wanted the new capacity to be built in St Helens to preserve jobs, whereas the board knew the company had to construct new plants overseas if it were to compete in overseas markets. Exporting was not a long-term option. Sterling was over-valued, and UK labour costs were too high. Sir Harry was strongly affected by the animosity of the strike and his personal failure to see the problems arising. In a very open paper to the board he was self critical that he was so out of touch; there was little criticism of

David Pilkington.
PILKINGTON ARCHIVE

the workers and even grudging admiration for the way in which the militants had used the media.[3]

The new adversarial employee–union–company relationship was a defining characteristic of the whole of this period 1970–85. Throughout, the director seeking to diminish this friction was David Pilkington. David, a fourth generation member of the family, joined the company in 1947 (the same year as Alastair). He had graduated in engineering from Cambridge and his early career with Pilkington was in the works. He was appointed to the board in 1959. David's character was well suited to the difficult, post-strike industrial relations role. At the time some regarded him as too gentle and too ready to concede to the union demands, but these comments were made by managers remote from the expediency of keeping the factories running at least cost. The works management–union relationship became very adversarial, and the links with senior officials at the national level became increasingly political. David, a gentle, empathetic and eminently reasonable negotiator, forestalled many of the standard criticisms. He was not a capitalist, red in tooth and claw, but a member of the family with a long history of slightly paternalistic but nevertheless labour friendly policies. His emphasis was on the company's long-term culture of looking after the workforce, not the recent industrial culture of constant warfare.

Not only did David have to contend with the increasingly militant climate, but the unions were well aware that the company could not afford another strike. While the constant drive was for job security and better terms and conditions, the workforce knew that float technology would inevitably lead to job losses, especially in St Helens. Pilkington was later criticised for being too slow to reduce numbers and too generous when they did. What was forgotten was that any stoppage on a continuous output plant was disastrous, potentially damaging to the plant and losing custom that could not be recovered. The climate, at least until after the miners' strike in 1984, was very much in favour of the workers, and competitors with surplus capacity were eyeing the lucrative UK market for the slightest slip in Pilkington's ability to supply. There was a pace and cost of redundancy which struck the balance between necessary de-manning and labour reaction. David had the difficult task of representing both the hawks and the doves on the board with a degree of consistency.

British management of this era was often criticised for being out of touch with the efficiencies of their foreign competitors until it was too late. This was not true of Pilkington. Because of the engineers' visits to competing plants and the exchange of improvements to the float process the company was fully aware of what was going on elsewhere. There were often reports to the board of comparative studies. In one report to the board of a study of Japanese practice, it was noted that there were no maintenance teams on standby at the works in addition to the operating personnel (as was the Pilkington practice). The operators were trained in maintenance (without demarcation issues) and there were racks of tools on the wall available at a moment's notice. One ex-works manager on the board promptly remarked, 'They wouldn't last five minutes at Cowley Hill!' There was no question that management knew what could be done; the difficulty was applying that knowledge in the context of a UK works culture. Improving efficiency in St Helens was a matter of the correct sticks and carrots, and the right timing of their deployment.

Sir Alastair had warned the St Helens town council that technology

> … had to mean a big reduction in our numbers if we were to survive as a company making glass. It is a curious thing to come to the realisation that companies like ours in established industries were going to be creators of unemployment in order to remain competitive and survive.[4]

Closing obsolete plant had produced its own difficulties in Queenborough, Pontypool and in St Helens, but there were going to have to be float plant redundancies among a workforce who felt that they had contributed to the development of float. The 1970 strike was still fresh in everybody's minds, and there were still plenty of people who had been involved in the instigation of that strike who were vociferous in St Helens and were willing the company to fail. St Helens was a Labour town, and there was a sympathetic Labour government in power. Any reductions had to be taken at an acceptable pace if the company were to avoid damaging confrontation and to phase the cost of redundancy and pension make-up at an affordable rate. As Figure 8.2 shows, numbers employed in St Helens fell through the 1970s (although 2,000 were as a result of the closure of the TV glass plant in 1974), even though new float plants were built. There was a plan to reduce numbers further over time. What the company had not expected was another oil shock and the resultant very deep recession. The impact was exacerbated by the strength of sterling, which gained 17 per cent in value over two years at a time when prices generally were falling. The recession doubled the number of redundancies that had been planned as a result of technology.[5]

In the face of the 1980s recession, the change in union legislation and a shift in public sympathy after the 1979 'winter of discontent', there was a grudging recognition by the unions that refusing to accept redundancies would be damaging in the long run. Changes would have to be accepted if the company were to survive, but the union policy was to limit job cuts to natural wastage and voluntary redundancy on the best possible terms. In addition to job cuts, substantial changes had to be made to outmoded, restrictive working practices. The company had said that it would open the new float plant, UK5, only if it was a state of the art plant, both in terms of technology and working practices. The prolonged period of construction (it

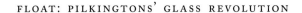

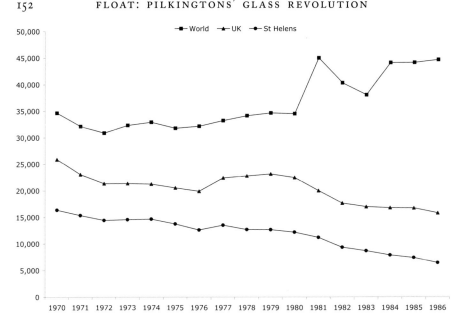

Figure 8.2   Employment, 1970–1986.

SOURCE: PILKINGTON ARCHIVES

was being built on regenerated land, which had been complex to clear, and with the state of the market there was no hurry to bring it on stream) gave time for the negotiations to go through and the men to be trained. In 1978 Cowley Hill employed 2,938 people; this number had dropped to 1,432 in 1984, with further announced reductions to 960. UK5, which opened in 1981, started up with 400 people, a level that was thought to be state of the art, but even there reductions were soon planned.

By 1985 Sir Antony and David were the last of the Pilkington family on the executive board (see Appendix 1). Sir Antony had changed the policy of directors serving out their retirement in a non-executive capacity. Executive directors now left the board on reaching retirement age, and Sir Alastair and John Leighton-Boyce were the last of the retired executives serving in a non-executive role, although they both retired later in 1985. Despite the departure from the board of many years of experience, the remaining executive directors had mainly spent their careers with the company, including a number of years on the board. They had all been involved in board decisions relating to the enforcement of the float licensing policy, and more than half of them had had direct personal responsibility for aspects of licensing. There was no shortage of relevant personal experience on the board.

The key advisers to the board in legal matters, and therefore key players in the final decision examined, were Ken Borrows, the Group Legal Adviser, and Tony Hartley, the manager of the legal department. Ken Borrows had for many years provided the technical backing to Leslie Wall in the application and evolution of the float licensing policy. A barrister, he was an accomplished draughtsman of licensing documentation and an understated but successful negotiator of detail. He had little experience of litigation, but was fully aware of the potential risks of legal battles in the USA. Tony Hartley was a solicitor with a property and pensions background, but his succession to the role of Manager, Legal Department, coincided with a number of court actions and arbitrations in relation to the technology, and he quickly became adept at directing the litigation teams and briefing Borrows and the board. Naturally a cautious man, he was not prone to risky decisions and was well aware of, and if anything fearful of, the consequences of US litigation.

Pilkington expansion overseas

As soon as Pilkington recognised that float could be a major influence on the glass industry it had planned to capitalise on the company's new strength to consolidate in its existing sphere of influence, and expand if it could. There were early lists of possible future overseas float plants for Australia, Canada, India and South Africa.[6] However, as float developed further it was realised that an economic float plant required an output of at least 2,500 tpw and perhaps twice this size if it was to compete with sheet. Consequently an overseas plant needed a very large local market for glass if the bulk of the output was to be sold locally. In addition, an overseas plant would replace the lucrative loading on the St Helens plants and it would be difficult to provide technical support at a time when there was a shortage of experienced engineers to build the UK plants and advise the licensees. Despite continual reviews of the prospects for overseas plants, only one (in Canada) was built prior to 1970.

Each country earmarked for expansion had its own complexity. Canada was always regarded as the first place for expansion. The company already had a sheet works at Scarborough, near Toronto, and had a minority interest with PPG in Duplate, a large glass processor. There was a large indigenous market and there was the prospect of supplying the enormous US market, particularly in the periodic times of shortage of supply from the US manufacturers. The company was anxious to guarantee as much downstream demand as possible, and spent some five years trying to persuade PPG to merge Duplate into the Pilkington Canadian company, although they were only prepared to offer PPG a minority in the merged company once float was planned. PPG were never very keen on the merger, probably because they did not want to become too close to Pilkington and lose their freedom of action, although antitrust

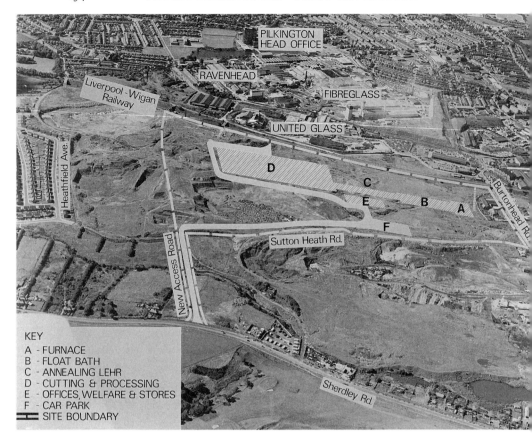

KEY
A - FURNACE
B - FLOAT BATH
C - ANNEALING LEHR
D - CUTTING & PROCESSING
E - OFFICES, WELFARE & STORES
F - CAR PARK
═══ SITE BOUNDARY

Aerial view of the prospective site for UK5, St Helens, showing the old mines and brick quarries.

PILKINGTON ARCHIVE

was the excuse most often expressed. Eventually Pilkington decided to go it alone, despite the much higher cost of building in Canada (£8 million), and the float plant came on stream in 1967. It was a technical success from the outset, surprising St Helens that it made better ⅛ inch than had been achieved at home, and, although the financial results for the first twelve months were not as good as expected, immediately thereafter it was profitable, so much so that a second plant was planned in 1969, coming on stream in 1970.

Australia was seen as the second overseas country for float. The company had operations there but there was also a local glass-maker, Australian Consolidated Industries (ACI), manufacturing sheet. A series of negotiations took place to reach agreement with ACI that when the market was ready for float it would be put down by a joint company in which Pilkington would hold the majority. In 1960 it was agreed more glass capacity was needed in Australia and a new company was formed with ACI, of which Pilkington would own one third, to build the new sheet plant and to bring in the ACI sheet operations. It would be 1974 before the Australian market was deemed large enough to have a float plant of its own. In any event, as was pointed out in 1966,[7] the Canadian plant would reduce Cowley Hill exports by 10,000 tons a year. The Australian plant would reduce them by another 12,000 tons a year, and the company was in no hurry to move to overseas production and lose the UK loading and profits as long as the market was not open to anybody else.

The South African market was even further away from being ready for a float plant, but the groundwork was done by reaching agreement on rationalisation of the downstream market with the indigenous processor, Plate Glass and Shatterprufe Industries (PGSI), through the joint ownership of processing facilities and establishing priority for Pilkington in glass manufacture. Both Australia and South Africa received considerable investment in the interim as new sheet facilities were installed to keep up with local market demand, as shown by the following Table 8.1. The South African float plant started up in 1977.

Table 8.1   *Sheet and plate capacity, 1959–1968, home and overseas (000 tons per annum)*

	1958	1963	1968
plate, UK	180	93	26*
float, UK	24	131	247
float overseas			92
sheet, UK	262	356	353
sheet overseas	97	164	291

* Processing of polished wired only.

Source: Pilkington Archives

India had long been a site of Pilkington manufacture, but there were considerable doubts over the speed of development of the market, exacerbated by the difficulty of managing plants in that country. India did not encourage foreign-controlled businesses, and although a government licence to build a float plant was obtained early in the 1960s, the local manager was warned that a plant would be many years off yet.[8] The company also had manufacturing interests in Argentina, but the ownership of the local glass-makers was complex and the allegiances shifted regularly. The company made some

Halmstad, Sweden. A typical 1970s greenfield site.
PILKINGTON ARCHIVE

progress towards rationalising its holdings in combination with St Gobain in preparation for float. The planning involved machinations in Brazil, where Pilkington had only a processing operation (which it sold in 1966 'as we will never manufacture glass there'[9]), as it tried to ensure a strong partnership between the Europeans while bearing in mind that the company would prefer the first float plant in South America to be in Argentina, where it would have a controlling holding. Float plans were revived in the early 1980s and the project was well advanced when the Falklands War put everything on hold. The plant was eventually approved in 1987, with St Gobain being offered a minority shareholding to share the cost and the risk and in fulfilment of a long-standing arrangement. Brazil had been expected to be a joint venture between St Gobain and Glaverbel, but the latter did not have the resources to go ahead, and its interests in the local sheet manufacturer passed to Flachglas in the late 1970s. After selling its Brazilian holdings in 1966, the company had revived its interest in this territory, had acquired some (different) local interests and, after the acquisition of Flachglas, had a strong position. The first float plant was built by Pilkington in 1982 jointly with St Gobain.

Closer to home Pilkington also had eyes on Scandinavia, where there were a number of small sheet producers and, apart from a minority held in one of them by St Gobain, the major European manufacturers were only interested as exporters. Although the company was reluctant to start manufacture on the Continent, Scandinavia had been identified as a separate market which would soon justify float and which was not obviously the territory of a licensee. From 1972 to 1974 negotiations with all those who had an interest in the Scandinavian glass market left the company as the only party who wished to commit to a float plant to serve this market. Sir Antony masterminded this complex campaign. By involving all those interested, although refusing to allow procrastination, the company was not seen as overly aggressive when it announced that it was going to build a float plant on its own. During negotiations the market had been prepared for float by exports from St Helens, and, by the time the plant came on stream in 1977, Pilkington had *de facto* control of a substantial share of the market without an excuse for retaliation by its competitors. A manufacturing plant had been achieved on the edge of the Continent without the overt hostility of St Gobain or the incumbent sheet glass manufacturers.

The growth in industrial development in South East Asia produced few chances for Pilkington to expand. In the early days the Japanese market was not seen as particularly important and the major concern was not allowing proliferation of float plants and the inevitable exporting of glass to the detriment of the company's Australian and New Zealand producers. By the time the company recognised the possibilities in South East Asia the best opportunities had been taken by the Japanese, who regarded this as their territory, had built local relationships, and were in pole position when the markets were ready for their own float plants. The first full study on South East Asia by the company was started in 1978 and identified Indonesia as the best site, but Asahi had already got a government licence for the first plant which was built in 1983. There was felt to be room for a second plant and there was much jockeying for a government licence with Asahi (who did not want local competition), local interests and the appearance, inevitably, of Guardian. In the event it was the late 1980s before a second plant was built with Guardian's help, although it was rumoured that there was a plant based on Chinese technology in the remote north of Java on the Straits of Singapore. By this time the company had decided not to expand its interests in glass any further.

Malaysia was thought to be ready for float in the mid-1980s, but Nippon already had ownership of the local sheet works and were reluctant to allow

Pilkington to take part in any float plant, which they built in 1985. The Korean company Hankuk had already built its first plant in 1981 and the company had never shown any interest in an investment in Korea, although growth was rapid and Hankuk built their second float plant in 1985. Thailand had an Asahi-owned sheet operation which changed to float in 1984. Only Taiwan offered any chance for Pilkington, and they took a 25 per cent interest in the sheet operation of Taiwan Glass to obtain a foothold. However, at the time Taiwan Glass came to convert to float in 1983 the company was already questioning the level of its commitment to flat glass and allowed its holding to fall to 6 per cent as the Taiwanese company was restructured. By the mid-1980s the group's intention was to protect its core markets, and the only development in the area was the second Australian plant, approved in late 1986 and the joint venture in China which, after many years' planning, came on stream in 1987.

With its potentially vast market, China had long been a prospect for float, but it had the disadvantages of no patent system and the difficulty of policing activity once the technology had been handed over. In 1979 Sir Alastair was invited to go to China to discuss the prospects for float and in April 1980 the board agreed that the company should make it clear to the Chinese that a licence for the technology for the whole of a float plant (not just the float bath) in China was possible.[10] A protocol was signed in August 1980 with a feasibility study commencing in the following year. A joint venture with the Chinese to install a plant near Shanghai was agreed at the end of 1981. The negotiations were the longest yet for the transfer of technology and a licence. Every aspect of the conventional Western agreements had to be explained and negotiated with at least three levels of bureaucracy. Some concepts, such as the formation of a company for the joint venture vehicle, required new legislation. However, Shanghai Yaohua Pilkington Glass Company Limited was formed at the end of 1983 and the plant started up in 1987.

During the negotiations it was discovered that a glass plant using the float principles had been built as a 'trial' plant in China at Loyang with the help of a number of retired American float plant engineers. There were attempts to bring Loyang within the scope of the Chinese float licence to avoid the risk that there would be competition from the Chinese in offering their 'float' technology. There was also the concern that, as with Guardian a decade earlier, unauthorised use of the company's technology could bring it into the public domain. The company was not overly concerned, however, because the reports were that the plant was having difficulty making glass and, when it did appear on the market, the glass was of such inferior quality that it did not compete with conventional float. Although the Chinese built a number of plants based on Loyang technology within China, only one was rumoured to be outside China, that in the north of Indonesia, and they were not a competitive threat, neither from their inferior glass nor from the risk of others wanting the technology. In fact the failure of Loyang may have helped to secure the licence from Pilkington as it showed the Chinese that they needed the backing of an experienced glass-maker with good technology. The successful negotiations for the joint venture encouraged Pilkington to contemplate a licence for the whole of China with a huge potential reward. There was a vast, virtually untapped market available.* The discovery that PPG were building a float plant in Shenzen, southern China required the company to consider how PPG could be prevented from building an unlicensed plant, with the consequent leak of know-how into the public domain and the prejudice to the all-China licence negotiations.

The expansion of float, by both the company and its licensees, meant that by the end of 1986 there were 100 float plants in operation (and some 17 in the course of design or planning) with the ability of producing about 350,000 tonnes of glass per week and with over 85 per cent of the total free world's clear flat glass capacity, of which Pilkington owned, in whole or in part, 20 plants. With the exception of the plant under construction in Shenzen, China by PPG and the Loyang plants, all of the plants were built under licence from Pilkington. The company had kept remarkable control over its technology for 35 years. This was not without a considerable amount of legal enforcement, as explained in Chapter 10.

The technical progress

The focus in the 1970s was to make the float process capable of substituting sheet glass in all its thicknesses, to improve the efficiency of the whole of the glass production line, and to develop new products unique to float.

The company had for some time been planning substituting 4 mm sheet with float and pricing it so that their competitors were driven to follow suit, and this was confirmed at the FGDB in July 1970. It would entail the closure of a number of sheet tanks, and in the aftermath of the strike only one tank was to remain in St Helens, with the balance of the production at both Pontypool and Queenborough. There were difficulties in the implementation of this strategy as the continental producers had large capacities in sheet which they were unwilling to write off with the consequent heavy job losses. In December 1971 the CCC complained that St Gobain were slow to exploit float and build large efficient float plants to replace sheet, despite their declared intent to help rationalise the European glass industry.[11]

CH2, which eventually came on stream in September 1972, was the largest

---

* In 2007 there were thought to be over 100 plants in China using technology derived from float.

Cowley Hill, 1972 showing the congested nature of the site after the completion of CH2.

PILKINGTON ARCHIVE

of the company's plants to date at 5,000 tpw, and was designed to provide the efficiencies to produce 4 mm at prices fully competitive with sheet. The board were told in February 1972 that the plan for substituting 4 mm had been postponed. However, it was only for a few months, and by the end of the year the company was offering only float in 4 mm and above, with the inevitable loss of some of the market to sheet imports. Immediately the company started planning for the replacement of sheet down to 3 mm.

In April 1974 it was reported that the American producers had stated their intention to substitute all sheet down to 2.2 mm. Ford would be using only float, and both Ford and PPG were building new float plants.[12] There was some consternation at this report as the company could only make down to 3 mm in the UK and 2.5 mm in Canada. There was a risk that the licensees were gaining a significant lead. It was therefore vital that the company had the technology to make these thinner substances to US automotive quality. 'It was considered to be of such great importance to the future profitability of the group that priority over current trading would have to be given as and when required by development work.'[13] Within two months the board was being told that 2.5 mm and 2.3 mm had been made on CH4 to the required standard.

Each time a competitor announced that it was to make thinner float glass the board was concerned that the company was falling behind. But the operators only needed to be asked. Worries about the company's ability to make thin glass appear to have diminished by the end of the decade. The Swedish plant, with all the latest technology and with spare capacity to allow time for development work, was now contributing to the group's technical base. In September 1978 the board were told: 'Following development trials on SK1 it is thought that Pilkington has all the necessary technology to make thin float down to 1.8 mm commercially, when necessary.'[14] This was the practical limit of a conventional float plant with normal handling facilities. Thinner glass might be required, but the demand was small and the glass was so fragile that it needed specialist plant.

The attitude of the Americans gave the company greater confidence about the replacement of sheet; where the USA went, Europe was bound to follow. Immediate planning started for a new UK float plant (UK5), and by December initial ideas were being tabled at the board. At this stage it was stated that the new plant would not be sited in St Helens, but by June 1974 the FGDB were recommending that UK5 be built in St Helens for economic and personnel reasons. The new plant would provide some 450 jobs (later downgraded to 400), which would go some way to compensate for the jobs which would be lost from the sheet works when it closed.

Europe did indeed follow the US lead, although not at the pace the company might have liked, and by mid-1977 the expected full switch to 3 mm float was planned by all the European producers (which implies a degree of consensual co-ordination) for April 1979. This shift required a great deal of investment in new plant across Europe. Pilkington had brought in CH2, was well advanced in the construction of UK5 (which was due on stream in 1980) and had built the new plant in Sweden in 1976, a total of 15,500 tpw new capacity. Despite Pilkington's complaints about St Gobain's sloth in building float capacity, they had in fact built eight new plants in Europe (and a ninth in partnership with SIV) in the decade and had another one due on stream in 1980. Boussois had built four, three of them in Germany via their subsidiary Flachglas A.G. In contrast Glaverbel had built only one, a reflection of their difficulties in getting out of sheet with a consequent loss in their overall share in the flat glass market. PPG and SIV, with one plant each in Italy, were the only other European constructors in this period.

The financial environment

Over the period 1970–85 (see Table 8.2) Pilkington largely followed the manufacturing cycle in each of its geographic markets, although it tended to lag by about a year (typically, glass is used late in an economic cycle). This meant that the company could report good results as the economy generally was starting to decline but conversely it would still report poor results when others had already shown a recovery. While it was often criticised for the latter it rarely got credit for the former. Although the profits followed the cycle, the sales showed almost unbroken growth. In some years inflation might have concealed a slight dip, but for the 15 years prior to the investment in LOF the company's turnover, both organically and by acquisition, was growing.

Table 8.2 *Financial performance, 1970–1987 (£ m)*

	1970	1971	1972	1973	1974	1975	1976	1977	1978
Turnover	117	123	136	177	226	242	303	390	469
Profit before tax	17	14	18	34	44	23	34	63	72
Royalty income	6.7	8.6	9.6	13.4	17.4	15.2	19.9	30.5	32.8
Loan capital	17	35	36	29	37	61	106	141	129

	1979	1980	1981	1982	1983	1984	1985	1986	1987
Turnover	549	629	786	958	1,021	1,214	1,225	1,321	2,103
Profit before tax	90	91	81	53	50	88	116	105	256
Royalty income	37.9	37	35.3	39.4	28	24	30	26.2	32
Loan capital	156	136	235	300	404	446	405	403	719

Source: Pilkington accounts

The last three years of Sir Harry's term as Chairman showed a rapid recovery from the effects of the 1970 strike. All the markets for the company's products were strong. Although certain UK customers were now second-sourcing glass from the Continent, and the company never recovered its pre-strike share of the UK market, it could still report record sales each year and, by 1973, Sir Harry's last annual statement, he could report record profits (see Table 8.2). In reflecting on the changes during his time with the company he stressed that float had made a huge impact on the glass world. Since 1930 sheet glass had risen by 380 per cent in price whereas float was only 76 per cent higher than the equivalent plate glass. Indeed in US dollar terms float was cheaper than 1930 plate, and this over a period when wages had risen by 1,500 per cent. Glass, relatively, was far cheaper than it had been forty years earlier.[15]

Sir Alastair could also report a good first year as Chairman in 1974, but the next two years saw the impact of the first oil crisis both on the company's own profits and the royalty receipts. The company only broke even in the first half of 1974/75 and in both 1975 and 1976 the royalties were higher than the profit from the group's manufacturing activities. However, the market was relatively quick to recover and there were record profits again in 1977 and in each year for the rest of Sir Alastair's tenure as Chairman. He could retire in 1980 reporting profits (including £37 million of royalties) of £91 million on sales of £630 million, an apparently superb return.

The company knew that this return was artificially high and there was bound to be a downturn. The royalties were near their peak as licences would start to expire in 1981. There was concern that the pound was over-valued, making competitive exports from the UK less profitable. In addition UK prices made the home market very attractive to importers and BSN (particularly Glaverbel) and St Gobain were already increasing their share of the UK float market. They would no longer feel inhibited by their licences and until the downturn the two companies had not had a persistent excess of float to export. What was not known that the second oil price shock in 1979 would trigger a far more severe recession than the first.

In 1981, in Sir Antony's first report as Chairman, he had to report that the UK operations as a whole had made the first loss since 1921. Despite this there was only a small drop in total profit as the overseas operations, which now comprised half of the Pilkington group, had done well. In particular the newly acquired Flachglas had had a record year. The next year, 1982, proved to be even worse as the overseas performance eased and once again royalties (at their peak of £39.4 million) exceeded trading profit from the operations. Thereafter total profits recovered, although it was not until 1984 that Sir Antony could report that the UK operations were no longer making a loss, a total of four years of UK losses while the company undertook a radical reorganisation.

Financially the early 1980s was a critical period for the company. The European recession was exacerbated by the arrival, in 1981, of Guardian and its low-priced glass in Europe (Chapter 10). It was also a period of adjustment as the new owners of the old BSN assets at Glaverbel (Asahi) and Boussois (PPG) tried to justify their investments. Over-capacity and the drive to sell at almost any price to cover costs made the market very competitive and the company faced the steady erosion of its market share in the UK. It was the new acquisitions of Flachglas and LOF which had the lucrative, relatively secure markets to survive this pressure and they provided valuable support for the group. The UK operations had been in loss and the trade cycles in the 1980s were too brief to allow full recovery from each downturn. The costs of reducing labour to take full advantage of the efficiency of float were high and prolonged. The relatively low level of reported profits required the company to change its conservative replacement-cost depreciation policy to the conventional historical cost method, largely because the City was critical that Pilkington should be the only company in step. The company's reputation declined to such an extent that BTR Industries plc launched a hostile bid for the company in late 1986, which was foiled by a drastic review of the company's internal accounting procedures (which enhanced the reported profitability), some drastic housekeeping and a fortuitous rapid upturn in all the company's markets (see Chapter 11).

With the difficulties in trading in the early 1980s, the royalties and technical fees from float licensing became even more important, as they could provide a cushion until trading recovered and costs were reduced to a more competitive level. There had been an expectation that the royalties would reduce rapidly in the early 1980s as the earliest and largest licences became fully paid up. In fact royalties were holding up quite well as new plants came on stream in new markets and various extensions were negotiated with existing licensees (see Table 8.2). There was a strong drive to extend the life of the royalties, either by the grant of new licences or by ensuring that there was no excuse for the existing licensees to withhold payment.

Licensing

After the radical shift in policy forced by Guardian's new plant in the USA, the company quickly offered licences to other flat glass manufacturers in the USA and granted licences to Combustion Engineering Glass in 1970, AFG Industries (formerly St Gobain's subsidiary ASG, which was the last company in the world to build a plate plant) in 1971 and Fourco Glass Co. in 1973. None of these companies was very successful, and they eventually merged under the name of AFG in 1982.

Licensing policy was constantly reviewed during the 1970s. Initially there was the significant change to offer float to sheet producers in the wake of the threat from Guardian and the need to bring them into the fold. In February 1972 Leslie Wall wrote a paper to the CCC raising the question as to whether the company was licensing too much. There was a risk of creating too much capacity and the royalties were a wasting asset. Should the company be doing more to broaden its manufacturing base? In particular it should be doing more in Europe:

> We must not stand still but it would be preferable to go ahead (e.g. with talks with BSN) at a time when our strong technical standing was backed up with a good manufacturing and trading position.[16]

During 1973 Wall wrote some five papers on float policy, raising issues of export rights and royalty rates, particularly to encourage the transfer of sheet to float in the smaller markets. The board considered a major float policy review paper in February 1974 looking at the timing of the expiry of the major licences in 1980 when the royalties would diminish rapidly, and the expiry of the major patents in the period from 1978 to 1985.[17] There was still the express wish to expand the group's trading interests, and licences should be granted as soon as possible to any country looking viable in the next few years; for example Sweden, India, Brazil, Argentina, Turkey, Iran, South Korea and Taiwan. Europe still appeared to be short of capacity and there were other possibilities in eastern Europe, China and the Middle East.

It was agreed to reduce royalty rates for developing countries and to be prepared to grant export rights to any country where the company did not have an interest. There is ambivalence here. The company was planning float in Australia, South Africa, Argentina and Brazil, either alone or in conjunction with partners. It was part of the practice to announce the intention to build plants well in advance of actual construction. This warned customers of the transition to give them time to prepare for the arrival of float, but it also pre-empted other potential manufacturers. But in most of the discussions with potential licensees and partners the negotiations focused on the potential market for the plant and, implicitly, the knock-on effect of depriving the UK of exports. Many potential licensees were discouraged by being told that the plant required a market of at least 3,000 tpw, far greater than most of the local markets, and of the realities of trying to export the balance at a realistic price when they had no established sales or distributor network. The company wanted to expand float but was also the biggest source of discouragement to licence applicants. The reality was that the markets in the developing world were not ready for the huge output of an efficient float plant, and it was not until the 1980s, and in particular the very rapid expansion in South East Asia, that a float plant outside the industrialised West or Japan was viable.

Despite numerous enquiries and extensive and often convoluted negotiations there were surprisingly few new licences during the 1970s and early 1980s. Although there were misgivings about the threat to Western Europe, licences were granted to Poland (1975) and East Germany (1977) after much hard bargaining over export rights. However, there was no East German plant until 1985, while the Polish plant was not built (and then in partnership with Pilkington) until 1989. Taiwan Glass eventually got a licence in 1983 after the company had spent years trying to persuade them that there was not a sufficient market for a float plant and that they should team up with firstly Hankuk of Korea (who were granted their own licence in 1977) and then the other Taiwanese glass-maker, Hsinchu. Despite the pressure from both Taiwan Glass and Hankuk, it was still some years before either company had a plant in operation. Turkiye Sise ce kam Fabrikalari of Turkey also signed a licence in 1977, although it was four years before their first plant came on stream. These delays were a mixed blessing for Pilkington. The markets, at least outside eastern Europe, were being met by existing licensees who were building new plants to meet demand (see Appendices 2B and 2C) and paying royalties. As the royalties expired on those early licences in the 1980s so the new licensees' plants came on stream carrying royalties for terms which ran from the first date of production. This added considerably to the period when Pilkington were in receipt of royalties and helped to ease the impact of the drop in royalty receipts in the early 1980s.

The only two new licensees of the 1970s who quickly built plants were Vernante and SIV, both of Italy, who signed in 1972 and had plants operating in 1974. Pilkington were not enthusiastic about either licence. SIV were a sheet glass maker who were part-owned by LOF and had the reputation of not playing the game on pricing in Europe. Sir Harry tried to persuade SIV to work with St Gobain, who were planning to put down a second small plant in Italy, when the company thought it would make more sense to jointly put down one large efficient plant with the purpose of replacing sheet. It was noted that negotiations between the two on a merger had broken down in August 1971, and in December LOF were reported to have sold their share in SIV, possibly because of the coming demands for capital.

There was a measure of frustration with Italy, especially as at the same time Vernante, another small sheet producer, had told the company that they were going to build a float plant without a licence and with the help of Guardian. The frustration was caused by the fact that the Europeans had done a great deal to rationalise the industry elsewhere in Europe but would not, or could not, do the same in Italy. The Italians would inevitably (and in fact did) become very disruptive in the market as they would have surplus capacity. The company did take an option over 50 per cent of SIV's shares at the time they granted the licence, but relinquished it in 1976 when it was realised that the company could never influence a company which was supported by the State in order to preserve jobs and was rumoured by the mid-1980s to have lost its capital many times over.

It was clear that Guardian were involved in talks with a number of producers, but even the possibility of their involvement affected Pilkington's attitude to enquiries or projects. Guardian was expressly mentioned in relation to Brazil, Scandinavia, Turkey and Hsinchu in Taiwan, as well as Portugal and Venezuela, but every enquiry was treated as if Guardian was in the background. Even as late as 1989 Guardian were the *bête noire*. I was asked to go to Indonesia to investigate the possibility that Guardian were involved in a new float project, and on commenting to Tony Hartley, by now Group Legal Advisor, that he was paranoid about Guardian, the response was 'I know, but am I paranoid enough?' It was not until June 1979 that the threat of an unlicensed Guardian plant became real, in Luxembourg, and the repercussions of this are set out below (see pages 192–5).

Typical of the complex defensive negotiations was the story of Portugal, where there was an existing sheet glass maker, Covina, which was 20 per cent owned by St Gobain. There was certainly no sufficient local market for the output of a float plant, and Portugal would have to rely primarily on Spain, a market controlled, at least for float, by St Gobain. Covina first approached the company for a float licence in 1972, but St Gobain had asked for the discussions to be dragged out and the Covina management promptly went to Guardian who were prepared to provide technology in exchange for 25 per cent of Covina. During 1973 all the other Covina shareholders had been advised about the ownership of the Pilkington technology, and in June it was reported that Covina was split, one faction supporting Guardian and one supporting Pilkington. The Guardian faction was led by Feteira, a shareholder and director, and it was discovered that his daughter had been to Guardian and returned with 27 kilos of drawings. The CCC decided to offer Covina a licence on reduced terms in exchange for a 20 per cent holding.[18] At a Covina shareholders' meeting in July the decision of the majority was that Covina should take a licence from Pilkington, but Feteira, who had by now been sacked, issued an injunction to prevent Covina taking a licence from Pilkington, partly on monopoly arguments and partly on the grounds that a Mr Akfirat could supply all the technology. Shortly afterwards Mr Akfirat, an ex-Ford employee, was arrested in possession of the complete plans of a float bath, and the operating manuals, and was imprisoned for theft. This time Ford had been supportive of protection of the technology, in contrast to their attitude in relation to Sczesny and Guardian. This curtailed the Feteira faction and in mid-1974 the Covina factory was caught up in the political turmoil in Portugal and was occupied by the workers. St Gobain thought it would be ten years before Portugal would need a plant, but in November 1974 a protocol was signed with Covina for a licence, although no full licence was signed until 1984 and the plant, by now under the control of St Gobain, was eventually built in 1986.

The board was surprised that there was not an explosion of new applications for licences after the Guardian decision. The changes were gradual, and took place in the 1980s rather than the 1970s. But the policy shift as a result of Guardian's pressure resulted in structural changes which are still being worked through, over thirty years later.

CHAPTER NINE

The acquisition of
Flachglas and LOF

A CENTRAL PART of the float strategy from the beginning had been to extend Pilkington's ownership of the glass industry.[1] For reasons that will be explored in this chapter, the right opportunities did not present themselves as early as the company might have hoped, but in 1980 the company acquired Flachglas, the most profitable of Boussois' European manufacturing units, based in Germany, the most successful European economy of the time. Only two years later Pilkington agreed to buy a share of LOF, one of the leading US glass-makers, and became the largest flat glass manufacturer in the world, the culmination of the ambitions expressed in the early 1950s, when float was just an unexplored idea with potential.

Despite being the goal of a declared, long-term strategy, the final decisions were by no means straightforward. In both cases there were strong reasons for and against the acquisition, not all of which were expressed in the meetings. Comparing the two cases is instructive. The management teams advising the board were very similar. The decision-making process was almost identical. The express reasoning in both cases followed a similar, logical pattern and might have led to each acquisition being turned down, although for different, economic reasons. However, the unexpressed, intuitive drives founded in the company's culture led to both deals being consummated despite a changing environment and a new Chairman seeking a change of policy.

A remarkably effective use of glass for the new roof of the Great Court of the British Museum in Bloomsbury, London.

The acquisition of Flachglas

Pilkington had acquired 8 per cent of the capital in BSN at the time BSN had taken its float licence in 1962. From the beginning it was seen not only as a valuable opportunity to know what was going on in one of the major European producers, but also a prospective stepping stone to greater involvement in Europe. In December 1970 Sir Harry reminded the CCC that the company ought to be interested in getting into the BSN glass division. 'In all this we were looking at the period ten or twenty years ahead rather than any immediate point. I think we ought to encourage any thoughts in this direction.'[2] Riboud, the head of BSN, had huge ambitions for his company, and with the failure of his bid for St Gobain (and therefore the aim of becoming the biggest glass-maker in Europe) he began to turn his mind to becoming one of the biggest food companies in Europe, even to rival Nestlé. As early as 1970 BSN bought Evian and half of the French breweries; it was more profitable to fill the bottles than to make them. (The outcome of his strategy is BSN-Gervais-Danone, one of the leading food producers and brewing companies in the world.) Pilkington had a role to play in these plans, and throughout the 1970s the two groups worked towards some form of merger.

In 1970 BSN consolidated its position in Germany with the merger of Delog and Detag to form Flachglas A.G. Although BSN held the majority of the shares, the company was publicly quoted and as a result the management were entitled in law to be, and in fact were, very independent. (Riboud eventually admitted to Sir Antony that he wished the company luck with controlling Flachglas as he had never been able to.[3]) Flachglas was a profitable, well-managed company with modern plant and good technology, particularly downstream in processed glass where it was the major supplier to the prestige German automotive manufacturers. There was a feeling that BSN left Flachglas to look after itself as Riboud dealt with the more intractable problems of Boussois and Glaverbel.

During 1971 the future of Glaverbel was the subject of extended discussion between Pilkington, Boussois and St Gobain. It was feared that Glaverbel were on the verge of bankruptcy, but that they would be subsidised by the Belgian government to avoid the heavy loss of jobs if the sheet works were to be closed.[4] Their exports into the UK were disruptive and Pilkington were having to take some small steps into Europe in retaliation. It would be better if Glaverbel were more firmly controlled by Boussois, who were also also amenable to a closer relationship with Pilkington. Sir Harry wrote, 'My present view is that a merger with BSN and Flachglas alone, though important, would have only a small part of the value of one with Glaverbel included.'[5] It would be another eight years before these plans came to fruition.

Glaverbel were owned 25 per cent by BSN at the beginning of the decade, but it was clear that this gave BSN very little practical influence. As was seen at the end of the 1960s, Glaverbel were more committed to sheet than to plate and then float. They had far too much capacity for Belgium, where they were based, and had always relied on exports. With the attack by float on 'their' markets (initially the lucrative thick-drawn sheet market and later the substitution of 4 mm sheet) they became increasingly aggressive and were irritating Pilkington by selling cheap sheet in the UK and even failing to follow the price leadership in float in Pilkington's home market. Glaverbel had set up operations in Canada which were both loss-making and disruptive and had asked Pilkington if they could become involved in the company's operations in Canada as a means of salvaging their position. In August 1971 the board considered the draft of a letter from Sir Harry to Riboud which said that we could only contemplate this if Glaverbel were completely under the control of BSN and better behaved. The conclusions to covering notes said that, 'I cannot see anybody other than the BGD [BSN] group with whom we would do really well to get tied up', and that the company should try to agree a timescale for some form of merger, the time to run from the moment of the absorption of Glaverbel.[6]

Getting control of Glaverbel was no easy matter. Freudorfer, the head of Flachglas, had told Terry Bird at this time that the Belgian government would not be willing to sanction any arrangement that would lead to the control of the Belgian glass industry by French or German interests, particularly if this led to the closure of Belgian sheet plants.[7] However, BSN did manage to get control of Glaverbel, by putting Glaverbel, Flachglas and Boussois (i.e. all the glass-making companies) into a new Belgian company, Mecaniver S.A. This had upset the French government, and Riboud had had to promise that BSN would treat Mecaniver as a French company in getting French government approval for future actions. Riboud had only agreed to take on Glaverbel in the expectation that Pilkington would become a partner, and it was even discussed whether Pilkington should lend BSN money to help them out. This was not taken up, and it is likely that BSN had enough difficulty with the authorities, in particular the competition authorities, who were now beginning to flex their muscles in Europe, that he needed to keep at arm's length from Pilkington.

By June 1972 BSN had agreed to merge with Glaverbel, and the company had set out their case to BSN for some form of merger with Pilkington. Riboud did not respond until the autumn and then only to say that he did not want to talk about future relationships until the Glaverbel merger had settled down, particularly as there was some rationalisation of downstream activities with St Gobain and he admitted in early 1973 that there had been some difficulties with the authorities. Riboud was still anxious that the company keep its 2 per cent holding in BSN. (The reduction from 8 per cent had arisen as BSN were continually seeking new capital to expand and the company did not wish to invest in the broader scope of activities in which BSN was engaging.)

Although there was regular contact with BSN at their board meetings and discussions on other matters, there was no further debate on a merger until March 1978, just after Riboud and Sir Alastair had both been present at the annual economic conference in Davos. In great secrecy the company set up project 6601 (1066 in reverse), but the code name was later changed to Davos as the earlier one was considered too obvious. The first meeting between the parties was in March 1978, and Riboud tabled the proposal that Pilkington buy 25 per cent of Mecaniver, the glass holding company. A month later Riboud said he would be open to offers for the whole of Mecaniver, or even the whole of Boussois and Glaverbel, but it could not be Flachglas alone. This vacillation by Riboud typifies his approach throughout the negotiations. A letter would set out a formal proposal for discussion but at the meeting itself two or three other suggestions would be thrown out. The principle for BSN was that they wanted to maximise the return on the sale. They had invested a great deal in Mecaniver to manage the shift from sheet to float (although it later transpired that much cost was yet to be incurred), but it had to be a transaction that would obtain all the relevant government consents as well as approval from the European competition authorities. Pilkington were the best buyer. It was not sentimentality on Riboud's part because of the long close relationship. He knew how desperate Pilkington were to get into Europe without overt hostility from the incumbent manufacturers, that this was their only realistic opportunity on any scale, and that Pilkington would pay the highest premium.

There were further meetings between the parties, at which various options were mulled over. Pilkington were very keen but cautious, surprisingly so given that this had been in their minds for over fifteen years. While it was very attractive to have an unopposed investment in Europe with access to the downstream markets, it still appeared that there was much to be done in Boussois and Glaverbel. Neither of the companies had been making any profit and still faced considerable costs arising from the closure of sheet and other rationalisation. These actions had already created a high level of debt, with no certainty that the businesses would create the cash flow to service the debts. The price would be very high – it would be by far the biggest transaction the company had done – and there was little point taking a minority stake in Mecaniver unless there was a right to move to control in the near future.

In March 1979 an investigatory team was appointed in conditions of great secrecy. Obviously the project was price-sensitive, but it is not clear why there were no minutes of any of the discussions at board or committee meetings. There were records of the meetings in the team's personal files, but not in the formal record, and no briefing papers were kept with other board papers. Despite this the French gossip sheet *Le Canard Enchainee* published an outline of the negotiations early in the exchanges as they had picked up a radio telephone call between Riboud and a colleague. Luckily the readership did not extend to the analysts and there were no further breaches of security. The amount of information that could be given to the team by BSN was also constrained. There were outside shareholders in each of the main companies being examined, and Pilkington could not be given information that was not available to the other shareholders. BSN's team were much more open with the Boussois and Glaverbel data than they were with the Flachglas data, although it was not open book for any of the companies; little was proffered unless it was specifically asked for. Despite those constraints, the team presented their first report in May 1979. It was not over-enthusiastic. Riboud had valued the company at some £102 million, but Mecaniver was making no profit (although it might make some next year); it had debts of £200 million, and would need to borrow a further £30 million to cover social costs; the relationship with the unions in Belgium and France was very sensitive, and the transaction would require the consent of four governments and the EEC, with the German Bundeskartellamt (Competition Law enforcement agency) probably the most difficult.

In June 1979 both the CC and the board received a 26-page briefing document and a presentation from the team. The conclusions were disappointing. Buying Mecaniver would weaken the company for years, not only because of the purchase price but also because of the need for further finance, the demands on management to deal with the personnel problems and the inability to do other major transactions, however attractive, for some time. The business outlook in Europe was not optimistic enough in the near future to warrant such a risk. Flachglas on its own might be very attractive, but it did not appear that that option was on the table.

Riboud was told the company could not buy Mecaniver as a whole and received the reply that Flachglas alone was not for sale. Further investigation was done on Glaverbel and DeMaas, a small Dutch sheet maker within Mecaniver. The information was even worse; there was still much rationalisation to be done, and no account had so far been taken of the accrued social costs arising from previous closures. Through July to September various combinations were examined and tried with BSN, the company's target being to obtain Flachglas with the minimum burden. On 7 September 1979 the board approved the purchase of Flachglas, Glaverbel and DeMaas for £120 million. The minute is terse (see Appendix 3A) and only records the decision rather than the debate. But the folder presented to the meeting was comprehensive (see Table 9.1). The debate must have been lengthy, but it had all been said before. If the company wanted a significant manufacturing base in Europe without a vicious war, this was the price. After all, the company was buying five reasonably new float plants and a great deal of safety glass plant, bearing in mind that the cost of UK5, which was currently under construction, was budgeted for £78 million. The board also agreed that if the purchase of Flachglas was blocked by the authorities it would buy Glaverbel and DeMaas alone.

Table 9.1 *Flachglas and LOF – briefing documents' section headings*

Flachglas	LOF
• Management and labour	• Organisation and senior management
• Management and unions	• Employment and unions
• Financial	• Financial
• Profit, cash flow, balance sheet	• Profit, cash flow, balance sheet
• Assets	• Plants, products and markets
• Capacity utilisation	
• Market shares	
• R & D	
• Legal (competition law implications)	• Legal (antitrust law implications)
• Financial, valuations and impact	• Financial, valuations and impact
• Minority Shareholder attitude	
• Integration	• Integration
• Future strategy in the USA	

Postscript to the Flachglas acquisition

A memorandum of agreement was signed with BSN on the negotiated basis, the deal was announced, and the briefings for all the relevant agencies were dispatched. The crucial meetings were with the Bundeskartellamt, the German competition office, at which both the Pilkington team and that from BSN were present to argue their case. Despite the fact that the company had only 6 per cent of the market for flat glass in Germany, mainly from the new plant in Sweden, Flachglas had 35 per cent and Glaverbel 11 per cent, giving a combined total of 52 per cent. This was much more than that of St Gobain and, when combined with Pilkington's technical leadership, would give an unacceptable level of dominance. Their conclusion, delivered at the first meeting on 19 December 1979, was that the German authorities would prohibit the transaction. It was agreed that further information and argument would be supplied, but at the next meeting on 31 January 1980 the answer was still 'no'.

However, at the end of the meeting the Pilkington representatives were asked to stay behind. The Bundeskartellamt officials' attitude changed from very formal and negative to supportive, almost conspiratorial.[8] Their formal objection was based on the fact that Pilkington's small exports to Germany were sufficient to put the proposed combination above the threshold for an acceptable transaction. However, would Pilkington consider changing the transaction to keep the merged businesses below the threshold? For example, Pilkington could buy either Glaverbel and DeMaas alone or Flachglas alone? Either possibility would not be objected to by the Bundeskartellamt.[9]

The Pilkington team were jubilant with this outcome. Although the signed memorandum of agreement stipulated that if the whole transaction failed to get approval then the company would buy Glaverbel and DeMaas alone, there was a firm belief that this would not really satisfy BSN. Even during the negotiations BSN had been making acquisitions, and it was a joke between the two teams that BSN were spending on the Pilkington credit card. The purchase price for Glaverbel and DeMaas would not be sufficient for BSN to cover the cost of their other purchases. On 8 February 1980 the board decided to make an offer for Flachglas and DeMaas without Glaverbel[10] and on 15

The author signing the contract for the acquisition of Flachglas A.G., June 1980.

February Sir Alastair and Riboud agreed the price for Flachglas alone; BSN would not sell DeMaas without Glaverbel because their two businesses were too intertwined. Despite the firm statements throughout the negotiations that Flachglas alone was not for sale, the company had acquired the most modern plant in the healthiest European market unencumbered by debt and social costs. There were some worries as to what BSN would do with the unprofitable rump of their glass business, and whether this would be disruptive in the future, but the company would be one of the largest glass producers in the world with a power base in Europe to match that of St Gobain, owning seven float plants serving the market compared with St Gobain's eleven.

The decision over which the board had agonised in September was superseded. Whether the acquisition of Glaverbel would have been a commercially successful decision is academic (although the eventual purchaser, Asahi Glass of Japan, is still the owner), but if the board had declined to make the offer for Glaverbel and Flachglas then there would have been no debate leading to the acquisition of Flachglas alone. In terms of the actual outcome it was a good decision.

The transaction was completed on 2 June 1980 at a cost of £141 million. Almost immediately Riboud told Sir Antony that St Gobain were interested in buying Glaverbel, but only if Pilkington undertook to buy Boussois. The undertaking was given in the expectation that the transaction would be turned down by the authorities and in fact nothing more was heard of it. Glaverbel was sold to Asahi in early 1981, and Boussois was eventually sold to PPG in early 1982. At least the businesses were kept within the club.

The acquisition of LOF

The relationship with LOF, while not as close as that with BSN, had been very friendly. There was little direct competition between LOF and Pilkington as glass-makers. Although Pilkington Canada had an interest in the US market for glass, the market appears to have been orderly, without the internecine price-cutting that caused so much friction in Europe. There had been a close and friendly association through the float licence, and each had a respect for the other's technical ability, particularly as LOF supplied the majority of the processed glass to General Motors, requiring the highest quality thin glass for laminated windscreens. The fact that the Americans were leading the world in replacing sheet also endeared them to Pilkington.

There had also been a long-running relationship between the two companies in trying to resolve the difficulties in Canada. Despite the company's early success in building a float plant in Canada, with a consequent second plant coming on stream in 1970, the Canadian operations became a continual drain on the group. The occasional good year was more than offset by a number of bad ones. For years discussions were held with PPG to merge PPG's downstream operations in Duplate (in which Pilkington held 49 per cent) with Pilkington Canada, but as the company insisted on a majority in the merged operations the discussions came to nothing. LOF also had processing operations in Canada, and as early as 1970 LOF had instigated a closer association in Canada as they wished to expand there and admired the strength of Pilkington's R&D.

Nothing material was reported to the board in relation to this approach, but by mid-1972 the situation in Canada was so poor that the CCC accepted that control of Canada may have to be ceded to PPG if that was the only way to achieve a merger with Duplate. By the end of the year advice had been received that this would not get through the Canadian antitrust authority and further talks had been held with LOF although they said that were not interested in buying into Canada for some years.

The continuing discussions with PPG were also affected by the company's refusal to grant PPG a float licence for Canada to enable the latter to convert their Canadian sheet plant to float. Pilkington wanted to get some advantage in Duplate as part of the deal and were very concerned about having another float plant in Canada, where there was already surplus capacity, unless there was some guarantee of an outlet in the USA. The Canadian company only survived because of regulatory protection from US imports, and even then the company complained these were not effective in times of surplus US capacity.

All the talks seemed to drift, and early in 1977 it was reported that Ford were interested in buying all or part of Pilkington Canada, followed in October by an approach from Guardian. It was stated that LOF would be preferred partners, and project 1000 was set up to explore this route early in 1978, although it was anticipated that there would again be problems with antitrust. By the end of the year it was reported that LOF were looking warmer about Canada. However, in July 1979 advice had been received that the antitrust laws in Canada would mean that the sale to LOF would be impractical and that to test it publicly would be bad for morale.

Within two months it was reported that Ford were very interested, and it was agreed that the company should sell a minority interest to them. There was a prescient caveat. As the company might be interested in being involved in manufacture in the USA in the future, antitrust law might require the sale of the balance of Canada. The agreement with Ford should therefore contain a 'put' option, which gave Pilkington the right to insist on selling the balance of the shareholding to Ford at a time of Pilkington's choosing. The negotiations took nearly a year, but in December 1980 agreement in principle was reached for the sale of 51 per cent of the Canadian glass-making and downstream operations for C$30m. Only five months later PPG, who had been upset with the announcement, bought the company's interests in Duplate for C$58m.

Without any definite plans in mind, the company was now in a position to make a major move into the USA. There had been tentative thoughts about this over the previous ten years. There was no question of trying to build a plant in the USA as the reaction from the indigenous manufacturers would be very hostile. Ford, PPG and LOF had all been assiduous in exploiting float, rapidly building new float plants, and substituting sheet. The small sheet manufacturers, C.E. Glass, AFG and Fourco, who had taken float licences in the early 1970s, had not been successful, and had each approached the company with offers of partial or complete ownership. Each had been turned down, mainly because they were not of a scale that suited the company, and partly because the company did not want to establish operations that brought them within the jurisdiction of the US laws, particularly the antitrust laws. This latter reason was misplaced: the company was already within the jurisdiction by virtue of its licensing activities, although it had no assets within the USA against which any adverse judgement could be enforced.

Guardian had proved that it was possible for a newcomer to build a successful business (constructing four float plants in the USA in the 1970s), but only on the back of an existing downstream processing business and an established sales network. Despite the antipathy between the two companies and the obvious culture differences, in June 1977 Pilkington decided to investigate whether to acquire Guardian, but only a month later changed its mind.

Sir Alastair retired as Chairman in August 1980 and was succeeded by Sir Antony. At his first meeting as chairman of the Planning Panel (the body advising the board on strategic planning, which comprised the executive directors plus the head of Group Planning Department) Sir Antony set out his view of the group policy and strategy. The paper reiterated the long-standing core statement that the company would seek successful continuity which required a return on assets of 14 per cent. Flat and safety glass had long failed to reach this target. As glass was again becoming a commodity product, where no manufacturer's product was distinguishable from anybody else's, except on price and availability, the company's market share was deteriorating in all of its markets. As a result of the high value of the pound, UK prices were 20 per cent above those in Europe and 40 per cent above those in the USA. Although the company did not have a presence in the USA, there were no plans to do so. The meeting concluded:

It is possible that the Group should not plan materially to expand its flat and safety operations, although it should plan to maintain its position in those markets which it dominates ... It is possible that in the future the Group should concentrate more of its resources on expanding the Optical Division.[11]

This view was reiterated in early 1982, when it was remarked that the prevailing adverse position in the UK prompted the view that the group should diversify away from flat and safety.[12] The board's resolve was tested only two months later when the CC received a report that LOF were seeking a 'white knight' (see below). LOF had been experiencing poor results in the glass division. The management team which had made it one of the most profitable of the glass producers in the USA had retired or reached a less productive stage, and they had not succeeded in finding adequate successors. While half of LOF, in the newly acquired fluid power and plastics businesses, was very profitable, the glass business was not, annual profits having fallen from $40m to a loss of $14m. It had not managed to sustain much of a share of the glazing market, which accounted for about one third of its sales; 90 per cent of the other two thirds was the supply to General Motors, whose sales had fallen drastically as a result of the recession in the USA and the impact of the importing of Japanese cars into the USA. In early 1982 LOF noted that the company Gulf+Western had been acquiring a significant holding in the company, which was now over 20 per cent. This indicated a prospective hostile takeover and one method of escape was for a friendly 'white knight' to buy the shares from the potential predator, the theory being that it was preferable to have a new shareholder who was sympathetic to the business rather than one who had the reputation for imposing drastic cost savings. Pilkington were chosen by LOF, and invited by them to acquire Gulf+Western's holding.

A research team was quickly formed, including two of the managers who had produced the Flachglas reports, and the CC considered the preliminary report in April 1982.[13] There was little logic in investing in a minority holding without planning to move to control, and LOF profits were dominated by the hydraulic business to which the group could contribute nothing. Despite the attraction of eventually becoming the largest glass producer in the world (if control could be obtained), with some 25 per cent of the world's installed capacity of float, this was further investment in flat and safety which, it had only just been decided, was not the future route to successful continuity. However, it would give the company a substantial presence in the USA, a major gap in its portfolio, even if the return could barely justify the cost of the investment. The CC decided against any involvement, although it would be discussed further at the board two days later.

The board reversed the decision. As there is no record of individual contributions it can only be inferred where the balance of the change lay. If Sir Antony had been clearly against the purchase, then it is unlikely that there would have been more than an expression of alternative views. But if Sir Antony was ambivalent or neutral then the presence of Sir Harry and Sir Alastair (still non-executive directors) might well have been crucial. For them the core business of the company was flat glass, and to become the biggest producer in the world would have fulfilled the ambition of the previous thirty years, since the invention of float had offered the prospect of the company becoming the world leader. Of course the argument was based, as the minutes show, on the rationale of the immediate transaction (see Appendix 3B). Being the biggest was not sufficient in itself, but if everything else was finely balanced then this, rather than the remoter prospect of success in the Optical Division, was an exciting opportunity. One of the reasons of expanding into another field of manufacture was to counter the cyclical nature of the European glass business. As experience had shown with the glass plants in other parts of the world, geographical spread could also be counter-cyclic as the markets of the USA and Europe were rarely in sync. It was decided to investigate further.

In July the board remarked that any company up for sale was likely to have problems, and the key question was whether it was capable of recovery and whether the group had the resources to help it.[14] The final board discussion was held on 3 September 1982. This was a major opportunity, which was not likely to be repeated, to get a substantial base in the USA. If there was uncertainty about the future of glass in the USA then it raised the question of whether the group should be in the glass business at all. The USA was arguably more stable than Europe, and while the investment required the recovery of both the USA and General Motors, it was unlikely that either would fail. LOF required some management help, but not so much that it would overstretch the group. It would take the group near the limit of its financial resources, and postpone other major moves, but it was strategically desirable and the risks were acceptable. The company was acquiring a saleable asset, and the transaction was not irreversible. It was agreed that the 29 per cent holding should be bought for $108 million.

Postscript to the LOF acquisition

As the company had no existing business in the USA it was not thought that antitrust would be a problem. However, the size of the transaction was such that pre-notification and clearance by the US government were required under the Hart-Scott-Rodino legislation. The agreement was signed, but held in escrow, conditional on government clearance. This was the company's first experience of a US government investigation. They had been warned about the scale of the file-searching and paper delivery required, but were still taken aback by the time-consuming nature of the whole process. The US government regarded 30 per cent of a public company as equivalent to control, so that all of Pilkington's glass business was looked at in relation to the LOF glass business to see whether US antitrust tests were infringed. In addition, the deal was examined on the basis that there was a single North American market, which was an unexpected development. The US government objected to the proximity of Pilkington's other interests in Mexico and Canada. It took another six months of negotiating before agreement was reached, but the US government would require the disposal of the company's remaining interests in Pilkington Canada and the rearrangement of the relationships with Mexico. The shares came out of escrow in January 1984. Ford bought the balance of Pilkington Canada, the put option obtained at the time of the original sale proving invaluable.

The company's holding in LOF gave them little say in the business and was unacceptable in the long term. Consequently in 1986 the company swapped its 30 per cent holding in the whole of LOF for 100 per cent of LOF's glass business, retaining the company name.

The acquisitions of both Flachglas and LOF were economically very successful. The profits from Germany supported Pilkington when the recession of the early 1980s reduced the UK operations to losses. LOF quickly returned to profit, and was a key contributor to the successful defeat of the hostile takeover bid in 1986 from BTR and the subsequent delivery of the promised level of profits (see Chapter 11). The technology of Flachglas and LOF (despite some early scepticism) made significant contributions to increased efficiency and new products. The contribution of having a global presence is less tangible, but, for example, as General Motors pursued its global purchasing policies in the late 1980s and 1990s Pilkington would not have been able to retain or increase its share of that business without a global presence. Until the mid-1990s there was no question of the success of the acquisitions and it was only at that time, when the group's performance was stalling, that the long-term management of the acquired operations was questioned. By this time the efficiencies of Flachglas and LOF were lagging best practice elsewhere, and strong direction was again required from the centre.

Conclusions

The process of the decisions to purchase Flachglas and LOF each followed the conventional, rational model and then ignored its conclusions. In the case of Flachglas the rational economic conclusion was to avoid the acquisition of Glaverbel, yet the board decided to buy Glaverbel if that were to be the price for Flachglas. The decision involved the over-ruling of the expressly rational by the culture. The board's decision was rendered redundant by the intervention of the German government, who forced an economically rational (to Pilkington) conclusion. In the case of LOF the rational decision was not to purchase LOF and to follow the new policy to diversify away from flat and safety. Despite that expressly rational conclusion, intuition intervened and LOF was acquired.

In both cases the rational model was set out in the folders of papers prepared by management for the board. All the relevant information was collected, the alternatives weighed and the impact on the organisation calculated. It was a dispassionate exercise, trying to ignore the personal wishes of the authors, who, I can recall, were emotionally attracted by the idea of the acquisitions. In Pilkington the guiding principle for management in relation to the board was one of 'no surprises'. While bad news might not be welcomed by the board, delaying or concealing information, false hopes and wishful thinking were far worse crimes. The folders, therefore, were prepared by Cassandra rather than Pollyanna.

The board did not follow the conclusions in the folders, not because those conclusions were wrong, but because they were incomplete. The conclusions did not take into account the weight of history, nor the intangibles intuitively recognised by the directors nor, possibly, the personal ambitions of the directors for their status within the industry.

In addition to the formal analysis in the folders the following economic issues were expressly discussed:

- Global diversity would counteract the cyclicality of the UK and Commonwealth markets. Even though the new markets were also cyclical, the periods of the cycles did not normally coincide.

- The growth markets were Europe (especially Germany) and the USA; prospects for the UK and Commonwealth were pessimistic.

- Both acquisitions presented unique opportunities for unopposed investment in major markets. If these opportunities were spurned they might not arise again and could fall to competitors, compounding the omission.

- Size was still a goal in itself to counteract its competitors, in the form of Asahi's global ambitions, the European strength of St Gobain and the US power (with possible global expansion) of PPG. Geographic spread was also vital to match the globalisation of the major customers, the leading US and Japanese car makers.

- In both cases the purchase price was far below the construction cost of the relatively modern assets. Whatever the business forecasts, the assets should be capable of profitable returns at such reduced prices. If not, then the whole glass industry was in dire straights.

- LOF offered a leading presence in the biggest automotive industry in the world, not a dying UK base; the substitution of the British-owned car makers by foreign-owned car manufacturers based in the UK was not foreseen.

The intuitive issues were fewer, but positive, in favour of the acquisitions:

Industry

- If there were to be a change in ownership, it was better to have ownership within the club and with the least risk of disruption. It is important to note that in neither case were there any significant formal objections by other members of the industry (who would have been consulted by the authorities), although in each case strong objections lodged with the antitrust authorities would have been very prejudicial to Pilkington's cause.

Company

- It offered the prospect of Pilkington's Chairman being seen as the leader of the world's glass industry and to be one of the very few British chief executives of a world market leader.

- When the company decided in 1950 to look for the successor for the Twin process it was with the idea of strengthening its physical presence as well as its technical strength in the glass market. In 1959 the hope was that royalties could be commuted for shareholdings in some cases. The prospect of the acquisition of Flachglas and LOF was therefore the culmination of 30 years' ambition for a large proportion of the board, even if they had retired from executive office. Many of their plans and strategies had had this goal in mind, and for 15 years the board had been actively courting BSN. The momentum of past behaviour was considerable.

In both decisions the quantifiable economic analysis prepared by management was against the acquisition, but the board, taking a broader view, overruled these analyses on the grounds that the unquantified economic issues outweighed the quantified. As Sir Alastair said (albeit in the context of float development), 'After analysis has been made of the rewards ... and ... all the ... problems then judgement [intuition] plays a vitally important part in decision-making.'[15] The directors were applying an intuitive value to the unquantified economic issues in order to bridge the gap between the known outcomes of the decision and the intangible.

In applying this intuitive evaluation they were not fighting against the weight of culture; the tide of culture was running with them. The industry culture was to preserve the club rather than risk the unknown forces of new members. For the company the intuitive answer was to press for geographic expansion, almost regardless of cost. The momentum of past decisions was enormous; a major presence in Europe and the USA had been a goal for thirty years, and the float strategy had been focused on this precise outcome. All the company's other strategies revolved around expansion for float. The directors' personal strategies were centred on growth of the company. The careers of the executive directors were allied to the growth and status of the company. At the personal, company and industry levels the acquisitions were more a product of the past than the current, explicit and quantifiable economic analysis.

The Flachglas decision was difficult in the sense that the rational model of choice was in conflict with the intuitive decision. However, there is little evidence of the board agonising over the decision. There was only one round of meetings; the minutes reflect no conflict of opinion, nor do the peripheral papers. Perhaps this was because the conflict could be resolved by the purchase price; to the extent that the negative aspect of the transaction was the unknown liabilities of Glaverbel, some value could be put on Flachglas and the potential negatives of Glaverbel to arrive at a net price. As long as the intuitive filling of the gaps did not conflict with the conscious aspects of the rational model, the directors could rationalise the choice and not have to agonise over it.

The LOF acquisition was different in that the rational model was indicating a change of policy, to shift the focus of investment away from the flat and safety operations of the company. This was completely in conflict with the intuitive commitment to those operations and the ambitions of the directors to complete the investment portfolio with US assets. It was not a simple matter of getting the purchase price right to balance the equation. There was the difficult issue of deferring the Chairman's change of policy until after the completion of the long-term ambition. The difficulty of the decision is reflected in the fact that the board reversed the decision of the Chairman's Committee, which was unprecedented in any major matter over at least 50 years. When the matter was again discussed by the Committee it was taken to an open vote, again unprecedented over a similar timescale. The logic of the rational model was defeated, with great difficulty, by the intuitive weight of the past.

In the event the intuitive answer was more effective than the explicit. In both cases the medium term outcome of the acquisitions was successful, and the difficulties encountered much later with both Flachglas and LOF were as much a product of later management as inherent weaknesses at the time of acquisition. The suggested strategic move to concentrate new investment in the non-flat glass sector did become company strategy, counter to the company culture which centred on flat glass. The change was not successful either in economic terms or in managing to alter the culture, and (as revealed in Chapter 11) the company reverted to being a flat and safety glass company in the mid-1990s.

CHAPTER TEN

Legal action against PPG

I n April 1985, the board agreed to launch a UK arbitration against PPG as a tactical move in a broader negotiation in relation to the use of float technology in China. This final decision for examination is one which appeared to be trivial at the time but which had the consequence of the company expending over £60 million in legal costs. This was ten times the original cost of developing float (albeit in depreciated currency), and the litigation put at risk the future of the company, at least in the USA. The dangers of being involved in proceedings in the USA or with a US litigant had been recognised for most of the post-war period, and the board had been at great pains to avoid those risks. Yet the decision to commence proceedings was very low-key and the fear of then becoming involved in the US legal system (which was so critical in licensing Guardian in 1970) appears to have been replaced by a confidence in a successful outcome to litigation.

In 1970 the board expressed the concern that the advent of Guardian meant that the company had lost control of the technology. Despite this Pilkington was still collecting royalties some twenty-five years later. The activities of the legal and patents team had somehow preserved the substantial cash flow. In order to understand the background to these legal activities and the consequent actions taken against PPG it is necessary to set out the legal structure and actions that underpinned Pilkington's control of its technology.

The legal background

Patents are now recognised in almost every country in the world; adoption of the international patent treaties and the establishment of local patent legislation are pre-requisites for acceptance as an international trading country. But the existence of patent legislation is no guarantee of an effective court system to enforce the rights. Although Pilkington covered each of its major patent cases in a wide range of countries, it was found that enforcement of

General Board, 1987. Sitting: Dennis Cail, Lord Croham, Antony Pilkington. Standing: Derek Cook, Denys Cledwyn-Davies, Roger Hurn, Geoff Iley, Robin Nicholson, Peter Thompson, Peter Grunwell, Hilmar Kopper.

PILKINGTON ARCHIVE

the patents was often more problematic. Even if the court system was free from corruption and the judges were impartial, there was the risk that the local courts had very little experience of patent litigation with the consequent lack of procedural rules and relevant precedent, making litigation even more uncertain than normal.

Each major float invention was covered by its own patent, and Pilkington took out a series of these from 1952 to the mid-1960s. There was no overall patent for float. Each case covered a particular detail, not all of which were essential to make good glass, but it was impossible to make good glass without using the key patents taken out in the 1950s. Manufacturing thin glass required using the direct stretch patents that were taken out in the 1960s, considerably extending the life of the patent cover. Although most countries had a 16-year life for the patents, the time when this period started varied. For some countries it was the date the application was lodged, while for others it was the date when the patent was granted, which could be years later if the arguments with the patent examiner were prolonged. Each country also had its own rules for examination so that the admissible description for each invention could differ significantly from country to country. Some countries, particularly developing countries, had rules that required a patent to be worked, failing which it could be compulsorily licensed or forfeit. The Swedish version of such rules influenced the decision to put down the Scandinavian plant in Sweden rather than Denmark.

The loss of an action (or failure to bring an action) in one country did not have any binding effect in any other country, because subtle differences in rules could lead to a completely different result. But a loss would encourage potential infringers and allow the licensees to argue that they should no longer be paying royalties. In cases where there was a high risk of losing a patent action, it was better to reach some form of settlement to keep the infringer within the club of patent licensees.

Patents prevent the manufacture of goods using the patented technology, and also the sale of those products. In theory, someone without a licence who sells a product covered by a valid patent infringes that patent. Hence the Pilkington licences granted rights to manufacture in one country and separate rights to sell in that country and, depending on the circumstances, a number of other countries. While this was extremely effective in policing the sale of float by the licensees, most of whom stuck to their territories, it was essentially a moral obligation; the legal enforceability of the sales prohibition was largely an illusion. It was the seller of the glass in the unlicensed territory who committed the infringement, and if the manufacturer sold glass in his licensed territory to a purchaser who then imported it to an unlicensed country for onward sale, then it was the importer who infringed. This meant that Pilkington would have to sue importers, who were often wholesalers and therefore prospective customers, which it was reluctant to do. In any event the local law often made it difficult to sue successfully. When Guardian started to export to Scandinavia without a licence in the 1970s, the company found it was impracticable to get these imports prohibited or to sue anyone for the infringement.

Although any novel invention can be patented, patents are expensive to maintain, and publication in one country means that the technology can be used in any other country where there is no patent cover. In addition, much of the vital information for running a successful float plant was not patentable. For these reasons much of the new technology was kept strictly secret and claimed as confidential 'know-how'. As long as this is kept confidential, it is the property of the owner and cannot be used without his consent. Pilkington went to great lengths to collate all the construction and operating detail in drawings and manuals and to register them centrally. All Pilkington personnel who had access to the know-how had to sign a confidentiality agreement. Any drawing or manual issued to a third party was registered, and there would be no issue until the third party had signed a confidentiality agreement with Pilkington. This applied to both licensees and suppliers of components of the float bath. Suppliers were an essential link in the policing of the technology.

Some of the suppliers had an effective monopoly on essential components. A loyal supplier both refused to supply to an unlicensed manufacturer and informed Pilkington of the enquiry, who could then follow up the prospective infringement. The envelope of confidentiality had to be preserved.

Even in a well-regimented system, it is difficult to keep information confidential. As the licence programme expanded many individuals at suppliers and licensees had access to the technology. Experienced engineers carried much of the know-how in their heads, and, with the advent of photocopiers, it became increasingly easy to duplicate engineering drawings and manuals. By the 1980s there was a small group of engineers who made successful careers offering consultancy and design services, even if very few plants were ever built and, like Loyang in China, they were unsuccessful in making good glass. Press visits and open days for employees' families required every visitor to be covered by some form of confidentiality (this was a particular problem for royal visits), and any form of publication risked inadvertent disclosure.

Once Pilkington were aware of a breach of confidentiality steps had to be taken to remedy the breach. When Sczesny left Ford with confidential information he and Guardian had to be brought within the envelope, either by granting a licence for the use of that technology or by a court deciding that the information had been gained unlawfully, in breach of confidence. Failure to do so would mean that the information was 'published', meaning that it had entered the public domain and could subsequently be used by anyone else without payment. In addition, licensees would be able to argue that they need no longer pay the full royalty.

Know-how actions are complex and only the most advanced countries, both industrially and legally, have the systems for enforcement. Guardian was adept at choosing sites for prospective plants in countries where the legal system was inadequate, forcing Pilkington to grant licences to Guardian or pushing the company into negotiations with other parties for plants it did not really want to encourage, for example in Portugal (Chapter 8).

All of the licences were expressed to be governed by English law and all disputes were to be referred to arbitration, in most cases in England. This meant that Pilkington could appoint experienced patent counsel as arbitrators for confidential hearings under a well-developed system of law that recognised and protected the rights of the inventor. The company did, on occasion, choose to take certain matters to court, but the decision could be made on tactical grounds where it was thought that the law was favourable or particular remedies, such as injunctions to prevent certain behaviour, were sought and were not available from arbitrators.

The perpetual threat in any litigation, particularly with American companies, was that the other party would raise antitrust infringement as part of their case. As was seen with the Guardian plant in 1969 (Chapter 7), the company was not prepared to risk the enormous expense of an antitrust action with the possibility that the court would forfeit the float patents in the USA or impose punitive levels of damages. There was a hint that Pilkington were concerned that some aspects of its early licensing of float and its general commercial behaviour in the USA in the 1960s might be held to infringe the antitrust laws, despite the vetting of much of its behaviour by lawyers and its professed intent to act within the laws of the countries in which it operated. It was perfectly understandable that behaviour which seemed reasonable ten to twenty years earlier in St Helens was a cause of later nervousness on the part of the board when contemplating US antitrust advice from the lawyers, particularly as the interpretation of the antitrust laws changed over the years.

While a great deal of effort and expense was invested by Pilkington in their patents, it was the success of the protection of their know-how, by both the internal systems and the ability of their lawyers and patent agents, that preserved Pilkington's control of the float technology well into the 1990s.

The first PPG litigation

Although litigation was threatened against Guardian in 1969 (see Chapter 7), it was never taken past the preliminary stages. The threat of antitrust counter-claims was instrumental in persuading the company to change its policy and grant Guardian a licence. Apart from occasional posturing by various licensees in the course of negotiations, no serious claim was made against the validity of the patents, and the relatively rapid grant of the licence to Guardian meant that no licensee tried to get out of paying royalty by arguing that the infringement of patents was going unpunished. The assurance by Guardian that no Pilkington know-how was being used discouraged any licensee, at this stage, asserting a loss of confidentiality.

A greater potential threat arose in 1974. In September the CC was told by PPG that they had developed a new 'float' process which they called LB. When the parties met to discuss the development in the following February, PPG claimed that LB did not use Pilkington patents or know-how; nor did LB fall within the definition of improvement and therefore did not have to be passed to Pilkington. More importantly it also meant that PPG did not have to pay royalty on any output from an LB plant and could pass this technology on to third parties or use it themselves outside their licensed territory, i.e. the USA, without Pilkington's consent.[1]

It is probable that the LB technology was not fully developed in 1974, as it was not until late 1976 that PPG announced the intention to rebuild its plant in California with LB and to convert its sheet plant in Canada to LB. It is not clear when PPG converted its Wichita Falls plants to LB, although it might have been as early as 1974. The LB process was thought by Pilkington to be limited in its quality (it was later discovered that the process was nicknamed 'Loads of Bubbles' within PPG), otherwise PPG would have converted all of its plants. However, there was still the risk that other licensees would adopt LB to avoid Pilkington royalties or would argue that LB breached the confidentiality envelope as it used Pilkington know-how in an unauthorised way.

By February 1978 a full technical inspection had been carried out by the company, and the conclusion was that PPG infringed both the patents and the know-how, although PPG were arguing that the latter was now in the public domain because of Guardian and other leaks. PPG wanted the right to be able to exploit their LB technology throughout the world without the consent of Pilkington, but were prepared to pay a limited royalty for its use within the USA. Both the CC and the board examined the detailed legal arguments and came to the conclusion that, with the expiry of the main patents in the major countries over the next four years and the risk of failing to enforce the know-how, the company could not stop PPG in its ambitions, but at best could obtain some compensation.

> On the basis therefore that there is no major issue of principle that is likely to be won [by Pilkington] through litigation, it is considered that it would be best to offer PPG the rights that they want outside the USA in respect of the LB process and concentrate on ensuring that they pay an adequate sum for those rights, both to satisfy ourselves, and to avoid problems with other licensees.[2]

The negotiations with PPG were difficult, and in the autumn of 1978 Pilkington gave notice of arbitration to PPG and were examining the possibility of some form of court action in Canada. This show of strength appears to have worked as settlement was reported in December 1978. In return for a payment of $5.2m. PPG were granted immunity to exploit LB in the USA and Canada, with the option to pay a further sum if they wanted to use LB in Italy. The use of the concept of 'immunity' is important; the word means that Pilkington had agreed not to sue, implying that it still had the right to do so and that LB did fall within the Pilkington patents and know-how. It is interesting that PPG's ambitions abroad did not extend beyond the countries where they already had activities, and the implication was that PPG would have to pay for any other countries where they wanted to expand.

LB obviously had limitations. Although PPG built an LB plant in Italy in 1983, its second Mount Zion Plant in the USA was built using conventional float in 1985. (The evidence is conflicting in relation to Mount Zion 1: two near simultaneous reports list it as either LB or conventional.) By this time the obligation to pay royalty had expired, PPG had complete rights to use Pilkington's float technology in the USA, and it can be assumed that PPG would have chosen the best method to make glass.

The Russian arbitration

Although the Russians had been tough negotiators at the time of their original float licence, and ensured that they got their full entitlements under the licence, there had never been any question about the performance of their obligations. The company was therefore concerned when, in April 1975, it heard that the Russians were operating a second float plant which had not been licensed. When challenged, the Russians said that the plant was using their own 'Two Stage' technology, which was not within the licence. This position needed to be resolved, but difficulties of access and continued procrastination by the Russians meant that it was November 1978 before the CC had sufficient information to form the conclusion that the Russian Two Stage process involved considerable effort to avoid the know-how but still infringed the patents. Further negotiation got nowhere, and in January 1980 it was decided to institute an arbitration in Sweden (the neutral location prescribed in the licence).

Again the Russians applied for every possible postponement and the process, which was supposed to be rapid, was being prolonged. By the end of 1981 it had been discovered that there were in fact nine Two Stage lines in operation, which meant that the Russians owed the company some £30 million. The valid excuses for postponement were running out, and there was a risk that the Russians would have a commercially embarrassing finding against them at a time when they were trying to foster a reputation for commercial reliability. There were informal contacts from the Russians through their national embassy, offering a settlement. The Russians needed to build a second, conventional, float line to make higher quality glass and for which they were prepared to pay. They would not pay in respect of the Two Stage process, but they were in need of large quantities of high-quality glass for which they were prepared to pay a price over which there would not be too much haggling.

It took another 12 months of negotiation to achieve a settlement, when the Russians agreed to pay £20 million for the second licensed float line and to enter into a glass supply agreement which would deliver £15 million profit over two years. The potential breach in the confidentiality envelope had been contained, as the settlement cured any default by the Russians.

Guardian

The good relationship with Guardian fostered by the grant of a float licence in 1971 did not last very long. In 1975 Guardian told the company that they intended to terminate the float licence.[3] They had only taken it to avoid expensive litigation and to satisfy their financial backers. They still believed the patents to be invalid, and the licence was inhibiting them from their planned expansion overseas. After protracted negotiations a further agreement was signed with Guardian in 1977 whereby Guardian paid a lump sum to consolidate all future royalties. However, their rights to build plants overseas were not extended. The relationship was always difficult, despite Guardian's protestations of friendship. There was inevitably distrust on the part of Pilkington, who had always doubted that Guardian had developed their own technology to build their first float plant. In addition Guardian's name always seemed to crop up in relation to prospective pirate float projects, despite the fact they had no rights to use Pilkington technology outside the USA, whether for their own operations or to license to third parties.

Each falling-out with Guardian provoked a legal review, and by 1976 Kirkpatrick (the company's external US legal adviser) was reluctantly advising that changes in circumstances made it worthwhile giving further consideration to legal action against Guardian.[4] The alleged friendship came to an end in June 1979 when the company was told that Guardian were about to announce the construction of a float plant in Luxembourg which was due to come on stream in late 1981. This was far too close to home for the company easily to contemplate extending Guardian's rights. There were worries at this time about over-capacity in Europe, the other European licensees would expect Pilkington to protect their position and, although the main licences were due to expire in the early 1980s, there was the risk the royalties would cease to be paid for the rest of the term of the relevant licences. At the same time the company was negotiating to buy BSN assets in northern France, Germany and Belgium, only miles from the proposed Guardian site.

It was clear that Guardian were determined to have a European plant. The threat was not just a question of excess capacity. Guardian had the justified reputation of being a very competitive manufacturer. They had earned themselves a significant share of the US market by making high-quality glass at attractive prices. All their plants were built on greenfield sites. The plate producers, on the other hand, had largely built float plants on the sites of old plate or sheet plants, and they had inherited all the existing union protectionism and the problem of reducing manning levels to match the prospective efficiency of float. In addition, the other licensees tended to be full service providers, offering a full range of thicknesses, qualities and cut sizes to meet the requirements of all of their customers. Guardian, on the other hand, could build plants with the minimum manning levels and offer only a narrow range of products in the most lucrative sectors of the market. Despite breaking into the US oligopoly, Guardian had succeeded in being very profitable and expanding its market share in the USA from zero in 1970 to 11 per cent by 1982.[5]

It was obvious that Guardian thought they could do the same in Europe and significantly influence the pricing of glass throughout the Continent.

In Luxembourg they would be close to the industrial centres of France and Germany and as close to London as was St Helens. The advent of the roll-on, roll-off ferries meant that the Channel was no longer a discouragement to exporting glass to England. Despite its weight and fragility, glass was now moved in increasing quantities around Europe, the old territorialities having dissolved. Plants with surplus capacity were anxious to sell that surplus at any price as long as it made some contribution to the cost of running the plant, bearing in mind that float was not a process that could easily be switched on and off to match demand. It was said that one container of glass offered at a low price could affect the price of glass across Europe. As soon as the customers heard of low-priced glass for sale they were quick, in times of surplus, to argue that they should not pay more than the lowest quoted price, even if the cheap glass were not really available in the quantities they required. The prospect of Guardian making profit at new low price levels was not attractive at a time when the existing producers still had much to do in reducing their costs.

The immediate problem was that an action for patent infringement could not be brought until the plant was in operation, which would be too late. It was possible that an action to protect the know-how could be brought if the company was prepared to argue that it had been improperly acquired by Guardian. This would mean reopening a ten-year-old debate and proving that Guardian had misappropriated, or stolen, the technology. To avoid the argument that Pilkington were out of time in bringing the case, it would also have to be proved that in 1969–70 Pilkington did not know that their technology was being used by Guardian but had only relatively recently discovered this fact. It was soon clear that Luxembourg was well chosen from Guardian's point of view. While the laws were in line with the rest of Europe, the local courts had little or no experience of patent litigation, let alone know-how litigation. If in doubt, they would follow Belgian precedent, but even this was a bit sparse. Evidence that Guardian were using Pilkington know-how was collected over the next few months by talking to suppliers of equipment for the new plant. Proceedings were issued in Luxembourg on 1 December 1980.

The first proceedings, for an injunction to prevent construction of the plant, quickly failed. The advice from the local lawyers was not to appeal the decision but to issue new proceedings for patent infringement. It was agreed by the CC that some action had to be taken to preserve the company's credibility with the other licensees and to discourage other companies which might have been tempted to obtain float technology from Guardian. Soon thereafter Guardian announced another float plant in Austria (which came to nothing) and talks with Llodio in Spain. The latter was particularly galling as Llodio had been part owned by BSN, and Pilkington had been offered their shares at the time of the completion of the Flachglas transaction only months before. The company had turned the shares down as it did not want to acquire an obsolete sheet plant in the Basque region, with all the political problems of closure and the risk of a violent reaction from the Basque liberation movement, ETA.

Guardian did state that they wanted to legitimise the Luxembourg plant, but were not prepared to make any constructive suggestions and the actions in Luxembourg escalated, slowly, over the next two years. In the meantime the Guardian float plant had come into operation, although it was initially reported that it had severe technical difficulties. Pilkingtons were frustrated at the lack of progress, and in late 1983 both the CC and the board considered the possibility of an action for breach of confidentiality in the USA.[6] This was a huge step to take as it would enable Guardian to resurrect all of the antitrust arguments which had persuaded the company to concede a licence back in 1970. At this time there was not just pressure to inhibit Guardian (who had now announced yet another plant in Switzerland), but also AFG in the USA. AFG was an amalgam, in 1982, of C.E. Glass, Fourco and ASG, all of whom had been granted float licences in the wake of the Guardian licence, and had now been joined by Sczesny who appeared to have fallen out with Guardian. AFG were claiming that they had overpaid their royalties and were claiming a rebate and, more worryingly, that they had their own float technology, particularly in relation to low capacity plants, and were intending to offer it to potential licensees. They had to be discouraged, and an action in the USA against Guardian might have helped in negotiations with AFG. The company was advised that antitrust counter-claims would have little chance of success, and the company decided to go ahead as long as the action did not prejudice the negotiations currently taking place with the US government in relation to the acquisition of LOF.

The show of force did work in relation to AFG, and a settlement was reached in early 1984 in respect of payment of the royalties owed by AFG and granting them some limited rights to build mini float plants, still within the Pilkington confidentiality envelope. The possibility of a small float plant in Finland to be owned by Pilkington was mentioned, and in fact when the plant was built there was the strange position that it was a Pilkington float plant built with AFG's technical support (which was somewhat notional but fulfilled the terms of the settlement). Guardian failed to give in to the extra pressure and the action escalated to a mini-trial, to examine a number of legal issues and the related facts, in late 1985

There was only a brief report of the judgement of this action, delivered in June 1986, to the CC.[7] The company lost the preliminary action; the claim for misappropriation of Pilkington technology was too long after the original theft. The judge was persuaded by Guardian that they had misappropriated Pilkington's know-how, that the know-how had been used on the first

Guardian plant in 1970 and Pilkington should have known of that use despite Guardian's persistent denials that they were using it. If Pilkington were going to make a claim against Guardian, they should have done so within three years of when they should have suspected the theft. To counter Pilkington's claim in relation to Luxembourg, Guardian had cheerfully admitted misappropriation and misrepresentation (theft and lying) and, in Pilkington's eyes, had been rewarded for it. The board was astonished, and Sir Alastair was incandescent. It was a travesty of everything he believed in. Hard competition was one thing, but profiting from blatant dishonesty was totally unacceptable. It did not help that the judge thought Davidson was a credible witness but doubted some of Sir Alastair's testimony.

Guardian were strangely proud of this reputation, or at least not embarrassed by it. In 1989 Russ Ebeid, by then head of Guardian's glass division, ducked the question whether Guardian had aggressively copied competitors' technology and said; 'We broke up the clique. We don't play by other peoples rules. We earned some of our reputation out of not following the rules ... The rest of the industry has its pattern of conduct yet we came in like a raging bull.'[8] Coincidentally, 'The Raging Bull' was the title of a 1982 Fortune magazine article in which Guardian's relaxed attitude to the technology of others was also recited.[9]

The main action in the USA was not killed by the court's finding, but the CC agreed in July 1986 that success was doubtful and a settlement should be sought.[10] In October it was reported that settlement had been reached; all the actions were to be dismissed and Guardian was to get a licence for Luxembourg, Spain and a third plant in Europe in return for $4m. There were also provisions that Guardian would preserve the confidentiality of Pilkington technology in its possession and that Pilkington would not assert* its rights after five years in neutral countries, eight years in Pilkington territories and ten years in the UK. After those time periods Guardian would have complete freedom. The know-how envelope was preserved, but the spectre of an ambitious, efficient and eventually unhindered Guardian remained.

PPG reborn

There were occasional rumours that PPG's LB process was being considered by potential licensees, but a firmer rumour in mid-1984 that Hsinchu had taken a licence for LB for a plant in Taiwan led the company to challenge PPG about their attempts to license LB outside the terms of the 1978 agreement. The concern within Pilkington was even greater in early 1985

---

* The 'non-assertion' concept is clever. It gave Guardian protection from any further legal action by Pilkington, but made it clear that both parties agreed that the rights still existed.

when PPG announced an LB project in Shenzen, China. This announcement greatly increased the stakes in the outcome of the argument about the use of LB. If the plant in contention had been the one to be owned by Hsinchu in Taiwan, Pilkington could have simply granted PPG immunity, even for nothing. The public image of the continuing acceptance of the existence of the Pilkington know-how envelope (particularly by a company as independent as PPG) would have been preserved. However the prize at stake was a technology licence for the whole of China. With the success of the grant of the licence to the Chinese joint venture in Shanghai, the company had turned its attention to capturing the whole of the Chinese market for float and at the same time rationalising the Loyang technology and bringing it within the fold. This was not an outrageous ambition. Despite very hard negotiating, the company had persuaded the Chinese that the joint venture had to pay royalties for the float technology, although there were very few extant patents. The failure of Loyang to produce good glass had shown the Chinese that they needed Western technology and they had chosen Pilkington despite the alternatives they could have chosen without any real risk of Pilkington being able to enforce its rights in the Chinese courts. It was possible to offer a licence to each new float plant as it was built, but this would be difficult to police within China, as the experience within Russia had shown, and so it was decided that the Chinese would be offered a licence for the whole of China for as many plants as they wanted, for a lump sum of $30–35 million. (To put this figure in context, Pilkington profits in 1985 were £106 million, approximately $180m.) This would include Loyang and the 17 or more plants then rumoured to be operating in China based on the Loyang technology.

The possibility of an uncontested LB plant in China would undermine the argument that Pilkington were the only lawful source of technology and risk obvious competition with PPG for the whole of China and any other future licensees. When Pilkington reminded PPG that they had no immunity in relation to the use of Pilkington's technology in China, PPG's response was to question whether there was still any proprietary Pilkington know-how that could be misused. The company was advised that PPG could apply to the US courts for a declaratory judgement that Pilkington no longer had any proprietary know-how. In addition, the advice was that if a dispute was in arbitration then, in general, the US courts would decline to hear any claim in the dispute until the arbitration was concluded. Therefore as a tactical matter it was recommended that an arbitration be commenced to avoid the risk of an adverse declaratory judgement from a US court. In April 1985 the CC approved the decision to commence an arbitration against PPG with no recorded debate.[11] It was hoped that commencing an arbitration would induce PPG to talk (Borrows said to the board, '... should PPG put out feelers for a settlement, which is perhaps likely ...'[12]) so that the position in China could be resolved.

Conclusions

The decisions already studied in Chapters 6, 7 and 9 were clearly strategic, both at the time they were made and with the benefit of hindsight. The decision to arbitrate with PPG was not seen as strategic at the time it was made, but as the potential consequences of the arbitration became more apparent, the arbitration, and its successful resolution, became critical for the company. However, at the time the decision was tactical; it related to a negotiating ploy, with some downside risk, to persuade PPG to agree some form of settlement in relation to their proposed plant in China.

By 1985 there was far less communication between the glass-makers than there had been in the 1960s, both as a result of the risk of antitrust litigation and the changing nature of the competition between the major glass-makers. However, there was still an industry culture. It might not have been reinforced by monthly meetings, but the shared assumptions of the small oligopolistic community of original plate manufacturers still prevailed. The shared intuitive elements of the decision to sue PPG can again be split at the industry and company level.

Industry

- Litigation threats were a normal part of the negotiating technique, particularly in the USA, and Pilkington would not be taken seriously without brandishing its weapons. Both sides knew that a full-scale arbitration would be very costly and uncertain in its outcome. There is some anecdotal evidence that PPG's decision was taken away from the negotiators by the then CEO of PPG who disliked Sir Antony and saw the litigation as a matter of personal pride. It was only when he left PPG, some ten years later, that the dispute could be settled.

- The prize of an all-China licence was significant, both in terms of cash and in terms of influence in an enormous emerging market.

- Companies would seek to protect their technology and reap its rewards for as long as possible. None of the glass-makers would expect Pilkington to give up its rights without a fight. Indeed some of the later licensees would be concerned if another company could get away with an infringement of the technology for which they were still paying.

Company

- The financial pressure on the company made the defence of royalties essential and the all-China licence highly desirable.

- If there had been activities by Pilkington in the 1960s which might have given rise to antitrust claims they were out of time twenty years later. They could not be sued on directly, although they could be cited as 'dispositive behaviour', i.e. evidence that Pilkington were disposed to behave in an anti-competitive manner.

- There had been extensive exploration of the company's documents in the Guardian actions and the LOF acquisition, and nothing had come to light which could be regarded as unequivocal, condemnatory evidence, although there was plenty of ambiguous material which required explanation.

- The litigation team were confident following their run of successes that if the dispute did escalate then they would prevail. In all previous cases the other side had declined to test the uncertainty of the courts or arbitration and had settled.

- The litigation team leaders, Ken Borrows and Tony Hartley, were not risk-takers. They were well aware of the antitrust risks. Borrows had been in a senior position at the time of the Guardian licence, and scolded the future Chairman for his rash note on licensing policy at that time.

- Above all, the company believed strongly that the confidentiality of the float know-how was still intact and valuable and therefore they had right on their side.

The decision was easy. The shared intuitions, or culture, at both the industry and company levels was supportive of the litigation. In deciding to sue PPG Pilkington was not having to disturb the culture. Over a period of ten years the experience of the company had been of relative success in litigation, and the board could be confident that the mere threat of an action would bring PPG to the negotiating table.

Postscript

This decision turned out to be more than merely tactical. The company's bluff was called, and PPG chose to treat the arbitration as a full-blown war. The war was to last for ten years and cost the parties a total of £150 million (my estimate).

My access to the archive terminates in 1987 and the following summary of the subsequent legal actions is based on publicly available information. This does not include any of the arbitration or court documents as all of the litigation was conducted *in camera*, on the basis that there was to be no public disclosure of the content of the proceedings nor of the confidential documents of the parties.

By the middle of 1987 the reaction of the Chinese authorities made it clear that the possibility of obtaining the all-China licence was remote. The PPG arbitration was therefore being fought over the continuing existence of Pilkington's protectable know-how, but without a specific goal in sight. Attempts were made to settle, but by this time the arbitration was developing a momentum of its own and PPG were developing counter-claims which they were reluctant to give up. The parties could not agree on terms.

Despite the fact that arbitration was supposed to be a quick and cheap process, the facts were very complex. Pilkington were asserting some 900 different items of confidential know-how, their combinations and combinations of those combinations. The whole of the history of float had to be explored (in far more detail than in this book) to establish whether or not there had been disclosure outside the envelope of confidentiality.

The arbitration lasted until 1992. The finding was that Pilkington in 1985 did still have protectable know-how, that the LB process utilised some of it and that therefore the PPG plant in China infringed that know-how, as PPG had no right to use it in China. However, damages were much lower than claimed, being assessed at £5 million, and Pilkington were entitled to its costs and were awarded a further £16 million. It is worth noting that awarded costs by no means covered the whole of the cost of the arbitration and typically the full cost, particularly allowing for the cost of management time, would have been at least 50 per cent higher and possibly double the amount awarded.

PPG were incensed by the outcome. As well as the award of damages and costs, PPG's costs of the action were at least as much as those of Pilkington and the decision inhibited their plans for expansion. They took two steps. They instituted proceedings in the USA for breach of the antitrust laws and also complained to the US government, who instituted their own criminal investigation into the activities of Pilkington in relation to the licensing of float. The stakes were now very high. PPG were claiming the costs of the arbitration (including the damages), as well as all the income they had lost in relation to Pilkington's alleged behaviour, and there was the prospect of triple damages as a punishment for illegal behaviour. It was impossible to guess what the outcome might be, especially as the case had been brought in Tucson, Arizona, a court not noted for its sophistication in antitrust matters, nor for its sympathy towards an overseas oligopolist. But it was clear that hundreds of millions of dollars were at stake. The government action was hardly less daunting. The risk was a finding of criminal behaviour, with personal penalties, including jail, for the directors and possibly enormous fines on the company. The company now had considerable assets in the USA, in the form of LOF and other significant businesses which it had acquired, against which any judgement could be enforced, and there was a risk that the whole of that business could be forfeit and the USA effectively closed to the company for the foreseeable future.

Pilkington managed to settle both of the actions. First, in 1994 the US government were persuaded that there was not a sufficiently strong case for Pilkington to be penalised. It was agreed that in future Pilkington would not assert its technology against any US manufacturer anywhere in the world and would not prevent anyone putting down a float plant in the USA. Pilkington had already got sufficient value from its know-how and should not assert (i.e. seek to enforce) its know-how rights to inhibit US glass-makers further. The terms of the settlement did not deny that the confidentiality envelope was still there; they only said that Pilkington was giving US glass makers freedom within the envelope.

PPG did not settle their action until 1995. It was agreed that neither side had committed any offence against the other and consequently Pilkington agreed to repay to PPG the sums they had been awarded in 1992 plus interest, a total of £31 million.[13] The settlement did not imply any weakness in respect of either Pilkington's rights against any other float licensee or the value of the know-how to any prospective float licensee. The confidentiality envelope had survived the concerted attack of the most determined of critics. The total cost to Pilkington was over £60 million in legal costs (my estimate), although over the ten years after the decision to sue PPG (i.e. 1985–95) the company reported receipts of over £250 million in royalties, the bulk of which were attributable to float. Arguably the action had preserved this income, which more than outweighed the costs.

It is important to note that none of the behaviour recorded in this history has been found to be illegal, despite the fact it has been explored in far more detail in a number of venues by teams of hostile lawyers. There is a natural tension between intellectual property law, which grants a monopoly, and antitrust law, which militates against monopolies. It is particularly difficult to stay within the law when there is a significant difference between the laws of the different countries in which a company operates and where interpretation of that law varies with the change of ruling parties. What is legal today in one country might tomorrow be found to be illegal, retrospectively, in another country. To optimise the return from its invention Pilkington had to tread a fine line between legality and illegality. It tested the law occasionally, but did not overstep the line, or, more cynically perhaps, was not caught when it did.

CHAPTER ELEVEN

Addendum

T HE NEED for internal cost-cutting during the early 1980s continued longer than Sir Antony had hoped. The succession of short periods of recovery interspersed with minor recessions in the general economy, combined with increasing competition as glass majors enjoyed the freedom from royalties and sought to recoup some of the ground lost to Pilkington over the previous fifteen years, meant that Pilkington was trying to catch a moving target. In 1986, despite the fact that trading had improved, it was decided to make a further £21 million provision for redundancy, so that there was a decrease in profit from the previous year, disappointing the City. This dissatisfaction triggered a bid for the company from BTR Industries plc, a very successful predator and a company very popular with the analysts. Their bid happened to coincide with a sharp upturn in the glass market world-wide: for once all of the markets were in sync, and, combined with a complete revision of all the conservative accounting policies and some substantial housekeeping, the company could forecast more than a doubling of the profits in the coming year and a tripling over three years. BTR dropped their bid, but retained the shares they had acquired in the run up to the bid, with the implied threat that the bid would be renewed if the company faltered.

The promised level of profitability was delivered, but only with aggressive financial policies, leaving the reserves and contingency funds depleted. In addition to the increased profits the company had also promised a shift in the balance of the company; the target was to have a third of the business in differentiated products rather than the commodity products which hitherto formed the bulk of the business. The company wanted to be able to sell on product performance, which commanded a price premium, rather than merely on price-cutting. Pilkington's investment in plastic spectacle lenses had been growing with excellent prospects, and a tentative investment in contact lenses was providing some expertise in this growing market. Accordingly, when the largest US producer of contact lenses, Barnes Hind Inc., came on the market in 1988 the company acquired it for £368 million (at a very high multiple of profit reflecting its high-tech status). While the acquisition was logical strategically, extending a known business, it is questionable whether the company's innate financial conservatism would have allowed the purchase if BTR had not still been a threatening shareholder and the City had not expected a more adventurous attitude from the company.

The company also had investments in the defence sector, broadly grouped as the Electro-Optical division, which enjoyed good profits and prospects; further investment was made in this area, also at relatively high multiples of earnings. The high multiples entailed extended borrowing as the company's shares were valued as a UK commodity manufacturer, not a US high-tech company. It was not realistic to use shares to make these acquisitions. The new investments had to perform well to meet their ambitious expectations and if they were to cover their cost. Not long after the completion of the Barnes Hind acquisition, the contact lens market was hit by health scares related to extended-wear lenses. In addition, Johnson & Johnson decided to enter the market, with their huge retailing resources, and the company found that this 'high-tech' business was in fact very dependent on large numbers of low-grade workers and that the key to its success was the efficiency of its mail order, not an area in which the company could provide expertise. To compound the difficulties of the change in strategy the Cold War ended and peace broke out with the rapid reduction in orders in a defence business which had hitherto enjoyed healthy growth for fifty years or more.

The company now had to re-balance its investments and, with the end of the boom in flat glass in 1991, it also faced another round of cost-cutting and the prospect of having to get tighter control on the German and US companies. After the successful BTR bid defence, all parts of the business felt they deserved a reward for their contribution. The unions in the UK would not contemplate job cuts in times of good profits; the overseas operations felt they deserved autonomy as they had delivered the promised profits, despite the fact that drastic reorganisation was required in Germany and to some extent the USA. Neither company wanted to take on their unions, and head office was reluctant to reduce the level of profits by having to make provision for redundancy at a time when any hesitation in delivering the promised level of profit would almost inevitably result in a further, indefensible, bid. By 1992 the recession in the flat glass market had become the worst since 1945. Glass prices in Europe were down by 25 per cent. Drastic steps were required to restore the company's financial strength.

In the early 1990s the insulation business, the spectacle lens business and the South African flat and safety business were sold at a profit, but the sale of the defence businesses and the contact lens business entailed large write-offs, and the company entered a long period of defensive trading. Sir Antony retired in 1996 and the new non-executive Chairman, Sir Nigel Rudd, waited only a year before dismissing the chief executive of five years, Roger Leverton, replacing him with Paolo Scaroni, who had made his reputation with St Gobain and by putting straight the company's relatively recent acquisition of SIV, the Italian float manufacturer. The company was put on a sounder financial footing, with much closer control of the overseas companies, the completion of the reorganisation of the company into two global businesses (flat glass and safety glass) and some cautious further investment in flat and safety. Despite its difficulties, Pilkington remained the second largest glass-maker, after Asahi, and still one of the technology leaders in its field. Turnover remained static, however, into the new century (see Table 11.1), and there was growing pressure from the City to improve the return to shareholders.

Table 11.1   *Pilkington financial performance, 1988–2003 (£m)*

	1988	1989	1990	1991	1992	1993	1994	1995
Turnover	2,333	2,573	2,915	2,650	2,611	2,573	2,737	2,676
Profit	306	349	360	208	182	88	104	120
Royalty income	25	28	28	26	23	17.5	19.1	16
Loan capital	789	941	994	1,235	1,260	1,469	1,335	1,084

	1996	1997	1998	1999	2000	2001	2002	2003
Turnover	2,899	3,096	2,991	2,709	2,707	2,820	2,805	2,754
Profit	214	152	191	214	238	288	283	221
Royalty income	11	11	11					
Loan capital	1,388	1,099	1,063	964	1,194	1,166	1,330	

Source: Pilkington accounts

At the time LOF was acquired it was in partnership with Nippon (the second largest Japanese float and safety glass company) in two North American safety glass companies designed to serve the Japanese car companies moving into the North American market. To strengthen this connection Nippon were offered a share in LOF rather than the subsidiaries. It proved to be very difficult to manage the minority relationship, and it was ultimately agreed that Nippon would take 10 per cent of Pilkington in exchange for the shares in LOF in 2000. Nippon soon increased the holding to 20 per cent, and at the end of 2005 it was announced that there were negotiations for Nippon to acquire the whole of the company. Pilkington became a subsidiary of Nippon in June 2006. The big four, Asahi, NSG/Pilkington, St Gobain and

Antony Pilkington's welcome after the successful defence of the takeover bid from
BTR, 1986.

PILKINGTON ARCHIVE

Guardian now control over 60 per cent of the flat glass produced in the world
(see Figure 11.1).

Since 1987 there has been a radical change to the shape of the world's glass
industry. Growth has averaged over 4 per cent per year, so that there are now
(Spring 2009) over 250 high-quality float lines in the world. But while the
USA has reduced capacity, the major growth has been in the new markets,
with China, which only started making float in 1987, now having some 40 per
cent of the world's capacity. The members of the Western plate glass oligopoly,
which Pilkington had sought to defend, have all but disappeared from the
scene. The three largest companies, Asahi, Nippon and Guardian, are not even

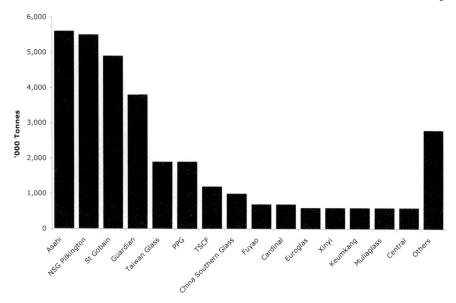

Figure 11.1   Approximate float glass market share, 2007
SOURCE: FROM PILKINGTON MATERIALS

members of the original club. PPG has not grown at all after the litigation with Pilkington which had been carried out to give them their freedom to expand. Glaverbel, Boussois and LOF have been absorbed by others. Ford glass has been spun off into Visteon (now owned by Zeledyne) and has been overtaken by Cardinal in the USA and many of the newcomers. A number of the countries (for example Taiwan and Turkey) with four or five float plants (equivalent to the market leaders in plate in the 1950s) were not even on the prospective list when the licensing policy was opened up in 1970.[1]

The description of the technique of making float in definitive manuals for the benefit of licensees has converted glass-making from an art to a science, relatively easily taught to non-glass-makers. It is still not simple to make good glass; only now are the Chinese plants that use the Loyang technology approaching the quality of a conventional float plant. But there is a huge change from the early days of float when the technology transferred was only comprehensible to an experienced glass-maker. The float glass process has reduced the threshold for high-quality glass both technically and financially, so that it is relatively easy for newcomers to enter the market and expand rapidly.

The hope in 1959 was that float would be a premium-quality product, not a mere commodity trading primarily on price and therefore cost-effectiveness. The reality was that float quickly did become a commodity, with most of the output indistinguishable between producers, and glass manufacture became less attractive to the investors. Despite the attractive growth rates and the ability of efficient producers to make solid profits, the UK and US stock markets did not rate the glass industry at the same multiple of earnings as the Japanese markets. It was therefore inevitable that the Western world would cede control to the East; the Japanese would be prepared to pay more for the shares in glass-makers than the Western market value. It is an interesting question whether the Western stock markets have got it right. Guardian (after 15 years as a quoted company, it delisted in the mid-1980s) had always found the business profitable enough to justify very rapid investment (see Appendix 2F). Whether right or wrong, the Western demands of providing the shareholders with a significant short-term return in competition with banks and telecoms companies has removed a still successful and world-leading company from the UK stock market almost exactly 50 years after the decision to invest in the first float plant.

As of the time of writing (Spring 2009) the worldwide banner for the newly merged company is Pilkington, and key senior management are from Pilkington. Despite a change of shareholder (which is arguably no more significant than when the company went public in 1970) the management successors of the original brothers still control the largest share of the world's glass market.

CHAPTER TWELVE

Conclusions

T HE EMPHASIS in this account of the exploitation of float glass technology
has been the directors' viewpoint at the moment of a number of key
decisions. What did they know or assume at critical moments and how did
they resolve the issues? Although the postscript to each decision examined
the outcomes there is little analysis of whether the outcomes were successful.
This chapter will look briefly at whether the overall strategy was successful and
try to answer two questions; should the board have done something else and,
given the strength of the culture, could they have done something else?

Was the exploitation successful?

There are two points of view from which this question should be answered;
first, from Pilkington's perspective and, second, from that of the world at
large.

At the outset of the search for a replacement for grinding and polishing
plate glass the board had four goals: to keep the technical lead in high-
quality glass; to improve profitability, including the security of those profits;
to improve the company's strength in its markets; and, to ensure the new
technology was dominant.

The technical leap of float was well beyond the board's early ambitions. The
initial experiments looked to reduce the need for grinding and polishing, not
to replace it entirely. Initially the float bath was there for cleaner transport,
then to finish the glass, and it was only after a lot of preliminary work that
Sir Alastair conceived the idea of actually forming the ribbon in the bath and
eliminating the need for rollers, grinding and polishing. The float process was
the biggest single step forward in the manufacture of flat glass and was far
ahead of any work being contemplated by any other competitor at the time.
Most improvements in glass-making were incremental, such as changing the
form of polishing from mechanical to chemical or reducing the marking by

the rollers. Completely altering the method of forming a ribbon was outside the contemplation of the other experts.

A lead was established but it lasted only five years as the patents were in the public domain and the company had decided to licence the technology. Through most of that time the company was still developing the technology to a basic commercial level. When the first competitive plant, that of PPG, came on stream in 1963, Pilkington were still struggling to keep their first plant operating commercially at more than one thickness. Their profitable lead time was minimal. However, they were always at least level, if not ahead, with the application of the technology. They were always aware of the developments made by the competitors, either via the exchange of improvements or the support visits by the Pilkington engineers to competitors' plants. If there were problems to be solved, the first port of call was Pilkington's licensing department and their dedicated engineering consultants. As each new plant was built it incorporated the latest technology, and so there were times when the company felt it was behind its competitors. But their lead was short-lived. The company was building a new plant every two or three years and in the early days of float the life of a plant was relatively short so that improvements could be incorporated at each rebuild. In fact the company was surprised how few major improvements were made by competitors, who seemed to be content

Relatively inexpensive high-quality glass has given car designers the freedom to create complex and exciting glazing, as with the new (2009) Jaguar XJ saloon.
BY COURTESY OF JAGUAR CARS

A wall of glass: a new office building near Tower Bridge, London.

PHOTOGRAPH: CARNEGIE, 2009

to leave the expensive development work to Pilkington and to focus on minor improvements to improve efficiency.

Pilkington was always regarded as the technical leader, even after the developments of PPG's LB process and Guardian's claims of independence. It was typical that the Chinese turned to Pilkington when they wanted to make high-quality glass. Pilkington had the breadth of experience, the latest developments and the expertise to supervise construction, which kept them in the technical lead, at least to the end of the period covered by this book. The achievement of the first goal was an unqualified success.

The second goal was to secure future profitability. Early in the project it was decided to price float glass in competition with plate glass. With the expectation that the production cost of float would be well below that of plate, the prospect was of very high levels of profit. This expectation was unfulfilled. For some time the new process struggled to make the consistently high yields necessary to yield the expected profits. By the time yields did improve there were other competitive pressures on the price of float. As the graph of float profitability showed (Figure 6.1) after 1963 float was consistently profitable, but not at such a level as to excite comment. For example, in a record year, 1969, Pilkington made a profit of £19.8 million on a turnover of £113.9 million. If the royalties of £5.8 million are deducted, the resulting £14 million shows a return of just over 12 per cent, below the target of 14 per cent the company set itself for long-term continuity. While float was profitable, the competitive pricing of plate, float and thick-drawn sheet by Pilkington's competitors kept the profits reasonable. Certainly profits were below any level which could be described as abusive.

Once the process became mature, as the licences started to expire, and new competition entered Europe in the early 1980s, the company struggled to make a profit even in float. The premium for the new product had been eroded and high internal costs and the uncompetitive level of the pound meant that for three years the UK flat glass operations made a loss. The security of profitability had therefore lasted for about twenty years.

However, profits from the glass itself were only one part of the equation. The royalties earned from the process were significant in two ways. First, they enhanced the reported profits of the company; for a number of years the royalties exceeded the trading profit on all the company's other operations. Although the company as a whole was not saved from reporting a loss because of the royalties, there were years, such as 1982, when the royalties stopped the flat glass operations from making a loss. Second, the predictability of the stream of royalties gave the company the confidence to embark on projects they might otherwise have thought too risky. The growth in Pilkington's assets from 1961 to 1985 was almost exactly the same as the royalty receipts over the same period. Without the royalties the company would have found it difficult, if not impossible, to expand at the same rate. The company's expansion overseas, and the security this gave to the company's profitability, was a direct consequence of the float licence income.

The goal of security of profitability was certainly enhanced by float technology. Even if the riches beyond the dreams of avarice were not forthcoming, in the absence of float Pilkington might well have experienced the fate of other UK-based commodity industries and succumbed to overseas competition.

The third goal was that of strength in Pilkington's markets. The float licences, quite legitimately, allowed the company to allocate territorial markets, and it gave no selling rights to its competitors in the UK, British Commonwealth and Argentina, those territories in which it was the prime supplier immediately after the war. In addition, it was cautious in allocating manufacturing rights outside the home countries of the licensees, reserving to itself the possibility of manufacturing in these new territories as their markets developed. Until the licences started to expire in the early 1980s this segregation was largely respected. There were occasional incursions by Glaverbel and Guardian, but they tended to be short-term and resolved in discussion. This protection certainly gave Pilkington a great deal of added strength. When they planned a new plant, it was with some certainty that the bulk of the expected market would remain theirs for some time. When there were new markets to be exploited, such as in Brazil, the company had a very strong negotiating position to obtain the share of ownership it required. It might not be able to prevent pirate plants in quite the way it hoped, but most potential pirates were deterred.

Throughout the period covered by this book, despite the challenges by Guardian, the company had a large measure of control over the direction and rate of expansion of the world's flat glass industry. While it was never found guilty of abusing this power, the degree of control was at least as great as the company had hoped for, and it lasted a good deal longer. At the time the licences were being granted, Lesley Wall was warning that the company's control could only last a few years; he thought it had gone when Guardian entered the fray, yet there were no plants outside the licensing framework until the Loyang plants in the mid-1980s, and these were not regarded as a competitive threat. Pilkington certainly saw itself in control of its own destiny, at least until the recessions of the 1980s.

The last goal was to ensure that the new technology was dominant. To have the lead was not enough. If there were other competing technologies the profits, and security, would not be as great. Having the best technology gave a short-term competitive edge. Dominance gave long-term control. For some time the company expected more challenges to the technology. At the time of its launch in 1959 the board were not sure that they could make thin glass or simplify the production of high-quality glass, and the early licence negotiations were rather defensive in the exchange of improvements, expecting the licensees would make a major contribution. The granting of licences and their terms were based on the policy that Pilkington should not be too aggressive; the company might want to take a grant back of significant technology in the future and did not want to be the victim of retaliation.

A test for dominance is the speed at which the technology was diffused through the industry. Float replaced plate instantly, in the sense that the only plate plant built after the announcement of float was the St Gobain plant in the USA to which they were already committed. Studies of the speed of replacement of plate and sheet by float glass indicate that by the standards of equivalent industries it was very rapid.[2] The licensees, once they had studied the process and made their own evaluations, decided that there was no alternative but to adopt float, and they did so with gusto, or at least with as much gusto as the working out of their plate assets would allow.

Over time the board realised that it was retaining the lead in developments, and that the float process was even more versatile in operation than they could have hoped, even if the engineers had never doubted it. There seemed to be little scope for a better process for forming the glass. Even PPG's rival LB process was an exercise in patent avoidance, rather than a technical

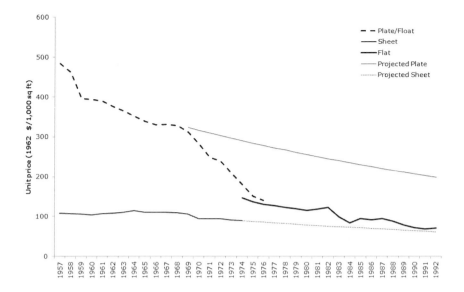

Figure 12.1 This graph shows the fall in US glass prices over the period 1957 to 1992 (adjusted for inflation). The price of high-quality glass fell, as Pilkington had predicted, to below the 1957 price of sheet glass, and to a mere 20% of the price of plate glass at the time the first float plant was built. (The projected prices of sheet and plate indicate what the prices would have been if the price reductions of those products had continued at the same rate.) *Source*: Teece 2000

improvement. Float technology proved to be dominant, to the extent that, fifty years later, it is still the only process for forming glass.

Judged on the basis of the company's own goals, the float process was a success. But was it a success from the customers' point of view? David Teece,[3] examines the savings in manufacturing costs made by the glass manufacturers over thirty years, the savings accruing to consumers over the same period and the profits made by Pilkington from the float process. He concludes that the industry saved some $117 billion by adopting float glass as a result of the lower capital costs of the plant and the lower operating costs. The consumer saved some $105 billion in lower prices for glass, i.e. the producers kept about 10 per cent profit, which seems a reasonable sharing of the benefit. Over the same period Pilkington made some $5.3 billion in royalties and extra profits (do not attempt to reconcile the figures with the tables in this book as all of Teece's figures are rebased to 1992 values) or between 4 per cent and 5 per cent of the savings. In his view, based on the returns of other dominant technology owners, this is at the low end of the range of returns. Not only did the glass industry and the consumer benefit enormously from the development of float, but Pilkington only took a modest return from the total benefits.

Could Pilkington have done anything else?

Critics and case-study authors have posed the question whether Pilkington could have exploited the technology in a more favourable way. Would they have made more profit if they had retained the monopoly in float technology or exploited it in different ways? One could do the sums on the assumption that Pilkington's competitors just stood back and let them become the only float producer, but this would be unrealistic. For all the reasons discussed in Chapter 5 Pilkington's competitors would not simply have stood to one side, but had a variety of strategies to damage float, possibly fatally.

Sir Alastair wrote that if the company had known all the difficulties at the outset it would never have gone ahead.[4] A surprisingly illogical comment from him; if he had known the difficulties he would also have known the outcome and there never would have been any doubt about proceeding. In the same way, if the board had known, in 1960, that their engineers would solve all the problems they might have been more robust with PPG on the licence terms, and if they had known the outcome of all the litigation they might have been more emphatic in enforcing any breach of their rights. But to sit here with the benefit of hindsight and say that the board could have done better is to judge them when the outcomes are known. The intention of this book is to try to understand the board's point of view and to examine their decisions in the context of their knowledge.

The board were acting, as far as they could judge, rationally. The structure of the decision-making was as rational as they could make it, yet the analysis set out in this book shows that the directors' rational contemplation was only a part of their decision-making process. There was also the powerful influence of the cultures of both Pilkington and the glass industry ingrained into the directors' psyche and unconsciously affecting the outcome.

When the board decided to build the first production plant it was the natural progression of a development project. For over 100 years the company had, with frequent success, taken ideas from the drawing board through experiment to final production. That was the way things were done in the company and the sums involved, at this stage, were not out of the ordinary for such a capital-intensive industry. As the project progressed there was no cultural pressure to stop it. The senior members of the board could remember how long all major developments took and there was no great surprise when float proved to be the same. In fact, the difficulties were heartening; if the development engineers were struggling, then so would a competitor who tried to replicate the technology.

The decision to license was purely a matter of culture. It was so ingrained in the glass industry that it was not even discussed formally. From all the evidence, or lack of it, licensing was a mutual assumption. It was with the advent of Guardian that the comfort of riding the wave of culture was removed. It is reminiscent of Asimov's science fiction classic *Foundation Trilogy*, in which sociologists had worked out the equations governing the future behaviour of the human race, only to be confounded when a mutant arose who did not abide by the rules. The decision to license Guardian, albeit under duress, had to counter the culture of keeping glass-making within the confines of the club and the expectations, quite correct in the event, that newcomers would not abide by the rules. The economically rational conclusion, that Pilkington would benefit from widening the licensing base, could only overcome the culture of exclusion when there was a threat of potentially damaging litigation.

The acquisitions of Flachglas and LOF were as much the product of culture as economic rationality. The outcomes of both decisions were economically satisfactory, but at the time there were doubts that were overridden by the deeply held ambitions to have strong bases in Europe and the USA, ambitions which were fostered by the goal to use float to improve the company's strength and its long-term stability. The final decision, to sue PPG, was arguably a mistake, a tactic which proved to be a strategy, but it was wholly in keeping with the culture of litigating in such circumstances to enforce the company's position.

With the notable exception of the Guardian decision the choices made were in line with the prevailing culture. The board could have done something else (in the case of Flachglas and LOF they very nearly did), and their behaviour was not deterministic, where they were left with no choice. But to turn against culture required a great deal of effort. In the case of Guardian it needed Terry Bird's powerful economic argument and the threat of damaging outcome from litigation to produce the cultural shift that would change the whole structure of the industry. If the economic argument had been weak the company might have risked the litigation. If there had been no threat from Guardian it might have been years before the licensing base was widened.

Succumbing to cultural pressure is not necessarily irrational. In an organisation the culture, 'the way we do things around here' is usually based on experience. It is the way that is expected to optimise the economic outcome based on previous analysis and the outcome of past events. But the emphasis is on the past. Culture has the tendency to perpetuate the past. This is not always wrong. Culture often encapsulates hard-won experience which it would be foolish to ignore. But in a dynamic environment the solutions of the past do not take into account changing circumstances, and changing the culture, possibly to create a new culture, might be the optimum economic solution.

This account shows that in general Pilkington got the balance right. They took an extraordinary invention, made the most of a unique window of opportunity, and successfully balanced culture and rationality to make the most of what they had created. In doing so they revolutionised, not only themselves, but the glass industry as a whole.

The directors of the company

(year joined company; years as director)

1959	1970	1979	1985
† Geoffrey Pilkington (1909; 1919–64)	‡ Sir Harry Pilkington (1927; 1934–80)	† Sir Harry Pilkington (1927; 1934–80)	† Sir Alastair Pilkington (1947; 1955–85)
† Guy Pilkington (1909; 1919–64)	† Douglas Phelps (1927; 1934–73)	† Arthur Pilkington (1934; 1943–79)	David Pilkington (1947; 1959–85)
† Lord Weeks (1912; 1928–60)	† Lord Cozens-Hardy (1932; 1937–71)	† Lawrence Pilkington (1935; 1943–81)	† John Leighton-Boyce (1966; 1971–85)
‡ Sir Harry Pilkington (1927; 1934–80)	Arthur Pilkington (1934; 1943–79)	‡ Sir Alastair Pilkington (1947; 1955–85)	Sol Kay (1951; 1973–86)

1959	1970	1979	1985
Douglas Phelps (1927; 1934–73)	**Lawrence Pilkington** (1935; 1943–81)	**David Pilkington** (1947; 1959–85)	‡ **Sir Antony Pilkington** (1959; 1973–95)
Lord Cozens-Hardy (1932; 1937–71)	† James Watt (1914; 1950–71)	† Terry Bird (1935; 1962–83)	Denis Cail (1947; 1975–87)
Arthur Pilkington (1934; 1943–79)	† Sir Alan Hudson-Davies (1946; 1952–71)	* Sir Barrie Heath (1960; 1967–84)	Geoffrey Iley (1968; 1977–90)
Lawrence Pilkington (1935; 1943–81)	Sir Alastair Pilkington (1947; 1955–85)	* Ted Judge (1968–80)	Dennis Oliver (1968; 1977–86)
James Watt (1914; 1950–71)	**David Pilkington** (1947; 1959–85)	Leslie Wall (1956; 1970–84)	* Lord Croham (1978–92)
Sir Alan Hudson-Davies (1946; 1952–71)	Terry Bird (1935; 1962–83)	John Leighton-Boyce (1966; 1971–85)	Denys Cledwyn Davies (1956; 1979–87)
Sir Alastair Pilkington (1947; 1955–85)	* Sir Humphrey Mynors (1964–77)	Sol Kay (1951; 1973–86)	Bill Snowdon (1952; 1979–85)
George McOnie (1927; 1958–69)	* Sir Norman Kipping 1965–73	**Sir Antony Pilkington** (1959; 1973–95)	Mervyn Windsor (1950; 1979–85)
	Sir Barrie Heath (1960; 1967–84)	* Sir Arnold Franc (1973–81)	* Hilmar Kopper (1983–95)
	* Ted Judge (1968–80)	Denis Cail (1947; 1975–87)	Derek Cook (1970; 1983–92)

1959	1970	1979	1985
		*Sir Leonard Neal (1976–83)	*Sir Roger Hurn (1984–94)
		Geoff Iley (1968; 1977–90)	
		Dennis Oliver (1968; 1977–86)	
		*Lord Croham (1978–92)	
		Denys Cledwyn Davies (1956; 1979–87)	
		Bill Snowdon (1952; 1979–85)	
		Mervyn Windsor (1950; 1979–85)	

Notes:
bold type denotes members of the Pilkington family

* Non-executive

‡ Chairman

† Retired Executive

Licensed float plants

2A Licensed float plants at the end of 1970

Country	Company	Licence Date	Plant	Start-up Date	Design Load tpw
USA	PPG	27/07/62	Cumberland	Dec. 1963	2,500
			Crystal City	Dec. 1965	2,000
			Meadville I	Oct. 1968	2,500
			Meadville II	April 1970	2,500
	LOF	19/04/63	Lathrop	Sept. 1964	2,500
			Rossford	Sept. 1966	2,500
			East Toledo	June 1969	2,750
			Ottawa	April 1970	3,000

Country	Company	Licence Date	Plant	Start-up Date	Design Load tpw
	Ford	29/07/64	Rossford II	June 1970	3,750
			Nashville	March 1966	2,400
			Dearborn	Feb. 1967	2,400
			Nashville II	June 1968	2,400
			Nashville III	Dec. 1970	2,800
	Guardian	18/05/71	Carleton	Oct. 1970	2,500
France	BSN	14/12/62	Boussois	Feb. 1966	2,800
Belgium	Glaverbel	19/08/62	Moustier	March 1965	3,150
	St Gobain	10/04/63	Auvelais	Feb. 1970	4,200
Germany	St Gobain	06/01/64	Portz	Feb. 1966	2,200
Italy	St Gobain	03/04/63	Pisa	Dec. 1965	1,200
Japan	Asahi	06/03/64	Tsurumi	May 1966	2,000
			Amagasaki	Oct. 1968	1,300
	Nippon	06/03/64	Maizuru	Nov. 1965	2,000
	Central	07/02/68	Matsuzaka	May 1969	2,100
Canada	PB(Canada)	01/02/67	Scarborough	Feb. 1967	2,500
			Scarborough	Dec. 1970	2,500
Mexico	Viplamex	29/03/65	Mexico City	June 1968	1,200
Russia	Technopromimport	29/03/67	Bor	Aug. 1970	2,000
Czechoslovakia	Sklo Union	06/12/66	Teplice	Oct. 1969	2,000
Spain	St Gobain	03/06/64	Aviles	Feb 1967	1,400

2B Licensed float plants, 1971–1980

Country	Company	Licence date (if new)	Plant	Start up date	Design load tpw
USA	PPG		Carlisle 1	April 1972	4,000
			Carlisle 2	June 1972	4,000
			* Wichita Falls 1	July 1974	4,500
			* Wichita Falls 2	Feb. 1975	4,500
			* Fresno	Dec. 1977	3,500
			* Owens Sound	Oct. 1978	4,000
	LOF		Laurinburg 1	June 1973	5,500
			Laurinburg 2	March 1980	5,500
	Ford		Tulsa 1	Aug. 1974	4,100
			Tulsa 2	Dec. 1975	4,100
	Guardian		Floriffe	Aug. 1971	2,200
			Carleton	May 1973	3,150
			Kingsburg	July 1978	3,150
			Corsicana	Dec. 1980	3,150
	AFG	July 1971	Greenland	April 1973	3,500
			Cinnaminson	Nov. 1973	3,340
			Clarksburg	Jan. 1976	3,200
Germany	St Gobain		Herzogenrath	Jan. 1971	6,200
	St Gobain		Stolberg	Nov. 1974	4,900

Country	Company	Licence date (if new)	Plant	Start up date	Design load tpw
	Flachglas		Gladbeck 1	March 1974	4,550
	Flachglas		Gladbeck 2	Dec. 1976	5,250
	Flachglas		Weiherhammer	Oct. 1979	4,900
Spain	St Gobain		Arbos	Oct. 1973	2,450
	St Gobain		Aviles	Sept. 1980	5,000
France	St Gobain		Chantereine	July 1972	4,200
	St Gobain		Aniche	June 1978	3,850
	Boussois		Boussois 2	April 1979	4,900
Belgium	St Gobain		Auvelais	Feb. 1976	4,200
	Glaverbel		Moustier 2	Oct. 1974	5,250
Italy	St Gobain		Caserta	April 1973	4,200
	PPG Vernante	April 1972	Cuneo	Oct. 1974	2,950
	SIV	May 1972	San Salvo	May 1974	3,800
	SIV/ SG	March 1978	San Salvo	Sept. 1979	3,570
Japan	Asahi		Aichi	May 1972	5,000
	Nippon		Chiba	Aug. 1971	3,800
			Maizura	June 1978	4,200
	Central		Matsuzaka	May 1976	2,940

* Built using PPG's LB process

2C New licensed float plants, 1981–1987

Country	Licensee	Date of new licence	Plant	Start up date	Design load tpw
USA	PPG		Mount Zion 1	April 1982	4,000
			Mount Zion 2	1985	4,000
	AFG		Greenland	Jan. 1984	3,800
			Kingsport	Oct. 1984	3,900
			Victorville	1987	3,500
Germany	St Gobain		Portz 2	May 1985	4,200
Portugal			Covina	1986	2,800
Holland	Asahi				
	(Glaverbel)		Tiel	Aug 1984	3,500
Belgium			Mol	1987	1,800
Italy	Vernante		Salerno	Au.g 1983	3,000
Luxembourg	Guardian		Luxguard	Nov. 1981	3,150
Spain			Llodio	Aug. 1985	
E.Germany	Industrienlagen	Oct. 1977	Torgau	July 1985	3,500
Turkey	TSCF	June 1977	Kirklareli	Sept. 1981	4,200
Russia	Technopromimport		Bor 2	Dec. 1986	4,000
Japan	Nippon			1987	
	Asahi		Kashima	April 1981	5,600
	Central		Sakai	Nov. 1982	3,850

Country	Licensee	Date of new licence	Plant	Start up date	Design load tpw
S. Korea	Hankuk	Nov. 1977	Kunsan 1	June 1981	3,500
			Kunsan 2	Dec. 1985	3,500
Taiwan	TGC	May 1983	Taichung 1	July 1983	2,500
			Taichung 2	Nov. 1987	3,250
China	PPG		*Shenzen	1987	
Indonesia	Asahimas		Jakarta	Jan. 1983	2,500
Thailand	Thai–Asahi		Samut Prakarn	April 1984	2,500
Malaysia	Nippon		Kuala Lumpar	Sept. 1985	2,500

* Built using the LB process

2D   *Pilkington-built float plants in 1987 not listed as licensees*

Plant	Location	Start–up date	Design load, tpw
CH1 *	UK	1957	1,200
CH3	UK	April 1962	3,000
CH4	UK	July 1963	3,000
CH2	UK	Sept. 1972	5,000
UK5	UK	April 1981	5,500
Dandenong	Australia	Feb. 1974	3,250
Halmstad	Sweden	July 1976	5,000
Springs	South Africa	April 1977	3,000
Cebrace	Brazil	Nov. 1982	4,500
Shanghai	China	Sept. 1987	5,000
Lahti	Finland	Sept. 1987	1,500

* Closed 1982

2E   *Plate plants 1969*

PPG	3	
LOF	3	
Ford	2	
ASG	1	
Boussois	2	(France)
St Gobain ('SG')	2	(France)
Cristalaria (SG)	1	(Spain)
St Roch (SG)	2	(Belgium)
Glaverbel	1	(Belgium)
Germanica	1	(Germany)
Vereigete (SG)	1	(Germany)
St Gobain	1	(Italy)
SIV	1	(Italy)
Central	1	(Japan)
Total	**22**	

2F   *Guardian float plants*

1971	Carleton, Michigan
1973	Carleton, Michigan
1978	Kingsburg, California
1980	Corsicana, Texas
1981	Bascharage, Luxembourg
1983	Floreffe, Pennsylvania (purchased from AFG)
1985	Llodio, Spain
1988	Richburg, South Carolina
1988	Dudelange, Luxembourg
1990	Maturin, Venezuela
1991	Oroshaza, Hungary
1992	Saraburi, Thailand
1993	Gujurat, India
1993	Tudela, Spain
1996	DeWitt, Iowa
1996	Al-Jubail, Saudi Arabia
1996	Thalheim, Germany
1997	Rayong, Thailand
1998	Geneva, New York
1998	Porto Real, Brazil
2002	Czestochowa, Poland
2003	Goole, England
2004	El Marques, Mexico

Source: Guardian Industries; http://www.guardian.com/en/about-timeline.html

APPENDIX THREE

Minutes of acquisition

3A *Minutes of Flachglas acquisition approval*

DRAFT
721/T/Y
24.9.79

MINUTES of Meeting of the Board of
Pilkington Brothers Limited
held on Friday, 7th September, 1979

Present:

Sir Alastair Pilkington (Chairman)
Lord Pilkington
Mr. A. C. Pilkington
Dr. L. H. A. Pilkington
Mr. D. F. Pilkington
Mr. G. W. T. Bird
Mr. E. T. Judge
Mr. L. N. Wall
Mr. J. Leighton-Boyce
Mr. S. E. Kay
Mr. A. R. Pilkington
Sir Arnold France
Mr. D. Cail
Sir Leonard Neal
Mr. G. N. Iley
Dr. D. S. Oliver
Lord Croham

In attendance:

Mr. W. J. Almond
Mr. D. J. Bricknell
Mr. J. W. E. Helliwell
Mr. L. B. Pinnell
Mr. R. A. Scholefield (part-time)
Mr. J. B. Tyler (Secretary)

Sir Alastair reported that Sir Barrie Heath was making vigorous and satisfactory recovery from his recent operation.

The Minutes of the Meetings held on the 13th and 31st July, and the 1st August, 1979, were signed.

4035. ACQUISITION OF FLAT AND SAFETY GLASS INTERESTS IN CONTINENTAL EUROPE

(Present W. J. Almond, D. J. Bricknell, J. W. E. Helliwell, L. B. Pinnell and R. A. Scholefield)

Following consideration of a draft memorandum of understanding dated the 4th September, 1979, and of a paper presented by L. B. Pinnell and the investigating team, the Board approved the proposal that the Company enter into agreement, in general accordance with the terms set out in the draft memorandum of understanding, with BSN Gervais Danone S.A. (BSN) and Mecaniver S.A. for the acquisition of the

- 2 -

following interests which are owned by Mecaniver S.A.:

1.   12.38 per cent interest in Flachglas A.G. ("Flachglas");

2.   56.48 per cent interest in Dahlbusch Verwaltungs-A.G. ("Dahlbusch")

3.   100 per cent interest in Glaverbel S.A. ("Glaverbel"); and

4.   100 per cent interest in Machinale Glasfabriek De Maas B.V. ("De Maas").

The above agreements are subject to the preparation of detailed contracts which will be submitted to the Board for approval in due course. It was noted that the transaction would be conditional on the approval of statutory and governmental bodies in the United Kingdom and elsewhere in Europe and on the approval of the shareholders of Pilkington.

Sir A.P. referred to the thoroughness with which L. B. Pinnell and his team had carried out their investigation over a long period and to the comprehensiveness of their report, which had been of great assistance to the Board in reaching their decision. On behalf of the Board, Sir A.P. thanked the investigating team for all the work they had done on the project.

4036.   APPOINTMENT OF A DEPUTY CHAIRMAN

The Board approved the proposal that A.R.P. be appointed a Deputy Chairman of the Company, with effect from 8th September, 1979. He will succeed L.N.W. who will retire from Executive duties at the close of the A.G.M.

4037.   LORD CROHAM: APPOINTMENTS

The Board noted that, following the retirement of E.T.J. from the Board and L.N.W. as an Executive Director, Lord Croham would take up the following appointments:

Chairman, Group Audit Committee.

A member of the Internal Audit Committee.

A member of the Sub-Committee and Working Party that keep the Executive Directors' emoluments under review.

3B   *Minutes of LOF acquisition approval*

- 2 -

ensure that they were aware of industry's views when discussing lending policy with the appropriate institutions.

The Board noted that the latest forecasts were regarded as pessimistic, as they did not make provision for certain major contracts in the course of negotiation.

The Company's costs of production compared with those of its competitors were being kept under continuous review in order to ensure that the Company could establish how competitive it was and the factors which influenced its competitiveness.

The Board approved, subject to certain amendments, the text of the Chairman's Statement to be made to the Annual General Meeting later that day.

4319   PROJECT 2181

ARP
DC
. B. Purvell
i. mckenna)

In introducing the papers before the Board the Chairman reported that it was essential that the Board make a firm decision as to whether it supported the acquisition of shares in 2181, as a definite answer had to be given to the Chairman of 2181 within the next few days. The question for the Board was whether the Company should make an offer for the 29.5% interest in 2181 held by G. & W., it having already been agreed by the Board that if it acquired any shares in 2181 it was with the intention of taking control of 2181 should this be possible, and desirable at some future date. It was necessary to determine firstly, whether an acquisition of shares in 2181 was strategically desirable and, secondly, if so, whether the Group could afford the acquisition at the present time.

In the course of discussion on the strategic issues the following points were made:-

1. It was the agreed strategy of the Group that the Group would not seek to expand its involvement in the flat and safety glass sector of the industry and would invest further in this sector only to maintain the viability of its present investments. However, it had also been agreed that the Group required a major presence in the U.S.A., as the largest single market in the free world. The project under review was a major opportunity, which was unlikely to be repeated, to provide a base in the U.S.A. It was possible that 2181 could act as a centre from which the Group could expand into electro-optics, although it was noted that it may not be ideal as an investment centre, as the management requirements of the electro-optical business were very different from the management employed by 2181.

2. If the Board decided not to invest in 2181 on the grounds that the future of the flat glass industry is uncertain, it would raise the question as to whether we should remain in the industry, particularly in the U.K. The U.S.A. market, although very competitive, did not have the uncertainties associated with the European market, with its severe cross-

- 3 -

frontier competition exacerbated by fluctuating, and
currently adverse, exchange rates. It was arguable that the
Group's future would be more stable with a U.S.
manufacturing base rather than a U.K. base. Taking the
present opportunity would give the Group more freedom of
choice in the future.

3.   The glass division of 2181 had a relatively poor record in
     the last few years, which raised questions as to the
     competence of its management and its ability to recover to
     its former level of profitability. It was argued that the
     Company was seeking to invest in 2181 at a time when its
     management were having difficulty in maintaining the
     profitability of its existing operations, and may therefore
     experience difficulties in assisting the 2181 management.
     However, it was stressed that the glass operations of 2181
     were, at heart, strong. Technically, especially in safety
     glass, it had been a leader in its field, and the technical
     support of the Company in the flat glass operations should
     have a material effect. Similarly it appeared that its
     financial reporting system was not as strong as the Group's,
     and could be improved with some help. 2181 had already taken
     major steps to improve its management, mainly with assistance
     from Aeroquip, who were recognised by external analysts as
     being a strong, well-managed company. It would be wrong to
     describe 2181 as weak managerially. Whilst help from the
     Group in some areas would benefit 2181, they were not in need
     of so much assistance that it would overstretch the
     management resources of the Group.

4.   The future success of 2181 was dependent upon the recovery of
     the U.S. economy and the recovery of its major customer,
     General Motors. It was considered that the U.S. economy
     would recover, although slowly, and the present low levels of
     activity may continue for some while. 2181 would be a poor
     investment if a rapid recovery in the U.S. market was
     essential to its return to good profitability. The future of
     General Motors was also difficult to assess, although
     analysts differed in their views as to the timing and extent
     of any recovery, few believed that General Motors would fail.
     It was emphasised that the 1983 forecasts provided by 2181
     showed a return to profitability by the glass division on the
     basis of the U.S. economy remaining static and a fall in its
     share of General Motors business. 2181's recovery was based
     on pessimistic rather than optimistic assumptions, only its
     ability to improve its share of the general trade market was
     questionable, especially in view of the strength of its
     competitors in this field.

5.   It was important to recognise that the Company was not being
     asked to perform a rescue operation. 2181 were completely
     confident, with apparent justification, that the re-
     organisation of their flat glass operations, coupled with the
     strength of Aeroquip, would lead to a secure future. The
     opportunity to invest had only arisen because of the
     unwelcome investment by G. & W., and the low market value of

- 4 -

2181 reflected the depressed state of the whole U.S. market
as much as its recent, relatively poor, performance.

6. The raising of funds to acquire the 30% interest in 2181
    would inhibit the Group in pursuing its agreed strategy of
    diversifying its manufacturing base. Although no investment
    opportunities had been firmly identified, a great deal of
    work was being done in this area and proposals for investment
    would, in due course, be presented to the Board. It was
    accepted that a balancing of the Group's product base could
    not be achieved quickly without the disposal of flat or
    safety glass assets, but equally a further investment in flat
    and safety would materially postpone the time when investment
    in, and the growth of, products such as electro-optics
    achieved a balance between these and traditional products.

7. The investment in 2181 is not irreversible. The shares would
    be a marketable asset at any time in the future if it was
    decided that the Group should no longer retain them.

It was agreed that the general statement of policy should not be
so inflexible that a major opportunity is declined, particularly where
it gave the Group a good position in the planned goegraphical area for
expansion. Strategically the investment in 2181 was desirable and the
risks inherent in the acquisition, when balanced against the geographic
and overall strengthening of the Group, were acceptable.

Following agreement on the overall strategic desirability of the
project, the Board considered the financial implications of the
acquisition. The following points were made:-

(a) Assuming a purchase price of $31.2 per share, the acquisition
     of 3,273,700 shares from G. & W. would cost $102.3 million
     (£59.1 million). This would give G. & W. a 25% premium over
     their original purchase price.

(b) It would be possible for the Group to borrow the funds
     necessary but there would be the following major
     consequences:-

(i)   The effect on the cash flow of the Group would be adverse to
      the extent of £5.1 million p.a., assuming a 14% rate of
      interest, a continuation of the existing dividend of 2181 and
      an incoming technical fee of £1 million p.a.

(ii) The Debt/Equity ratio was forecast to deteriorate from
      1 : 3.0 to 1 : 2.6.

(iii) Interest cover by trading profits would remain largely
      unaltered provided 2181 and the Group achieved the forecast
      profits.

(iv) The relatively high level of borrowing resulting from the
      project would increase the risk of the Group having to give
      security for any further loans, or indeed providing security
      for existing loans if covenants are breached.

Notes and references

Notes to Chapter 1: Introduction

The reference PB *** relates to the number of the box of documents in the Pilkington Archive, Records Management System.

1. Elkadi, H. 2006. *Cultures of Glass Architecture*. Ashgate, Aldershot. p.12.
2. Teece, D.J. 2000. *Managing Intellectual Capital*. Oxford University Press, Oxford. p.225.
3. For more on the history of glass-making see Wiggington, M. 2002. *Glass in Architecture*. Phaidon, London. Cable, M. 1999. Mechanisation of Glass Manufacture. *Journal of the American Ceramic Society* **82**(5) 1093–1112, www.glasslinks.com/history, and for Pilkington specifically, see Barker, T.C. 1977. *The Glass-makers*. Weidenfeld and Nicolson, London. and Barker, T.C. 1994. *An Age of Glass*. Boxtree, London.
4. Pilkington, L.A.B. 1969. The Float Glass Process. *Proceedings of the Royal Society of London* **314** 1–25.
5. The Monopolies Commission. 1966. A Report on the Supply of Flat Glass.
6. Grenfell, J. 1979. *In Pleasant Places*. Macdonald Futura, London.
7. Chandler, A.D. 1990. *Scale and Scope; The Dynamics of Industrial Capitalism*. Belknap Press, Cambridge MA. pp.511–12.

Notes to Chapter 2: The 1950s: a decade of optimism

1. Pilkington Archive/Records Management System Document Box (hereafter RMS Doc. Box) PB 524 General Board Papers, 13 Dec. 1968.
2. The Monopolies Commission, A Report on the Supply of Flat Glass. 1966. para. 35.. They concluded (largely on the basis of Pilkington's evidence) that the agreements were not very effective.
3. Pilkington Archive, RMS Doc. Box PB 257 General Board Minutes, 29 Nov. 1945.
4. Pilkington Archive, RMS Doc. Box PB 257 General Board Minutes, 28 Nov. 1946.
5. Pilkington Archive, RMS Doc. Box PB 257 General Board Minutes, 25 Nov. 1948.
6. Pilkington Archive, RMS Doc. Box PB 257 General Board Minutes, 30 Sept. 1948.
7. Pilkington Archive, RMS Doc. Box PB 257 General Board Minutes, 30 Nov. 1950.
8. Pilkington Archive, RMS Doc. Box PB 257 General Board Minute 1332, 26 Jan. 1950.
9. Pilkington Archive, RMS Doc. Box PB 259 Group Executive Papers, 10 March 1953.
10. The Monopolies Commission. 1966. A Report on the Supply of Flat Glass.
11. Ibid.
12. Ibid.

13. Chandler, A.D. 1990. *Scale and Scope; The Dynamics of Industrial Capitalism*. Belknap Press, Cambridge MA. p.780.
14. Pilkington Archive, RMS Doc. Box PB 259 Group Executive Papers, 8 March 1955.
15. Pilkington Archive, RMS Doc. Box PB 50147 Chairman's statement to shareholders, 1955.
16. Pilkington Archive, RMS Doc. Box PB 349 Board Papers, 28 Nov. 1958.
17. Pilkington Archive, RMS Doc. Box PB 50147 Chairman's statement to shareholders, 1951.
18. Pilkington Archive, RMS Doc. Box PB 349 Board Papers, 30 Jan. 1958.
19. Pilkington Archive, RMS Doc. Box PB 50147 Chairman's statement to the shareholders, 1952.
20. Pilkington Archive, RMS Doc. Box PB 259 Group Executive Papers, 2 Jan. 1956.
21. Pilkington Archive, RMS Doc. Box PB 259 Group Executive Papers, 21 June 1955.
22. Pilkington Archive, RMS Doc. Box PB 50147 Chairman's statement to shareholders, 1955.
23. Pilkington Archive, RMS Doc. Box PB 50147 Chairman's statement to shareholders, 1956.
24. Chandler, A.D. 1990. *Scale and Scope; The Dynamics of Industrial Capitalism*. Belknap Press, Cambridge MA, p.390.
25. Personal communication from Sir Alastair Pilkington, c.1980.
26. Pilkington Archive, RMS Doc. Box PB 50147 Chairman's statement to shareholders, 1955.
27. Personal communication from Sir Alastair Pilkington, c.1980.
28. Pilkington Annual Accounts, 1973.
29. Pilkington Archive, RMS Doc. Box PB 259 Group Executive Papers, 2 Jan. 1956.
30. Mintzberg, H., B. Quinn. 1995. *The Strategy Process*, European Edition ed. p.867.
31. Pilkington Archive, RMS Doc. Box PB 349 Group Executive Minutes, 22 March 1955.
32. Boswell's Life of Johnson, 1979, Penguin, p.271.

Notes to Chapter 3: Building the first float plant

1. Pilkington Archive, RMS Doc. Box PB 257 General Board Minutes, 26 Jan. 1950.
2. Pilkington Archive, RMS Doc. Box PB 257 General Board Minutes, 30 Sept. 1954.
3. Pilkington Archive, RMS Doc. Box PB 51600 Minutes, of Manufacturing Conference, 19 July 1949.
4. Pilkington Archive, RMS Doc. Box PB 51600 Minutes, of Manufacturing Conference, 14 Nov. 1950.
5. Pilkington Archive, RMS Doc. Box PB 257 General Board Papers, 23 May 1951.
6. Pilkington Archive, RMS Doc. Box PB 50172 Alastair Pilkington's Misc. papers; Notes of 17 July 1950.
7. Pilkington Archive, RMS Doc. Box PB 51600 Minutes, of Manufacturing Conference, 16 Jan. 1951.
8. Pilkington Archive, RMS Doc. Box PB 51600 Minutes, of the Manufacturing Conference, 15 Jan. 1952.
9. Mintzberg, H., B. Quinn. 1995. *The Strategy Process*, European Edition ed. p.856.
10. Pilkington, L.A.B. 1963. The Development of Float glass. *The Glass Industry* (February) 80–100.
11. Pilkington Archive, RMS Doc. Box PB 257 General Board Minutes, 27 March 1952.
12. Pilkington Archive, RMS Doc. Box PB 50162 L.A.B. Pilkington file: float Finish Research.
13. Pilkington Archive, RMS Doc. Box PB 349 General Board Papers, 29 May 1958.

14. Grundy, T. 1990. *The Global Miracle of Float Glass*. Privately Published, St. Helens. p.14.
15. Ibid. p.35.
16. Ibid.
17. Pilkington Archive, RMS Doc. Box PB 349 General Board Papers, 26 March 1953 and 28 May 1953.
18. Pilkington Archive, RMS Doc. Box PB 349 General Board Papers, 26 May 1955.
19. Pilkington Archive, RMS Doc. Box PB 259 Minutes, of Group Executive, 19 Oct. 1954.
20. Pilkington Archive, RMS Doc. Box PB 51600 Minutes, of the Manufacturing Conference, 15 March 1955.
21. Pilkington Archive, RMS Doc. Box PB 259 Group Executive Papers, 19 April 1955.
22. For example, Barker, T.C. 1977. Business Implications of Technical Developments in the Glass Industry 1945–1965: A Case Study. B. Supple, ed. *Essays in British Business History*. Clarendon Press, Oxford, 187–204, Quinn, B. 1980. *Strategies for Change: Logical Incrementalism*. Irwin, Homewood, Ill.
23. Pilkington Archive, RMS Doc. Box PB 259 Group Executive Papers, 19 April 1955.
24. Pilkington Archive, RMS Doc. Box PB 349 General Board Papers, 23 May 1950.
25. Interview with A.S. Robinson, 12 April 2005; Barker, T.C. 1972. Float: A study in invention. *Pilkington Archive*.
26. Pilkington Archive, RMS Doc. Box PB 745 J.B. Watt's private files.
27. Pilkington Archive, RMS Doc. Box PB 259 Group Executive Papers, 22 March 1955.
28. Pilkington Archive, RMS Doc. Box PB 349 General Board Papers, 31 March 1955.
29. Pilkington Archive, RMS Doc. Box PB 349 General Board Papers, 27 Jan. 1955.
30. Pilkington Archive, RMS Doc. Box PB 349 General Board Papers, 26 May 1955.
31. Pilkington Archive, RMS Doc. Box PB 259 Minutes, of Group Executive, 19 April 1955.
32. Pilkington Archive, RMS Doc. Box PB 257 General Board Minute 1775, 26 May 1955.
33. Pilkington, L.A.B. 1969. The Float Glass Process. *Proceedings of the Royal Society of London* **314** 1–25.
34. Pilkington, L.A.B. 1976. Flat Glass: Evolution and Revolution Over 60 Years. *Glass Technology* **17**(5) 182–193.
35. Pilkington Archive, RMS Doc. Box PB 1242 'Costs and Implications of Float'; Sir Harry Pilkington's statement at the Press Conference, 20 Jan. 1959.

Notes to Chapter 4: Continuing development work

1. Pilkington Archive, RMS Doc. Box PB 259 Group Executive Papers, 2 Jan. 1958; the figure is approximate as the report relates to total float expenditure including the pilot plant.
2. Pilkington Archive, RMS Doc. Box PB 349 Board Papers, 26 July 1956.
3. Pilkington Archive, RMS Doc. Box PB 51600 Minutes, of Manufacturing Conference, 10 May 1955.
4. Pilkington Archive, RMS Doc. Box PB 50149 No1 Tank Minutes of Meetings.
5. Pilkington Archive, RMS Doc. Box PB 50149 No1 Tank Minutes of Meetings 03 Oct. 1955.
6. Pilkington Archive, RMS Doc. Box PB 349 General Board Papers, 27 Sept. 1956.
7. Pilkington, L.A.B. 1969. The Float Glass Process. *Proceedings of the Royal Society of London* **314** 1–25.
8. Ibid.
9. Pilkington Archive, RMS Doc. Box PB 51600 Minutes, of Manufacturing Conference, 10 Jan. 1956.
10. Pilkington Archive, RMS Doc. Box PB 259 Group Executive Minute 1007, 16 Oct. 1956.

11. Pilkington Archive, RMS Doc. Box PB 51600 Minutes, of Manufacturing Conference, 17 Jan. 1957.
12. Pilkington Archive, RMS Doc. Box PB 51600 Minutes, of Manufacturing Conference, 12 March 1957.
13. Pilkington Archive, RMS Doc. Box PB 349 General Board Papers, 28 March 1957.
14. Pilkington Archive, RMS Doc. Box PB 349 General Board Minute 1941, 28 March 1957.
15. Pilkington Archive, RMS Doc. Box PB 259 Group Executive Papers, 18 June 1957.
16. Pilkington Archive, RMS Doc. Box PB 50149 No1 Tank Minutes of Meetings.
17. Pilkington Archive, RMS Doc. Box PB 259 Group Executive Papers, 16 July 1957.
18. Pilkington Archive, RMS Doc. Box PB 349 Board Papers, 25 July 1957.
19. Pilkington Archive, RMS Doc. Box PB 50149 No1 Tank Minutes of Meetings 27 Nov. 1957.
20. Pilkington Archive, RMS Doc. Box PB 030500 Minutes of Flat Glass Management Committee, 12 March 1956.
21. Pilkington Archive, RMS Doc. Box PB 259 Group Executive Papers, 17 Sept. 1957.
22. Pilkington Archive, RMS Doc. Box PB 259 Group Executive Papers, 19 Nov. 1957.
23. Pilkington Archive, RMS Doc. Box PB 349 General Board Minute 2013, 29 Nov. 1957.
24. Pilkington Archive, RMS Doc. Box PB 349 General Board Papers, 29 Nov. 1957.
25. Pilkington Archive, RMS Doc. Box PB 259 Group Executive Papers, 2 Jan. 1958.
26. Pilkington Archive, RMS Doc. Box PB 259 Group Executive Minute 1476, 2 Jan. 1958.
27. Pilkington Archive, RMS Doc. Box PB 349 General Board Minute 2028, 27 March 1958.
28. Pilkington Archive, RMS Doc. Box PB 259 Group Executive Papers, 18 Feb. 1958.
29. Pilkington Archive, RMS Doc. Box PB 50149 No1 Tank Minutes of Meetings 01 Sept. 1958.
30. Pilkington Archive, RMS Doc. Box PB 349 General Board Papers, 25 Sept. 1958.
31. Pilkington Archive, RMS Doc. Box PB 349 General Board Minute 2067, 25 Sept. 1958.
32. Pilkington Archive, RMS Doc. Box PB 259 Group Executive Minutes, 22 Sept. 1958.
33. Pilkington Archive, RMS Doc. Box PB 349 General Board Minute 2084, 28 Nov. 1958.
34. Pilkington Archive, RMS Doc. Box PB 50149 No1 Tank Minutes of Meetings Sept-Nov 1958.
35. Pilkington, L.A.B. 1969. The Float Glass Process. *Proceedings of the Royal Society of London* **314** 1–25.
36. Personal communication, April 2005.
37. Pilkington Archive, RMS Doc. Box PB 349 General Board Papers, 28 Nov. 1958.
38. Pilkington Archive, RMS Doc. Box PB 259 Group Executive Papers, 10 Nov. 1958.
39. Pilkington Archive, RMS Doc. Box PB 349 General Board Papers, 28 Nov. 1958.
40. Pilkington Archive, RMS Doc. Box PB 259 Group Executive Papers, 5 Jan. 1959.
41. Pilkington Archive, RMS Doc. Box PB 349 General Board Papers, 28 July 1955.
42. Pilkington Archive, RMS Doc. Box PB 259 Group Executive Minute 404, 17 May 1955.
43. Pilkington Archive, RMS Doc. Box PB 259 Group Executive Papers, 19 Nov. 1957.
44. Pilkington Archive, RMS Doc. Box PB 349 General Board Minute 2051, 29 May 1958.
45. Pilkington Archive, RMS Doc. Box PB 1242 'Costs and Implications of float'; Sir Harry Pilkington's statement at the press conference, 20 Jan. 1959.
46. Skeddle, R.W. 1977. Empirical Perspectives on Major Capital Decisions. Ph.D.Thesis, Cape Western Reserve University. p.138.
47. Pilkington Archive, RMS Doc. Box PB 259 Group Executive Papers, 13 Oct. 1959.
48. Pilkington Archive, RMS Doc. Box PB 259 Group Executive Papers, 10 March 1959.
49. Pilkington, L.A.B. 1969. The Float Glass Process. *Proceedings of the Royal Society of London* **314** 1–25.

50. Pilkington Archive, RMS Doc. Box PB 50149 No1 Tank Minutes of Meetings, 23 July 1959.
51. Pilkington Archive, RMS Doc. Box PB 259 Group Executive Papers, 6 Aug. 1959.
52. Pilkington Archive, RMS Doc. Box PB 259 Group Executive Papers, 14 July 1959.
53. Pilkington Archive, RMS Doc. Box PB 349 General Board Minutes, 25 Feb. 1960.
54. Chairman's statement to shareholders, 1973.
55. Pilkington, L.A.B. 1971. Float: An Application of Science, Analysis, and Judgement. *Glass technology* **12**(4) 76–83.
56. Pilkington Archive, RMS Doc. Box PB 1242 'Costs and Implications of float'; Sir Harry Pilkington's statement at the press conference, 20 Jan. 1959.
57. Pilkington Archive, RMS Doc. Box PB 50154 LABP's files; Briefing Papers, for the Guardian litigation, 1969.
58. Pilkington Archive, RMS Doc. Box PB 1242 'Costs and Implications of float'; Sir Harry Pilkington's statement at the press conference, 20 Jan. 1959.

Notes to Chapter 5: The decision to license float glass technology

1. Pilkington Archive, RMS Doc. Box PB 318 Minutes, of Directors' Flat Glass Committee, 2 Feb. 1959.
2. Mintzberg, H., B. Quinn. 1995. *The Strategy Process*, European Edition ed. p.854. Professor Quinn prepared the first version of his case study in the 1970s and interviewed both Sir Harry and Sir Alastair. I have used a number of quotations from the study as they were originally obtained closer in time to the events covered in this chapter.
3. Pilkington Archive, RMS Doc. Box PB 30500 Flat Glass Management Committee Minutes, 12 April 1955.
4. Pilkington Archive, RMS Doc. Box PB 259 Group Executive Minutes, 2 Jan. 1956.
5. Pilkington Archive, RMS Doc. Box PB 349 General Board Papers, 29 March 1956.
6. Pilkington Archive, RMS Doc. Box PB 318 Directors' Flat Glass Committee Papers, 31 Oct. 1958.
7. Pilkington Archive, RMS Doc. Box PB 50147 Chairman's Statement with accounts for period to 31 March 1963.
8. Pilkington Archive, RMS Doc. Box PB 257 General Board Minutes, 30 May 1957.
9. Mintzberg, H., B. Quinn. 1995. *The Strategy Process*, European Edition ed., p.863.
10. Mintzberg, H., B. Quinn. 1995. *The Strategy Process*, European Edition ed., p.861.
11. Pilkington Archive, RMS Doc. Box PB 50142 Sir Alastair's PPG files – note of meeting 01 July 1962.
12. Pilkington Archive, RMS Doc. Box PB 259 Directors' Flat Glass Committee Papers, 5 Jan. 1959.
13. Interview with B. Milne, 13 April 2005.
14. Skeddle, R.W. 1977. Empirical Perspectives on Major Capital Decisions. Ph.D. Thesis, Cape Western Reserve University.
15. Barker, T.C. 1977. *The Glass-makers*. Weidenfeld & Nicolson, London. p.18.
16. Hofstede, G., G.J. Hofstede. 2005. *Cultures and Organisations: Software of the Mind*. McGraw-Hill, New York. p.4.
17. Pilkington Archive, RMS Doc. Box PB 1242 'Costs and Implications of float'; Sir Harry Pilkington's statement at the press conference, 20 Jan. 1959.
18. Pilkington Archive, RMS Doc. Box PB 259 Group Executive Papers, 19 Nov. 1957.
19. Pilkington Archive, RMS Doc. Box PB 259 Group Executive Papers, 12 May 1959.
20. Barker, T.C. 1994. *An Age of Glass*. Boxtree, London. p.71.
21. Pilkington Archive, RMS Doc. Box PB 259 Group Executive Papers, 22 April 1958.
22. Mintzberg, H., B. Quinn. 1995. *The Strategy Process*, European Edition ed. p.862.

23. Pilkington Archive, RMS Doc. Box PB 349 General Board Papers, 26 Nov. 1959.
24. Kynaston, D. 2007. *Austerity Britain 1945–51*. Bloomsbury, London. p.464.
25. Westall, O. 1996. British business history and the culture of business. A. Godley, O. Westall, eds. *Business History and Business Culture*. Manchester University Press, Manchester, p.32.
26. Pilkington Archive, RMS Doc. Box PB 259 Group Executive Papers, 16 Aug. 1960.
27. Pilkington Archive, RMS Doc. Box PB 316 Group Executive Minutes, 25 Oct. 1955.
28. Mintzberg, H., B. Quinn. 1995. *The Strategy Process*, European Edition ed.
29. Schein, E.H. 2004. *Organisational Culture and Leadership*, 3rd ed. Jossey-Bass, San Francisco. p.31.
30. Teece, D.J. 2000. *Managing Intellectual Capital*. Oxford University Press, Oxford.

Notes to Chapter 6: The 1960s: decade of revolution

1. I am indebted to David Pilkington for this account.
2. Pilkington Archive, RMS Doc. Box PB 318 Directors Flat Glass Committee Minutes, 1 July 1963.
3. Pilkington Archive, RMS Doc. Box PB 349 General Board Minutes, 25 July 1963.
4. Pilkington Archive, RMS Doc. Box PB 316 Group Executive Minutes, 14 April 1964.
5. Pilkington Archive, RMS Doc. Box PB 349 General Board Papers, 6 Oct. 1967.
6. Pilkington Archive, RMS Doc. Box PB 349 General Board Papers, 3 Feb. 1967.
7. Pilkington Archive, RMS Doc. Box PB 349 General Board Papers, 6 Oct. 1967.
8. Pilkington Archive, RMS Doc. Box PB 318 Directors' Flat Glass Committee Minutes, 1 Aug. 1966.
9. Pilkington Archive, RMS Doc. Box PB 527 Chairman's Consultative Committee Papers, 6 March 1970.
10. Pilkington Archive, RMS Doc. Box PB 349 General Board Papers, 29 July 1965.
11. Chairman's statement to shareholders, 1973.
12. Pilkington Archive, RMS Doc. Box PB 316 Group Executive Minutes, 19 Aug. 1957.
13. Interview with B. Milne, 13 April 2005.
14. Grundy, T. 1990. *The Global Miracle of Float Glass*. Privately Published, St. Helens.

Notes to Chapter 7: The Guardian controversy

1. Pilkington Archive, RMS Doc. Box PB 318 Directors' Flat Glass Committee Minutes, 29 June 1959.
2. Pilkington Archive, RMS Doc. Box PB 318 Directors' Flat Glass Committee Papers, 4 June 1960.
3. Skeddle, R.W. 1977. Empirical Perspectives on Major Capital Decisions. Ph.D.Thesis, Cape Western Reserve University.
4. Pilkington Archive, RMS Doc. Box PB 259 Executive Committee Minutes, 8 Oct. 1952.
5. Pilkington Archive, RMS Doc. Box PB 259 Executive Committee Minutes, 8 March 1955.
6. Pilkington Archive, RMS Doc. Box PB 318 Directors' Flat Glass Committee Minutes, 2 July 1962.
7. Pilkington Archive, RMS Doc. Box PB 349 General Board Minutes, 28 Feb. 1963.
8. Interview with B. Milne, 13 April 2005.
9. Pilkington Archive, RMS Doc. Box PB 54064 L.N. Wall's Ford file, Note by K.J.B. Earle, 21 Dec. 1973.
10. Pilkington Archive, RMS Doc. Box PB 527 Chairman's Consultative Committee Papers, 31 July 1967.

11. Pilkington Archive, RMS Doc. Box PB 349 General Board Papers, 6 Oct. 1967.
12. Pilkington Archive, RMS Doc. Box PB 50459 Flat Glass Divisional Board Papers, 26 July 1968.
13. Pilkington Archive, RMS Doc. Box PB 50459 Flat Glass Division Board Papers, 30 Aug. 1968.
14. Pilkington Archive, RMS Doc. Box PB 50459 Flat Glass Divisional Board Minutes, 25 Oct. 1968.
15. Pilkington Archive, RMS Doc. Box PB 524 General Board Papers, 13 Dec. 1968.
16. Pilkington Archive, RMS Doc. Box PB 50460 Flat Glass Divisional Board Papers, 31 Jan. 1969.
17. Pilkington Archive, RMS Doc. Box PB 50460 Flat Glass Divisional Board Minutes, 31 Jan. 1969.
18. Pilkington Archive, RMS Doc. Box PB 50460 Flat Glass Divisional Board Papers, 30 May 1969.
19. Pilkington Archive, RMS Doc. Box PB 527 Chairman's Consultative Committee Minutes, 3 Oct. 1969.
20. Pilkington Archive, RMS Doc. Box PB 524 General Board Papers, 12 Dec. 1969.
21. Pilkington Archive, RMS Doc. Box PB 527 Chairman's Consultative Committee Minutes, 2 Jan. 1970.
22. Hofstede, G., G.J. Hofstede. 2005. *Cultures and Organisations: Software of the Mind.* McGraw-Hill, New York. p.308.
23. Interview with B. Milne, 13 April 2005.
24. Pilkington Archive, RMS Doc. Box PB 49738 W.H. Pilkington's Guardian File.
25. Pilkington Archive, RMS Doc. Box PB 49738 W.H. Pilkington's Guardian File.
26. Pilkington Archive, RMS Doc. Box PB 49738 W.H. Pilkington's Guardian File.
27. Pilkington Archive, RMS Doc. Box PB 527 Chairman's Consultative Committee Papers, 2 April 1969.
28. Pilkington Archive, RMS Doc. Box PB 49738 W.H. Pilkington's Guardian File.
29. Pilkington Archive, RMS Doc. Box PB 49738 W.H. Pilkington's Guardian File.
30. Kinkead, G. 1982. The Raging Bull. *Fortune*(8th April 1982) 58–63.
31. Ibid.
32. The Monopolies Commission. 1966. A Report on the Supply of Flat Glass.
33. Pilkington Archive, RMS Doc. Box PB 316 Group Executive Minutes, 9 April 1963.
34. Pilkington Archive, RMS Doc. Box PB 51172 K.A. Borrows' files.
35. Pilkington Archive, RMS Doc. Box PB 527 Chairman's Consultative Committee Minutes, 6 March 1970.
36. Personal communication, c.1980.
37. Pilkington Archive, RMS Doc. Box PB 527 Chairman's Consultative Committee Papers, 5 Feb. 1971.
38. Pilkington Archive, RMS Doc. Box PB 527 Chairman's Consultative Committee Papers, 11 June 1971.

Notes to Chapter 8: Turmoil and consolidation, 1970–1985

1. Sampson, A. 1992. *The Essential Anatomy of Britain.* Hodder & Stoughton, London. p.101.
2. Lane, T., K. Roberts. 1971. *Strike at Pilkingtons.* Fontana, London.
3. Pilkington Archive, RMS Doc. Box PB 524 General Board Papers, 12 June 1970.
4. Hamilton-Fazey, I. 1987. *The Pathfinder: The Origins of the Enterprise Agency in Britain.* Financial Times, London. p.4.
5. Ibid. p.5.
6. Pilkington Archive, RMS Doc. Box PB 318 Directors' Flat Glass Committee Minutes, 30

April 1962.
7. Pilkington Archive, RMS Doc. Box PB 316 Group Executive Minutes, 28 Feb. 1966.
8. Pilkington Archive, RMS Doc. Box PB 349 General Board Papers, 29 Nov. 1962.
9. Pilkington Archive, RMS Doc. Box PB 349 General Board Papers, 25 Nov. 1965.
10. Pilkington Archive, RMS Doc. Box PB 50262 General Board Minutes, 18 April 1980.
11. Pilkington Archive, RMS Doc. Box PB 527 Chairman's Consultative Committee Papers, 3 Dec. 1971.
12. Pilkington Archive, RMS Doc. Box PB 527 Chairman's Consultative Committee Papers, 6 April 1973.
13. Pilkington Archive, RMS Doc. Box PB 526 General Board Minute 3282, 13 April 1973.
14. Pilkington Archive, RMS Doc. Box PB 50261 General Board Papers, 1 Sept. 1978.
15. Pilkington Annual Report, 1983.
16. Pilkington Archive, RMS Doc. Box PB 527 Chairman's Consultative Committee Papers, 5 Feb. 1971.
17. Pilkington Archive, RMS Doc. Box PB 50259 General Board Papers, 8 Feb. 1974.
18. Pilkington Archive, RMS Doc. Box PB 527 Chairman's Consultative Committee Papers, 1 June 1973.

Notes to Chapter 9: The acquisition of Flachglas and LOF

1. Pilkington Archive, RMS Doc. Box PB 318 Directors' Flat Glass Committee Papers, 2 Feb. 1959.
2. Pilkington Archive, RMS Doc. Box PB 527 Chairman's Consultative Committee Papers, 4 Dec. 1970.
3. Personal recollection, signature meeting, Brussels 21 Feb. 1980.
4. Pilkington Archive, RMS Doc. Box PB 527 Chairman's Consultative Committee Papers, 3 Dec. 1971.
5. Pilkington Archive, RMS Doc. Box PB 527 Chairman's Consultative Committee Papers, 6 Aug. 1971.
6. Pilkington Archive, RMS Doc. Box PB 526 General Board Papers, 13 Aug. 1971.
7. Pilkington Archive, RMS Doc. Box PB 526 General Board Minutes, 8 Oct. 1971.
8. Personal recollection.
9. Pilkington Archive, RMS Doc. Box PB 76765 Chairman's Committee Papers, 5 Feb. 1980.
10. Pilkington Archive, RMS Doc. Box PB 50262 General Board Minutes, 8 Feb. 1980.
11. Pilkington Archive, RMS Doc. Box PB 529 Planning Panel Minutes, 8 Dec. 1980.
12. Pilkington Archive, RMS Doc. Box PB 76797 General Board Minutes, 12 Feb. 1982.
13. Pilkington Archive, RMS Doc. Box PB 76766 Chairman's Committee Papers, 21 April 1982.
14. Pilkington Archive, RMS Doc. Box PB 76797 General Board Minutes, 9 July 1982.
15. Pilkington, L.A.B. 1971. Float: An Application of Science, Analysis, and Judgement. *Glass technology* **12**(4) 76–83.

Notes to Chapter 10: Legal action against PPG

1. The technical differences between LB and conventional float are set out in McCawley, R.A. 1980. Float Glass Production: Pilkington vs. PPG. *The Glass Industry* (April) 18–22.
2. Pilkington Archive, RMS Doc. Box PB 50261 General Board Papers, 10 Feb. 1978.
3. Pilkington Archive, RMS Doc. Box PB 50268 Chairman's Committee Papers, 2 Sept. 1975.
4. Pilkington Archive, RMS Doc. Box PB 51172 K.A. Borrows' Guardian File.

5. Pilkington Archive, RMS Doc. Box PB 76766 Chairman's Committee Papers, 21 April 1982.
6. Pilkington Archive, RMS Doc. Box PB 76798 General Board Papers, 14 Oct. 1983.
7. Pilkington Brothers plc v. Guardian Industries Corp. 1986 US Dist Lexis 24466 (ED Mich 1986).
8. Levy, D. 1999. The Great Philosopher. *US Glass* **34**(3).
9. Kinkead, G. 1982. The Raging Bull. *Fortune*(8th April 1982) 58–63.
10. Pilkington Archive, RMS Doc. Box PB 76776 Chairman's Committee Minutes, 28 July 1986.
11. Pilkington Archive, RMS Doc. Box PB 76769 Chairman's Committee Minutes, 24 April 1985.
12. Pilkington Archive, RMS Doc. Box PB 43560 A.J. Hartley's PPG file, K.A. Borrows' note 25 June 1985.
13. *The Times*, 15 April 1995.

Notes to Chapter 11: Addendum

1. The material for the current state of the world's float market is taken from Pilkington's website; http://www.pilkington.com/resources/pfgi2008final.pdf accessed 11th January 2009.
2. For example Teece, D.J. 2000. *Managing Intellectual Capital*. Oxford University Press, Oxford.
3. Ibid.
4. Pilkington, L.A.B. 1976. Flat Glass: Evolution and Revolution Over 60 Years. *Glass Technology* **17**(5) 182–193.

Bibliography

Barker, T.C. 1972. Float: A study in invention. *Pilkington Archive.*

Barker, T.C. 1977. Business Implications of Technical Developments in the Glass Industry 1945–1965: A Case Study. B. Supple, ed. *Essays in British Business History.* Clarendon Press, Oxford, 187–204.

Barker, T.C. 1977. *The Glass-makers.* Weidenfeld & Nicolson, London.

Barker, T.C. 1994. *An Age of Glass.* Boxtree, London.

Cable, M. 1999. Mechanisation of Glass Manufacture. *Journal of the American Ceramic Society* 82(5) 1093–1112.

Chandler, A.D. 1990. *Scale and Scope; The Dynamics of Industrial Capitalism.* Belknap Press, Cambridge MA.

Elkadi, H. 2006. *Cultures of Glass Architecture.* Ashgate, Aldershot.

Grenfell, J. 1979. *In Pleasant Places.* Macdonald Futura, London.

Grundy, T. 1990. *The Global Miracle of Float Glass.* Privately Published, St Helens.

Hamilton-Fazey, I. 1987. *The Pathfinder: The Origins of the Enterprise Agency in Britain.* Financial Times, London.

Hofstede, G., G.J. Hofstede 2005. *Cultures and Organisations: Software of the Mind.* McGraw-Hill, New York.

Kinkead, G. 1982. The Raging Bull. *Fortune* (8 April 1982) 58–63.

Kynaston, D. 2007. *Austerity Britain, 1945–51.* Bloomsbury, London.

Lane, T., K. Roberts. 1971. *Strike at Pilkingtons.* Fontana, London.

Levy, D. 1999. The Great Philosopher. *US Glass* 34(3).

McCawley, R.A. 1980. Float Glass Production: Pilkington vs. PPG. *The Glass Industry* (April) 18–22.

Mintzberg, H., B. Quinn. 1995. *The Strategy Process,* European Edition edn.

Pilkington, L.A.B. 1963. The Development of Float glass. *The Glass Industry* (February) 80–100.

Pilkington, L.A.B. 1969. The Float Glass Process. *Proceedings of the Royal Society of London* 314 1–25.

Pilkington, L.A.B. 1971. Float: An Application of Science, Analysis, and Judgement. *Glass technology* 12(4) 76–83.

Pilkington, L.A.B. 1976. Flat Glass: Evolution and Revolution Over 60 Years. *Glass Technology* 17(5) 182–193.

Quinn, B. 1980. *Strategies for Change: Logical Incrementalism.* Irwin, Homewood, Ill.

Sampson, A. 1992. *The Essential Anatomy of Britain.* Hodder & Stoughton, London.

Schein, E.H. 2004. *Organisational Culture and Leadership,* 3rd edn, Jossey-Bass, San Francisco.

Skeddle, R.W. 1977. Empirical Perspectives on Major Capital Decisions. Ph.D. thesis, Cape

Western Reserve University.

Teece, D.J. 2000. *Managing Intellectual Capital.* Oxford University Press, Oxford.

The Monopolies Commission. 1966. A Report on the Supply of Flat Glass.

Westall, O. 1996. British business history and the culture of business. A. Godley, O. Westall, eds *Business History and Business Culture.* Manchester University Press, Manchester.

Wiggington, M. 2002. *Glass in Architecture.* Phaidon, London.

Index

Index references in *italic* type indicate photographs.

Acknowledgements

My grateful thanks to the following in the research and preparation of this book:

Dr Geoffrey Tweedale and Professor David Jeremy for taking it in turns to be my Director of Studies throughout the Ph.D. process and for their support, guidance and patience in trying to teach an old dog new tricks; Nancy Barker at IM&S Limited, the custodians of the Pilkington Archive, for sharing her expertise of the records and her unfailing enthusiasm for my project while digging out the files; John McKenna, Company Secretary, Pilkington plc, for permission to use the archive, and to John McKenna, Chris Bailey and David Roycroft for their helpful comments on behalf of Pilkington Limited without in any way inhibiting me; Sid Robinson, Barry Milnes, Chris Moore and David Wood for their time and patience in interviews as they helped to remove some of my preconceptions; Kirsty Pilkington, Glen Nightingale and David Pilkington for the labour of reviewing the text, their constructive comments and above all their encouragement;

and

Ilush, for her IT skills and for providing the initial impetus to embark on this project and then living with the consequences without complaint as it became my latest obsession.

They have all done much to improve this book, but the errors are my own.

List of subscribers

1 Dr A. Ledwith, Standish, Wigan
2 Mr Anthony Shuttleworth, Winstanley, Wigan
3 William Barrow, St Helens
4 Sol Kay, Church Stretton
5 J.D. Ormesher, Huntingdon
6 Maurice Hilton, Shevington, Wigan
7 Mr H. Frank Green, Darley Dale, Derbyshire
8 Mr Arthur Brown, Eccleston, St Helens
9 Mr Anthony Hartley, Grange over Sands
10 Eric Bridge, Billinge, Wigan
11 Tom Latto, Southport
12 Mr Michael Hirst, Doncaster
13 Jim Franklin, Mackenzie Glass, Exeter
14 anonymous
15 Mr George Hoy, Lowton
16 Mrs E. Porter, Doncaster
17 Miss Jean Hind, Doncaster
18 Mr Derek Norman, Pilkington, 1964–99
19 Mark & Ann Unsworth, St Helens
20 Mr Douglas Twist, Hollywood, Birmingham
21 Mr Sam Reeves, Penmaenmawr
22 Eric A. Ventham, Northampton
23 Alan R. Nicholson, Tarporley
24 Mr J.R. Parr, Rainford, St Helens
25 Mr Roy Penny, Liverpool
26 anonymous
27 anonymous
28 Alan Havard, Southport
29 Mr Ron Berry, St Helens
30 Dr James W. Smith, Birkdale

31 Mr Robert J. Williamson, Eccleston, St Helens
32 Mr Charles Newby, Alcester
33 Mr Arthur W. Nixon, Shifnal, Salop
34 Edward Carroll, St Helens
35 Mr and Mrs David Pilkington, Belmont, Durham
36 Mr Peter Dixon, St Helens
36 J.R. Nield Esq., Prescot
37 Mr J.M. Jackson, Doncaster
38 John M. Virgoe, Parbold
39 Geoffrey M. Eaves, St Helens
40 John Currie, Eccleston, St Helens
41 Ken Pearson, Rainhill
42 Douglas Campbell, Dunfermline
43 Mrs Joyce R. Higham, Southport
44 Anthony De Martin, Buxton, New South Wales, Australia
45 Dr Stanley Lythgoe, Newburgh
46 C.R. Taylor, St Helens
47 Keith Knowles, St Helens
   Cyril Alan Knowles, Yattendon
48 John Allen, Doncaster
49 Mr Michael J. Davies, Knutsford
50 Robert G. Bannerman, Prescot
51 Mrs Joan Eaves, Southport
52 Blake Pinnell, Head Office, Pilkington
53 William Bettley, Thelwall
54 D. Ripley, Lathom and Doncaster; A. Tyson, Lathom and PPE; G. and J. Szymanski, Lathom, Cowley Hill, Scarborough
55 B.J. Kirkbride, Butterwick, Penrith
56 B.W. Oxley, Parry South, Canada
57 John Peter Glover, Doncaster
58 Edward Tomkinson, Lantswit Major,

Vale of Glamorgan
59 Roger Hele, Torquay
60 Mrs Ellen Busby, St Helens
61 Brian Riley, Tarleton, Lancashire
62 anonymous
63 James Hill, St Helens
64 Gordon Cochrane, Largs
65 Stuart Gardner, Sydney, Australia;
    Malcolm Cooke, Sydney, Australia
66 R.L. Rosbotham, Kingswood, Surrey
67 Peter Liley, Southport
68 John Gillespie, Formby
69 Harry Banks, Ashton-in-Makerfield
70 Andrew Vardy; Alan and Janet Vardy,
    Doncaster
71 John Baldry, Toronto, Canada
72 Percy James Cooke, Cowley Hill
    Springs; retired in Cornwall
73 Mrs Patrick Glennane
74 Russell Pickersgill, Scarborough,
    Ontario, Canada
75 Mrs Arthur Fairclough, St Helens
76 Mrs Lilian Grundy, Frodsham
77 A. Chaplin, Hartford, Northwich
78 Richard Guppy, Croesyceiliog,
    Cwmbran
79 B. Hughes, Exeter
80 Geoffrey A. Hedgecock, Holywell,
    Clwyd
81 anonymous
82 John MacDougall, Eccleston, St
    Helens
83 Professor Adrian C. Wright,
    Hermitage, Thatcham
84 Pilkington Group Limited
85 Robert Alexander, Longton, Preston
86 Martin McBride, Carterton, Oxon
87 anonymous
88 M. Bernard Savaete, Courbevoie,
    France
89 William Asson, Windle, St Helens
90 John Burton, Appley Bridge, Wigan